Selected Writings

Truman Capote

SELECTED WRITINGS

with an Introduction
by MARK SCHORER

The Modern Library
New York

Acknowledgments: The articles "A Ride through Spain," "The Muses Are Heard," and "The Duke in His Domain" appeared originally in *The New Yorker*. The stories "The Headless Hawk," "A Tree of Night," and "A Diamond Guitar" appeared originally in *Harper's Bazaar*. "House of Flowers" appeared originally in *Botteghe Oscure* and *Mademoiselle*. "Children on Their Birthdays," "Miriam," "A Christmas Memory," and "Ischia" appeared originally in *Mademoiselle*. The stories "Breakfast at Tiffany's" and "Among the Paths to Eden" appeared originally in *Esquire*. "Master Misery" appeared originally in *Harper's*. "Shut a Final Door" appeared originally in the *Atlantic Monthly*. "A House on the Heights" appeared originally in *Holiday*.

THE MODERN LIBRARY
is published by
RANDOM HOUSE, INC.

Manufactured in the United States of America

FOR

Phyllis and Bennett

Introduction

AMONG THE SURPRISING QUALITIES of Truman Capote's mercurial talent and a quality that is made very plain by such a selection from the entire body of his work as this is its range, the variety of its development over the nearly twenty years in which the author has been publishing. A prose of many moods, it is equally at ease in situations of black nightmarish horror and of high, often hilarious comedy, and perhaps its single constant quality is the unerring sense of style. By style one means, when speaking of Capote's work, not only the right words in the right places, but the body of detail precisely and freshly observed and the varieties of the speaking human voice accurately heard and quintessentially reported. The style moves, of course, with the movement of the subjects, and thus the variety is doubled at least and possibly squared. Within that multiplicity of interest one can yet mark out some major tendencies.

The earliest stories are written in what some people have called the "Gothic" tradition or in the tradition of what Hawthorne meant by the word "romance," stories that are set in a world where we continually move without transition or warning from the actual into the dream, from the real into the surreal, from the natural into the supernatural. They are stories whose central concern is with the theme of the *Doppelgänger,* the alter ego, and the supernatural is, in fact, a metaphor of the world in which that other self, which we cannot ever confront in the busy social world, exists. These are stories generally about lonely, loveless people—or, at any rate, they seem to be alone because they *are* loveless—who encounter strange, often offensive creatures with whom they are, in one way or another, trapped and whom they cannot and usually do not wish to escape, for these creatures are their selves, their fate, whom they are helpless to shun.

These are stories that, one feels, are written not out of any formal knowledge of the psychology of the irrational but directly out of the irrational itself. They evoke with a shocking directness the terrors of childhood and the vivid force and grip of dreams. And on these matters they seldom speculate; they are simply, dreadfully *there.* In one of the earliest of these stories, "A Tree of Night," Kay, a pleasant girl on her way back to college from a funeral, is forced by two grotesques with whom she is trapped on a train into a recognition of her own unconscious life and made at last to submit to it:

> Staring up into his hairless, vapid face, flushed brilliant by the lantern light, Kay knew of what she was afraid: it was a memory, a childish memory of terrors that once, long ago, had hovered above her like haunted limbs on a tree of night. Aunts, cooks, strangers—each eager to spin a tale or teach a rhyme of spooks and death, omens, spirits, demons. And always there had been the unfailing threat of the wizard man: stay close to the house, child, else a wizard man'll snatch you and eat you alive! He lived everywhere, the wizard man, and everywhere was danger. At night, in bed, hear him tapping at the window? Listen!

The "wizard man," in one guise or another, is everywhere in these stories. He is Mr. Revercomb in "Master Misery," and he is that Mr. Destronelli of "The Headless

Hawk" who is disguised in nearly all the characters and yet is none of them, and his is probably the voice on the telephone in "Shut A Final Door," that voice of doom which is also the hero's, Walter Ranney's.

"The Headless Hawk" is probably the story that most completely epitomizes the nightmare mood. Certainly, it is the story that depends most for its effect on the disordered surrealistic imagery of the dream state, and likewise the story that most explicitly announces the *Doppelgänger* theme in that extraordinary passage where Vincent, the hero, finds his other self, "old and horrid," clinging "spiderlike onto his back," and then, in the chaotic throng, sees "that many are also saddled with malevolent semblances of themselves, outward embodiments of inner decay." But it is everywhere in these early stories— the hopeless flight from identity and the final recognition of it in the darkest depths of the self. It appears, in an inverse way, in "Master Misery," where Sylvia, robbed of her dreams, is robbed finally of her very self. ". . . there was nothing left to steal."

This mood found its fullest treatment in Capote's first novel, *Other Voices, Other Rooms,* a work about which, eight years after its publication, he said, "I am a stranger to that book; the person who wrote it seems to have so little in common with my present self. Our mentalities, our interior temperatures are entirely different." The "interior temperature" was apparently undergoing its modification even when the nightmare mood was most upon him, for in an early story like "Children On Their Birthdays," and in such later stories as "House of Flowers" and "A Christmas Memory," a very different mood asserts itself.

These are stories about people who, inhabiting a world of love, live peaceably with their selves, and are even capable—as in the instance of Miss Bobbit in "Children On Their Birthdays"—of transforming those around them. These characters dream still (". . . a man who doesn't dream is like a man who doesn't sweat: he stores up a lot of poison," says the Judge in *The Grass Harp,* which is the novel that explores most fully this second mood), but their dreams are gentle, even happy, with none of the violent turbulence and alarming exposures of the nightmare stories. Violence gives way here to pathos, even sentiment, and melodrama to comedy. In this mood, where pathos joins with comedy, the natural universe is transformed, too. A story like "The Headless Hawk" ends with jangling violence: ". . . it was as if the sky were a thunder-cracked mirror, for the rain fell between them like a curtain of splintered glass"; and this harsh image of sky and rain is characteristic of the treatment of nature, where all is gnarled and stark, deformed and sub-marine, in the earliest stories. But in "Children On Their Birthdays," "it has been raining buoyant summer rain shot through with sun," and when the sun comes out at the end of the story, it brings "with it into the air all the sweetness of wisteria." For this more benign world, Royal's "house of flowers" is the symbol, or the tree house in *The Grass Harp.*

Isolating his characters once more—but in a differ-ent way—and transforming the soft humor of these stories into high outrageous comedy, Capote moves into still an-other mood and possibly the one that suits him best. Holly Golightly of *Breakfast at Tiffany's* is self-sufficient, un-committed to everything but her own need for freedom, a "wild thing."

"Never love a wild thing, Mr. Bell," Holly advised him. "That was Doc's mistake. He was always lugging home wild things. A hawk with a hurt wing. One time it was a full-grown bobcat with a broken leg. But you can't give your heart to a wild thing: the more you do, the stronger they get. Un-til they're strong enough to run into the woods. Or fly into a tree. Then a taller tree. Then the sky. That's how you'll end up, Mr. Bell. If you let your-self love a wild thing. You'll end up looking at the

sky. . . . Good luck: and believe me, dearest
Doc—it's better to look at the sky than live there.
Such an empty place; so vague. Just a country
where the thunder goes and things disappear."

Which predicts the end of the story, and her end. So
there is pathos still, of a sort, yet this choice is Holly's
own, which modifies the pathos, and it is under any circumstances qualified by the lacquered manners of this
brilliantly observed and re-created world of self-contained
misfits and stylish zanies.

With his great gift of observation, it is not surprising
that all the time that he was publishing fiction, Capote
was also writing reportage. The travel sketches that make
up the book called *Local Color* are among the first of his
attempts at reporting. Quite short, very pointed, they are
at once highly personalized through the particularizing
detail and at the same time without the intrusion of personal generalization. We are brought deftly, without fuss,
into the heart of these places, and left there, immersed in
the special quality of each.

From travel sketches, Capote moved on to a number
of profiles of persons of public prominence, and of these,
"The Duke in His Domain"—Marlon Brando in Japan,
"just a young man sitting on a pile of candy"—is among
the most successful. The quality of the place is evoked
with the now expected skill, the necessary facts of
Brando's enterprise in Kyoto are presented with journalistic grace, but it is the ear now that is most impressive as
the characterization is set before us almost entirely
through that speaking voice, ruminating through hours of
muted self-inspection. It is, of course, his experience and
discipline as a writer of fiction that makes Truman Capote
the superb reporter that he is.

The high point until now is *The Muses are Heard,*
one of the great satiric reports of our time, brilliant in its
deadpan presentation of a variety of very funny people in
situations which, when they are not alarming, are hilari-

ous and mad. So the reportage has moved, too, from places to people in places, from the lyric to the comic. And it will not stop there, one has reason to know. The narrator of *Breakfast at Tiffany's* speculates at one point as follows: "the average personality reshapes frequently, every few years even our bodies undergo a complete over-haul—dsirable or not, it is a natural thing that we should change."

Truman Capote's personality is hardly average; but his literary personality, at least, has undergone constant, always refreshing, change. The next change will become evident when he publishes the book at which he is now at work—*In Cold Blood,* the re-creation of a brutal Kansas murder and its consequences. Thoroughly unpredictable, it will be the most remarkable change of all, and the most exciting.

MARK SCHORER

June, 1962

Contents

NONFICTION

From LOCAL COLOR

FICTION

A Tree of Night

IT WAS WINTER. A string of naked light bulbs, from which it seemed all warmth had been drained, illuminated the little depot's cold, windy platform. Earlier in the evening it had rained, and now icicles hung along the station-house eaves like some crystal monster's vicious teeth. Except for a girl, young and rather tall, the platform was deserted. The girl wore a gray flannel suit, a raincoat, and a plaid scarf. Her hair, parted in the middle and rolled up neatly on the sides, was rich blondish-brown; and, while her face tended to be too thin and narrow, she was, though not extraordinarily so, attractive. In addition to an assortment of magazines and a gray suede purse on which elaborate brass letters spelled Kay, she carried conspicuously a green Western guitar.

When the train, spouting steam and glaring with light, came out of the darkness and rumbled to a halt, Kay assembled her paraphernalia and climbed up into the last coach.

The coach was a relic with a decaying interior of ancient red-plush seats, bald in spots, and peeling iodine-colored woodwork. An old-time copper lamp, attached to the ceiling, looked romantic and out of place. Gloomy dead smoke sailed the air; and the car's heated closeness accentuated the stale odor of discarded sandwiches, apple cores, and orange hulls: this garbage, including Lily cups, soda-pop bottles, and mangled newspapers, littered the long aisle. From a water cooler, embedded in the wall, a steady stream trickled to the floor. The passengers, who glanced up wearily when Kay entered, were not, it seemed, at all conscious of any discomfort.

Kay resisted a temptation to hold her nose and threaded her way carefully down the aisle, tripping once, without disaster, over a dozing fat man's protruding leg. Two nondescript men turned an interested eye as she passed; and a kid stood up in his seat, squalling, "Hey, Mama, look at de banjo! Hey, lady, lemme play ya banjo!" till a slap from Mama quelled him.

There was only one empty place. She found it at the end of the car in an isolated alcove occupied already by a man and woman who were sitting with their feet settled lazily on the vacant seat opposite. Kay hesitated a second then said, "Would you mind if I sat here?"

The woman's head snapped up as if she had not been asked a simple question, but stabbed with a needle, too. Nevertheless, she managed a smile. "Can't say as I see what's to stop you, honey," she said, taking her feet down and also, with a curious impersonality, removing the feet of the man who was staring out the window, paying no attention whatsoever.

Thanking the woman, Kay took off her coat, sat down, and arranged herself with purse and guitar at her side, magazines in her lap: comfortable enough, though she wished she had a pillow for her back.

The train lurched; a ghost of steam hissed against the window; slowly the dingy lights of the lonesome depot faded past.

"Boy, what a jerkwater dump," said the woman. "No town, no nothin'."

Kay said, "The town's a few miles away."

"That so? Live there?"

No. Kay explained she had been at the funeral of an uncle. An uncle who, though she did not of course mention it, had left her nothing in his will but the green guitar. Where was she going? Oh, back to college.

After mulling this over, the woman concluded,

"What'll you ever learn in a place like that? Let me tell you, honey, I'm plenty educated and I never saw the inside of no college."

"You didn't?" murmured Kay politely and dismissed the matter by opening one of her magazines. The light was dim for reading and none of the stories looked in the least compelling. However, not wanting to become involved in a conversational marathon, she continued gazing at it stupidly till she felt a furtive tap on her knee.

"Don't read," said the woman. "I need somebody to talk to. Naturally, it's no fun talking to *him.*" She jerked a thumb toward the silent man. "He's afflicted: deaf and dumb, know what I mean?"

Kay closed the magazine and looked at her more or less for the first time. She was short; her feet barely scraped the floor. And like many undersized people she had a freak of structure, in her case an enormous, really huge head. Rouge so brightened her sagging, fleshy-featured face it was difficult even to guess at her age: perhaps fifty, fifty-five. Her big sheep eyes squinted, as if distrustful of what they saw. Her hair was an obviously dyed red, and twisted into parched, fat corkscrew curls. A once-elegant lavender hat of impressive size flopped crazily on the side of her head, and she was kept busy brushing back a drooping cluster of celluloid cherries sewed to the brim. She wore a plain, somewhat shabby blue dress. Her breath had a vividly sweetish gin smell.

"You do wanna talk to me, don't you, honey?"

"Sure," said Kay, moderately amused.

"Course you do. You bet you do. That's what I like about a train. Bus people are a close-mouthed buncha dopes. But a train's the place for putting your cards on the table, that's what I always say." Her voice was cheerful and booming, husky as a man's. "But on accounta *him,* I always try to get us this here seat; it's more private, like a swell compartment, see?"

"It's very pleasant," Kay agreed. "Thanks for letting me join you."

"Only too glad to. We don't have much company; it makes some folks nervous to be around him."

As if to deny it, the man made a queer, furry sound deep in his throat and plucked the woman's sleeve. "Leave me alone, dear-heart," she said, as if she were talking to an inattentive child. "I'm O.K. We're just having us a nice little ol' talk. Now behave yourself or this pretty girl will go away. She's very rich; she goes to college." And winking, she added, "He thinks I'm drunk."

The man slumped in the seat, swung his head sideways, and studied Kay intently from the corners of his eyes. These eyes, like a pair of clouded milky-blue marbles, were thickly lashed and oddly beautiful. Now, except for a certain remoteness, his wide, hairless face had no real expression. It was as if he were incapable of experiencing or reflecting the slightest emotion. His gray hair was clipped close and combed forward into uneven bangs. He looked like a child aged abruptly by some uncanny method. He wore a frayed blue serge suit, and he had anointed himself with a cheap, vile perfume. Around his wrist was strapped a Micky Mouse watch.

"He thinks I'm drunk," the woman repeated. "And the real funny part is, I am. Oh, shoot—you gotta do something, ain't that right?" She bent closer. "Say, ain't it?"

Kay was still gawking at the man; the way he was looking at her made her squeamish, but she could not take her eyes off him. "I guess so," she said.

"Then let's us have us a drink," suggested the woman. She plunged her hand into an oilcloth satchel and pulled out a partially filled gin bottle. She began to unscrew the cap but, seeming to think better of this, handed the bottle to Kay. "Gee, I forgot about you being company," she said. "I'll go get us some nice paper cups."

So, before Kay could protest that she did not want a drink, the woman had risen and started none too steadily down the aisle toward the water cooler.

Kay yawned and rested her forehead against the windowpane, her fingers idly strumming the guitar: the strings sang a hollow, lulling tune, as monotonously soothing as the Southern landscape, smudged in darkness, flowing past the window. An icy winter moon rolled above the train across the night sky like a thin white wheel.

And then, without warning, a strange thing happened: the man reached out and gently stroked Kay's cheek. Despite the breathtaking delicacy of this movement, it was such a bold gesture Kay was at first too startled to know what to make of it: her thoughts shot in three or four fantastic directions. He leaned forward till his queer eyes were very near her own; the reek of his perfume was sickening. The guitar was silent while they exchanged a searching gaze. Suddenly, from some spring of compassion, she felt for him a keen sense of pity; but also, and this she could not suppress, an overpowering disgust, an absolute loathing: something about him, an elusive quality she could not quite put a finger on, reminded her of—of what?

After a little, he lowered his hand solemnly and sank back in the seat, an asinine grin transfiguring his face, as if he had performed a clever stunt for which he wished applause.

"Giddyup! Giddyup! my little bucker-ROOS . . ." shouted the woman. And she sat down, loudly proclaiming to be, "Dizzy as a witch! Dog tired! Whew!" From a handful of Lily cups she separated two and casually thrust the rest down her blouse. "Keep 'em safe and dry, ha ha ha. . . ." A coughing spasm seized her, but when it was over she appeared calmer. "Has my boy friend been entertaining?" she asked, patting her bosom reverently. "Ah, he's so sweet." She looked as if she might pass out. Kay rather wished she would.

"I don't want a drink," Kay said, returning the bottle. "I never drink: I hate the taste."

"Mustn't be a kill-joy," said the woman firmly. "Here now, hold your cup like a good girl."

"No, please . . ."

"Formercysake, hold it still. Imagine, nerves at your age! Me, I can shake like a leaf, I've got reasons. Oh, Lordy, have I got 'em."

"But . . ."

A dangerous smile tipped the woman's face hideously awry. "What's the matter? Don't you think I'm good enough to drink with?"

"Please, don't misunderstand," said Kay, a tremor in her voice. "It's just that I don't like being forced to do something I don't want to. So look, couldn't I give this to the gentleman?"

"Him? No sirree: he needs what little sense he's got. Come on, honey, down the hatch."

Kay, seeing it was useless, decided to succumb and avoid a possible scene. She sipped and shuddered. It was terrible gin. It burned her throat till her eyes watered. Quickly, when the woman was not watching, she emptied the cup into the sound hole of the guitar. It happened, however, that the man saw; and Kay, realizing it, recklessly signaled to him with her eyes a plea not to give her away. But she could not tell from his clear-blank expression how much he understood.

"Where you from, kid?" resumed the woman presently.

For a bewildered moment, Kay was unable to provide an answer. The names of several cities came to her all at once. Finally, from this confusion, she extracted: "New Orleans. My home is in New Orleans."

The woman beamed. "N.O.'s where I wanna go when I kick off. One time, oh, say 1923, I ran me a sweet little fortune-telling parlor there. Let's see, that was on St. Peter Street." Pausing, she stooped and set the empty gin bottle on the floor. It rolled into the aisle and rocked back and forth with a drowsy sound. "I was raised in Texas—on a big ranch—my papa was rich. Us kids always had the best; even Paris, France, clothes. I'll bet you've got a big swell house, too. Do you have a garden? Do you grow flowers?"

"Just lilacs."

A conductor entered the coach, preceded by a cold gust of wind that rattled the trash in the aisle and briefly livened the dull air. He lumbered along, stopping now and then to punch a ticket or talk with a passenger. It was after midnight. Someone was expertly playing a harmonica. Someone else was arguing the merits of a certain politician. A child cried out in his sleep.

"Maybe you wouldn't be so snotty if you knew who we was," said the woman, bobbing her tremendous head. "We ain't nobodies, not by a long shot."

Embarrassed, Kay nervously opened a pack of cig- arettes and lighted one. She wondered if there might not be a seat in a car up ahead. She could not bear the woman, or, for that matter, the man, another minute. But she had never before been in a remotely comparable situation. "If you'll excuse me now," she said, "I have to be leaving. It's been very pleasant, but I promised to meet a friend on the train. . . ."

With almost invisible swiftness the woman grasped the girl's wrist. "Didn't your mama ever tell you it was sinful to lie?" she stage-whispered. The lavender hat tumbled off her head but she made no effort to retrieve it. Her tongue flicked out and wetted her lips. And, as Kay stood up, she increased the pressure of her grip. "Sit down, dear . . . there ain't any friend . . . Why, we're your only friends and we wouldn't have you leave us for the world."

"Honestly, I wouldn't lie."

"Sit down, dear."

Kay dropped her cigarette and the man picked it up. He slouched in the corner and became absorbed in blowing a chain of lush smoke rings that mounted up- ward like hollow eyes and expanded into nothing.

"Why, you wouldn't want to hurt his feelings by leaving us, now, would you, dear?" crooned the woman softly. "Sit down—down—now, that's a good girl. My, what a pretty guitar. What a pretty, pretty guitar . . ." Her voice faded before the sudden whooshing, static noise of a second train. And for an instant the lights in the coach went off; in the darkness the passing train's golden windows winked black-yellow-black-yellow-black-yellow. The man's cigarette pulsed like the glow of a firefly, and his smoke rings continued rising tranquilly. Outside, a bell pealed wildly.

When the lights came on again, Kay was massaging her wrist where the woman's strong fingers had left a painful bracelet mark. She was more puzzled than angry. She determined to ask the conductor if he would find her a different seat. But when he arrived to take her ticket, the request stuttered on her lips incoherently.

"Yes, miss?"

"Nothing," she said.

And he was gone.

The trio in the alcove regarded one another in mysterious silence till the woman said, "I've got something here I wanna show you, honey." She rummaged once more in the oilcloth satchel. "You won't be so snotty after you get a gander at this."

What she passed to Kay was a handbill, published on such yellowed, antique paper it looked at if it must be centuries old. In fragile, overly fancy lettering, it read:

LAZARUS

The Man Who Is Buried Alive

A MIRACLE

SEE FOR YOURSELF

Adults 25¢—Children 10¢

"I always sing a hymn and read a sermon," said the woman. "It's awful sad: some folks cry, especially the old ones. And I've got me a perfectly elegant costume: a black veil and a black dress, oh, very becoming. *He* wears a gorgeous made-to-order bridegroom suit and a turban and lotsa talcum on his face. See, we try to make it as much like a bonafide funeral as we can. But shoot, nowadays you're likely to get just a buncha smart alecks come for laughs—so sometimes I'm real glad he's afflicted like he is on accounta otherwise his feelings would be hurt, maybe."

Kay said, "You mean you're with a circus or a sideshow or something like that?"

"Nope, us alone," said the woman as she reclaimed the fallen hat. "We've been doing it for years and years —played every tank town in the South: Singasong, Mississippi—Spunky, Louisiana—Eureka, Alabama . . ." these and other names rolled off her tongue musically, running together like rain. "After the hymn, after the sermon, we bury him."

"In a coffin?"

"Sort of. It's gorgeous, it's got silver stars painted all over the lid."

"I should think he would suffocate," said Kay, amazed. "How long does he stay buried?"

"All told it takes maybe an hour—course that's not counting the lure."

"The lure?"

"Uh huh. It's what we do the night before a show. See, we hunt up a store, any ol' store with a big glass window'll do, and get the owner to let *him* sit inside this window, and, well, hypnotize himself. Stays there all night stiff as a poker and people come and look: scares the livin' hell out of 'em. . . ." While she talked she jiggled a finger in her ear, withdrawing it occasionally to examine her find. "And one time this ol' bindlestiff Mississippi sheriff tried to . . ."

The tale that followed was baffling and pointless: Kay did not bother to listen. Nevertheless, what she had heard already inspired a reverie, a vague recapitulation of her uncle's funeral; an event which, to tell the truth, had not much affected her since she had scarcely known him. And so, while gazing abstractedly at the man, an image of her uncle's face, white next the pale silk casket pillow, appeared in her mind's eye. Observing their faces simultaneously, both the man's and uncle's, as it were, she thought she recognized an odd parallel: there was about the man's face the same kind of shocking, embalmed, secret stillness, as though, in a sense, he were truly an exhibit in a glass cage, complacent to be seen, uninterested in seeing.

"I'm sorry, what did you say?"

"I said: I sure wish they'd lend us the use of a regular cemetery. Like it is now we have to put on the show wherever we can . . . mostly in empty lots that are nine times outa ten smack up against some smelly fillin' station, which ain't exactly a big help. But like I say, we got us a swell act, the best. You oughta come see it if you get a chance."

"Oh, I should love to," Kay said, absently.

"Oh, I should love to," mimicked the woman. "Well, who ask you? Anybody ask you?" She hoisted up her skirt and enthusiastically blew her nose on the ragged hem of a petticoat. "Bu-leeve me, it's a hard way to turn a dollar. Know what our take was last month? Fifty-three bucks! Honey, you try living on that sometime." She sniffed and rearranged her skirt with considerable primness. "Well, one of these days my sweet boy's sure enough going to die down there; and even then somebody'll say it was a gyp."

At this point the man took from his pocket what seemed to be a finely shellacked peach seed and balanced it on the palm of his hand. He looked across at Kay and, certain of her attention, opened his eyelids wide and began to squeeze and caress the seed in an undefinably obscene manner.

Kay frowned. "What does he want?"

"He wants you to buy it."

"But what is it?"

"A charm," said the woman. "A love charm."

Whoever was playing the harmonica stopped. Other sounds, less unique, became at once prominent: someone snoring, the gin bottle seesaw rolling, voices in sleepy argument, the train wheels' distant hum.

"Where could you get love cheaper, honey?"

"It's nice. I mean it's cute. . . ." Kay said, stalling for time. The man rubbed and polished the seed on his trouser leg. His head was lowered at a supplicating, mournful angle, and presently he stuck the seed between his teeth and bit it, as if it were a suspicious piece of silver. "Charms always bring me bad luck. And besides . . . please, can't you make him stop acting that way?"

"Don't look so scared," said the woman, more flat-voiced than ever. "He ain't gonna hurt you."

"Make him stop, damn it!"

"What can I do?" asked the woman, shrugging her shoulders. "You're the one that's got money. You're rich. All he wants is a dollar, one dollar."

Kay tucked her purse under her arm. "I have just enough to get back to school," she lied, quickly rising and stepping out into the aisle. She stood there a moment, expecting trouble. But nothing happened.

The woman, with rather deliberate indifference, heaved a sigh and closed her eyes; gradually the man subsided and stuck the charm back in his pocket. Then his hand crawled across the seat to join the woman's in a lax embrace.

Kay shut the door and moved to the front of the observation platform. It was bitterly cold in the open air, and she had left her raincoat in the alcove. She loosened her scarf and draped it over her head.

Although she had never made this trip before, the train was traveling through an area strangely familiar: tall trees, misty, painted pale by malicious moonshine, towered steep on either side without a break or clearing. Above, the sky was a stark, unexplorable blue thronged with stars that faded here and there. She could see streamers of smoke trailing from the train's engine like long clouds of ectoplasm. In one corner of the platform a red kerosene lantern cast a colorful shadow.

She found a cigarette and tried to light it: the wind

(14) SELECTED WRITINGS OF TRUMAN CAPOTE

snuffed match after match till only one was left. She
walked to the corner where the lantern burned and
cupped her hands to protect the last match: the flame
caught, sputtered, died. Angrily she tossed away the
cigarette and empty folder; all the tension in her tight-
ened to an exasperating pitch and she slammed the wall
with her fist and began to whimper softly, like an irrita-
ble child.

The intense cold made her head ache, and she
longed to go back inside the warm coach and fall asleep.
But she couldn't, at least not yet; and there was no sense
in wondering why, for she knew the answer very well.
Aloud, partly to keep her teeth from chattering and
partly because she needed the reassurance of her own
voice, she said: "We're in Alabama now, I think, and
tomorrow we'll be in Atlanta and I'm nineteen and I'll
be twenty in August and I'm a sophomore. . . ." She
glanced around at the darkness, hoping to see a sign of
dawn, and finding the same endless wall of trees, the
same frosty moon. "I hate him, he's horrible and I hate
him. . . ." She stopped, ashamed of her foolishness
and too tired to evade the truth: she was afraid.

Suddenly she felt an eerie compulsion to kneel down
and touch the lantern. Its graceful glass funnel was warm,
and the red glow seeped through her hands, making
them luminous. The heat thawed her fingers and tingled
along her arms.

She was so preoccupied she did not hear the door
open. The train wheels roaring clickety-clack-clackety-
click hushed the sound of the man's footsteps.

It was a subtle zero sensation that warned her finally;
but some seconds passed before she dared look behind.

He was standing there with a mute detachment,
his head tilted, his arms dangling at his sides. Staring up
into his harmless, vapid face, flushed brilliant by the
lantern light, Kay knew of what she was afraid: it was a
memory, a childish memory of terrors that once, long
ago, had hovered above her like haunted limbs on a

tree of night. Aunts, cooks, strangers—each eager to spin a tale or teach a rhyme of spooks and death, omens, spirits, demons. And always there had been the unfailing threat of the wizard man: stay close to the house, child, else a wizard man'll snatch and eat you alive! He lived everywhere, the wizard man, and everywhere was danger. At night, in bed, hear him tapping at the window? Listen!

Holding onto the railing, she inched upward till she was standing erect. The man nodded and waved his hand toward the door. Kay took a deep breath and stepped forward. Together they went inside.

The air in the coach was numb with sleep: a solitary light now illuminated the car, creating a kind of artificial dusk. There was no motion but the train's sluggish sway, and the stealthy rattle of discarded newspapers.

The woman alone was wide awake. You could see she was greatly excited: she fidgeted with her curls and celluloid cherries, and her plump little legs, crossed at the ankles, swung agitatedly back and forth. She paid no attention when Kay sat down. The man settled in the seat with one leg tucked beneath him and his arms folded across his chest.

In an effort to be casual, Kay picked up a magazine. She realized the man was watching her, not removing his gaze an instant: she knew this though she was afraid to confirm it, and she wanted to cry out and waken everyone in the coach. But suppose they did not hear? What if they were not really *asleep?* Tears started in her eyes, magnifying and distorting the print on a page till it became a hazy blur. She shut the magazine with fierce abruptness and looked at the woman.

"I'll buy it," she said. "The charm, I mean. I'll buy it, if that's all—just all you want."

The woman made no response. She smiled apathetically as she turned toward the man.

As Kay watched, the man's face seemed to change

form and recede before her like a moon-shaped rock
sliding downward under a surface of water. A warm
laziness relaxed her. She was dimly conscious of it when
the woman took away her purse, and when she gently
pulled the raincoat like a shroud above her head.

Miriam

FOR SEVERAL YEARS, Mrs. H. T. Miller had lived alone
in a pleasant apartment (two rooms with kitchenette)
in a remodeled brownstone near the East River. She
was a widow: Mr. H. T. Miller had left a reasonable
amount of insurance. Her interests were narrow, she
had no friends to speak of, and she rarely journeyed farther than the corner grocery. The other people in the
house never seemed to notice her: her clothes were
matter-of-fact, her hair iron-gray, clipped and casually
waved; she did not use cosmetics, her features were
plain and inconspicuous, and on her last birthday she
was sixty-one. Her activities were seldom spontaneous:
she kept the two rooms immaculate, smoked an occasional cigarette, prepared her own meals and tended a
canary.

Then she met Miriam. It was snowing that night.
Mrs. Miller had finished drying the supper dishes and
was thumbing through an afternoon paper when she saw
an advertisement of a picture playing at a neighborhood
theatre. The title sounded good, so she struggled into
her beaver coat, laced her galoshes and left the apartment, leaving one light burning in the foyer: she found
nothing more disturbing than a sensation of darkness.

The snow was fine, falling gently, not yet making an
impression on the pavement. The wind from the river
cut only at street crossings. Mrs. Miller hurried, her head

bowed, oblivious as a mole burrowing a blind path. She stopped at a drugstore and bought a package of peppermints.

A long line stretched in front of the box office; she took her place at the end. There would be (a tired voice groaned) a short wait for all seats. Mrs. Miller rummaged in her leather handbag till she collected exactly the correct change for admission. The line seemed to be taking its own time and, looking around for some distraction, she suddenly became conscious of a little girl standing under the edge of the marquee.

Her hair was the longest and strangest Mrs. Miller had ever seen: absolutely silver-white, like an albino's. It flowed waist-length in smooth, loose lines. She was thin and fragilely constructed. There was a simple, special elegance in the way she stood with her thumbs in the pockets of a tailored plum-velvet coat.

Mrs. Miller felt oddly excited, and when the little girl glanced toward her, she smiled warmly. The little girl walked over and said, "Would you care to do me a favor?"

"I'd be glad to, if I can," said Mrs. Miller.

"Oh, it's quite easy. I merely want you to buy a ticket for me; they won't let me in otherwise. Here, I have the money." And gracefully she handed Mrs. Miller two dimes and a nickel.

They went over to the theatre together. An usherette directed them to a lounge; in twenty minutes the picture would be over.

"I feel just like a genuine criminal," said Mrs. Miller gaily, as she sat down. "I mean that sort of thing's against the law, isn't it? I do hope I haven't done the wrong thing. Your mother knows where you are, dear? I mean she does, doesn't she?"

The little girl said nothing. She unbuttoned her coat and folded it across her lap. Her dress underneath was prim and dark blue. A gold chain dangled about her neck, and her fingers, sensitive and musical-looking, toyed with it. Examining her more attentively, Mrs. Miller decided the truly distinctive feature was not her hair, but her eyes; they were hazel, steady, lacking any child-like quality whatsoever and, because of their size, seemed to consume her small face.

Mrs. Miller offered a peppermint. "What's your name, dear?"

"Miriam," she said, as though, in some curious way, it were information already familiar.

"Why, isn't that funny—my name's Miriam, too. And it's not a terribly common name either. Now, don't tell me your last name's Miller!"

"Just Miriam."

"But isn't that funny?"

"Moderately," said Miriam, and rolled the peppermint on her tongue.

Mrs. Miller flushed and shifted uncomfortably. "You have such a large vocabulary for such a little girl."

"Do I?"

"Well, yes," said Mrs. Miller, hastily changing the topic to: "Do you like the movies?"

"I really wouldn't know," said Miriam. "I've never been before."

Women began filling the lounge; the rumble of the newsreel bombs exploded in the distance. Mrs. Miller rose, tucking her purse under her arm. "I guess I'd better be running now if I want to get a seat," she said. "It was nice to have met you."

Miriam nodded ever so slightly.

It snowed all week. Wheels and footsteps moved soundlessly on the street, as if the business of living continued secretly behind a pale but impenetrable curtain. In the falling quiet there was no sky or earth, only snow lifting in the wind, frosting the window glass, chilling the rooms, deadening and hushing the city. At all hours it was necessary to keep a lamp lighted, and Mrs. Miller lost track of the days: Friday was no different from Saturday and on Sunday she went to the grocery: closed, of course.

That evening she scrambled eggs and fixed a bowl of tomato soup. Then, after putting on a flannel robe and cold-creaming her face, she propped herself up in bed with a hot-water bottle under her feet. She was reading the *Times* when the doorbell rang. At first she thought it must be a mistake and whoever it was would go away. But it rang and rang and settled to a persistent buzz. She looked at the clock: a little after eleven; it did not seem possible, she was always asleep by ten.

Climbing out of bed, she trotted barefoot across the living room. "I'm coming, please be patient." The latch was caught; she turned it this way and that way and the bell never paused an instant. "Stop it," she cried. The bolt gave way and she opened the door an inch. "What in heaven's name?"

"Hello," said Miriam.

"Oh . . . why, hello," said Mrs. Miller, stepping hesitantly into the hall. "You're that little girl."

"I thought you'd never answer, but I kept my finger on the button; I knew you were home. Aren't you glad to see me?"

Mrs. Miller did not know what to say. Miriam, she saw, wore the same plum-velvet coat and now she had also a beret to match; her white hair was braided in two shining plaits and looped at the ends with enormous white ribbons.

"Since I've waited so long, you could at least let me in," she said.

"It's awfully late. . . ."

Miriam regarded her blankly. "What difference does that make? Let me in. It's cold out here and I have on a silk dress." Then, with a gentle gesture, she urged Mrs. Miller aside and passed into the apartment.

She dropped her coat and beret on a chair. She was indeed wearing a silk dress. White silk. White silk in February. The skirt was beautifully pleated and the sleeves long; it made a faint rustle as she strolled about the room. "I like your place," she said. "I like the rug, blue's my favorite color." She touched a paper rose in a vase on the coffee table. "Imitation," she commented wanly. "How sad. Aren't imitations sad?" She seated herself on the sofa, daintily spreading her skirt.

"What do you want?" asked Mrs. Miller.

"Sit down," said Miriam. "It makes me nervous to see people stand."

Mrs. Miller sank to a hassock. "What do you want?" she repeated.

"You know, I don't think you're glad I came."

For a second time Mrs. Miller was without an answer; her hand motioned vaguely. Miriam giggled and pressed back on a mound of chintz pillows. Mrs. Miller observed that the girl was less pale than she remembered; her cheeks were flushed.

"How did you know where I lived?"

Miriam frowned. "That's no question at all. What's your name? What's mine?"

"But I'm not listed in the phone book."

"Oh, let's talk about something else."

Mrs. Miller said. "Your mother must be insane to let a child like you wander around at all hours of the night—and in such ridiculous clothes. She must be out of her mind."

Miriam got up and moved to a corner where a covered bird cage hung from a ceiling chain. She peeked beneath the cover. "It's a canary," she said. "Would you mind if I woke him? I'd like to hear him sing."

"Leave Tommy alone," said Mrs. Miller, anxiously. "Don't you dare wake him."

"Certainly," said Miriam. "But I don't see why I can't hear him sing." And then, "Have you anything to eat? I'm starving! Even milk and a jam sandwich would be fine."

"Look," said Mrs. Miller, arising from the hassock, "look—if I make some nice sandwiches will you be a good child and run along home? It's past midnight, I'm sure."

"It's snowing," reproached Miriam. "And cold and dark."

"Well, you shouldn't have come here to begin with," said Mrs. Miller, struggling to control her voice. "I can't help the weather. If you want anything to eat you'll have to promise to leave."

Miriam brushed a braid against her cheek. Her eyes were thoughtful, as if weighing the proposition. She turned toward the bird cage. "Very well," she said, "I promise."

How old is she? Ten? Eleven? Mrs. Miller, in the kitchen, unsealed a jar of strawberry preserves and cut four slices of bread. She poured a glass of milk and paused to light a cigarette. *And why has she come?* Her hand shook as she held the match, fascinated, till it burned her finger. The canary was singing; singing as he did in the morning and at no other time. "Miriam," she called, "Miriam, I told you not to disturb Tommy." There was no answer. She called again; all she heard was the canary. She inhaled the cigarette and discovered she had lighted the cork-tip end and—oh, really, she mustn't lose her temper.

She carried the food in on a tray and set it on the coffee table. She saw first that the bird cage still wore its night cover. And Tommy was singing. It gave her a queer sensation. And no one was in the room. Mrs. Miller went through an alcove leading to her bedroom; at the door she caught her breath.

"What are you doing?" she asked.

Miriam glanced up and in her eyes there was a look that was not ordinary. She was standing by the bureau, a jewel case opened before her. For a minute she studied Mrs. Miller, forcing their eyes to meet, and she smiled. "There's nothing good here," she said. "But I like this." Her hand held a cameo brooch. "It's charming."

"Suppose—perhaps you'd better put it back," said Mrs. Miller, feeling suddenly the need of some support. She leaned against the door frame; her head was unbearably heavy; a pressure weighted the rhythm of her heartbeat. The light seemed to flutter defectively. "Please, child—a gift from my husband . . ."

"But it's beautiful and I want it," said Miriam. *"Give it to me."*

As she stood, striving to shape a sentence which would somehow save the brooch, it came to Mrs. Miller there was no one to whom she might turn; she was alone; a fact that had not been among her thoughts for a long time. Its sheer emphasis was stunning. But here in her own room in the hushed snow-city were evidences she could not ignore or, she knew with startling clarity, resist.

Miriam ate ravenously, and when the sandwiches and milk were gone, her fingers made cobweb movements over the plate, gathering crumbs. The cameo gleamed on her blouse, the blond profile like a trick reflection of its wearer. "That was very nice," she sighed, "though now an almond cake or a cherry would be ideal. Sweets are lovely, don't you think?"

Mrs. Miller was perched precariously on the hassock, smoking a cigarette. Her hair net had slipped lopsided and loose strands straggled down her face. Her eyes were stupidly concentrated on nothing and her cheeks were mottled in red patches, as though a fierce slap had left permanent marks.

"Is there a candy—a cake?"

Mrs. Miller tapped ash on the rug. Her head swayed slightly as she tried to focus her eyes. "You promised to leave if I made the sandwiches," she said.

"Dear me, did I?"

"It was a promise and I'm tired and I don't feel well at all."

"Mustn't fret," said Miriam. "I'm only teasing."

She picked up her coat, slung it over her arm, and arranged her beret in front of a mirror. Presently she bent close to Mrs. Miller and whispered, "Kiss me good night."

"Please—I'd rather not," said Mrs. Miller.

Miriam lifted a shoulder, arched an eyebrow. "As you like," she said, and went directly to the coffee table, seized the vase containing the paper roses, carried it to where the hard surface of the floor lay bare, and hurled it downward. Glass sprayed in all directions and she stamped her foot on the bouquet.

Then slowly she walked to the door, but before closing it she looked back at Mrs. Miller with a slyly innocent curiosity.

Mrs. Miller spent the next day in bed, rising once to feed the canary and drink a cup of tea; she took her temperature and had none, yet her dreams were feverishly agitated; their unbalanced mood lingered even as she lay staring wide-eyed at the ceiling. One dream threaded through the others like an elusively mysterious theme in a complicated symphony, and the scenes it depicted were sharply outlined, as though sketched by a hand of gifted intensity: a small girl, wearing a bridal gown and a wreath of leaves, led a gray procession down a mountain path, and among them there was unusual silence till a woman at the rear asked, "Where is she taking us?" "No one knows," said an old man marching in front. "But isn't she pretty?" volunteered a third voice. "Isn't she like a frost flower . . . so shining and white?"

Tuesday morning she woke up feeling better; harsh slats of sunlight, slanting through Venetian blinds, shed a disrupting light on her unwholesome fancies. She opened the window to discover a thawed, mild-as-spring day; a sweep of clean new clouds crumpled against a vastly blue, out-of-season sky; and across the low line of rooftops she could see the river and smoke curving from tugboat stacks in a warm wind. A great silver truck plowed the snow-banked street, its machine sound humming on the air.

After straightening the apartment, she went to the grocer's, cashed a check and continued to Schrafft's where she ate breakfast and chatted happily with the

waitress. Oh, it was a wonderful day—more like a holiday—and it would be so foolish to go home.

She boarded a Lexington Avenue bus and rode up
to Eighty-sixth Street; it was here that she had decided
to do a little shopping.

She had no idea what she wanted or needed, but
she idled along, intent only upon the passers-by, brisk
and preoccupied, who gave her a disturbing sense of
separateness.

It was while waiting at the corner of Third Avenue
that she saw the man: an old man, bowlegged and
stooped under an armload of bulging packages; he wore
a shabby brown coat and a checkered cap. Suddenly she
realized they were exchanging a smile: there was nothing friendly about this smile, it was merely two cold
flickers of recognition. But she was certain she had never
seen him before.

He was standing next to an El pillar, and as she
crossed the street he turned and followed. He kept quite
close; from the corner of her eye she watched his reflection wavering on the shopwindows.

Then in the middle of the block she stopped and
faced him. He stopped also and cocked his head, grinning. But what could she say? Do? Here, in broad daylight, on Eighty-sixth Street? It was useless and, despising her own helplessness, she quickened her steps.

Now Second Avenue is a dismal street, made from
scraps and ends; part cobblestone, part asphalt, part
cement; and its atmosphere of desertion is permanent.
Mrs. Miller walked five blocks without meeting anyone,
and all the while the steady crunch of his footfalls in the
snow stayed near. And when she came to a florist's shop,
the sound was still with her. She hurried inside and
watched through the glass door as the old man passed;
he kept his eyes straight ahead and didn't slow his pace,
but he did one strange, telling thing: he tipped his cap.

"Six white ones, did you say?" asked the florist.
"Yes," she told him, "white roses." From there she went

to a glassware store and selected a vase, presumably a replacement for the one Miriam had broken, though the price was intolerable and the vase itself (she thought) grotesquely vulgar. But a series of unaccountable purchases had begun, as if by prearranged plan: a plan of which she had not the least knowledge or control.

She bought a bag of glazed cherries, and at a place called the Knickerbocker Bakery she paid forty cents for six almond cakes.

Within the last hour the weather had turned cold again; like blurred lenses, winter clouds cast a shade over the sun, and the skeleton of an early dusk colored the sky; a damp mist mixed with the wind and the voices of a few children who romped high on mountains of gutter snow seemed lonely and cheerless. Soon the first flake fell, and when Mrs. Miller reached the brownstone house, snow was falling in a swift screen and foot tracks vanished as they were printed.

The white roses were arranged decoratively in the vase. The glazed cherries shone on a ceramic plate. The almond cakes, dusted with sugar, awaited a hand. The canary fluttered on its swing and picked at a bar of seed.

At precisely five the doorbell rang. Mrs. Miller *knew* who it was. The hem of her housecoat trailed as she crossed the floor. "Is that you?" she called.

"Naturally," said Miriam, the word resounding shrilly from the hall. "Open this door."

"Go away," said Mrs. Miller.

"Please hurry . . . I have a heavy package."

"Go away," said Mrs. Miller. She returned to the living room, lighted a cigarette, sat down and calmly listened to the buzzer; on and on and on. "You might as well leave. I have no intention of letting you in."

Shortly the bell stopped. For possibly ten minutes Mrs. Miller did not move. Then, hearing no sound, she concluded Miriam had gone. She tiptoed to the door and opened it a sliver; Miriam was half-reclining atop a cardboard box with a beautiful French doll cradled in her arms.

"Really, I thought you were never coming," she said peevishly. "Here, help me get this in, it's awfully heavy."

It was not spell-like compulsion that Mrs. Miller felt, but rather a curious passivity; she brought in the box, Miriam the doll. Miriam curled up on the sofa, not troubling to remove her coat or beret, and watched disinterestedly as Mrs. Miller dropped the box and stood trembling, trying to catch her breath.

"Thank you," she said. In the daylight she looked pinched and drawn, her hair less luminous. The French doll she was loving wore an exquisite powdered wig and its idiot glass eyes sought solace in Miriam's. "I have a surprise," she continued. "Look into my box."

Kneeling, Mrs. Miller parted the flaps and lifted out another doll; then a blue dress which she recalled as the one Miriam had worn that first night at the theatre; and of the remainder she said, "It's all clothes. Why?"

"Because I've come to live with you," said Miriam, twisting a cherry stem. "Wasn't it nice of you to buy me the cherries . . . ?"

"But you can't! For God's sake go away—go away and leave me alone!"

". . . and the roses and the almond cakes? How really wonderfully generous. You know, these cherries are delicious. The last place I lived was with an old man; he was terribly poor and we never had good things to eat. But I think I'll be happy here." She paused to snuggle her doll closer. "Now, if you'll just show me where to put my things . . ."

Mrs Miller's face dissolved into a mask of ugly red lines; she began to cry, and it was an unnatural, tearless sort of weeping, as though, not having wept for a long time, she had forgotten how. Carefully she edged backward till she touched the door.

.   .   .

She fumbled through the hall and down the stairs to a landing below. She pounded frantically on the door of the first apartment she came to; a short, redheaded man answered and she pushed past him. "Say, what the hell is this?" he said. "Anything wrong, lover?" asked a young woman who appeared from the kitchen, drying her hands. And it was to her that Mrs. Miller turned.

"Listen," she cried, "I'm ashamed behaving this way but—well, I'm Mrs. H. T. Miller and I live up-stairs and . . ." She pressed her hands over her face. "It sounds so absurd . . . ."

The woman guided her to a chair, while the man excitedly rattled pocket change. "Yeah?"

"I live upstairs and there's a little girl visiting me, and I suppose that I'm afraid of her. She won't leave and I can't make her and—she's going to do something terrible. She's already stolen my cameo, but she's about to do something worse—something terrible!"

The man asked, "Is she a relative, huh?"

Mrs. Miller shook her head. "I don't know who she is. Her name's Miriam, but I don't know for certain who she is."

"You gotta calm down, honey," said the woman, stroking Mrs. Miller's arm. "Harry here'll tend to this kid. Go on, lover." And Mrs. Miller said, "The door's open—5A."

After the man left, the woman brought a towel and bathed Mrs. Miller's face. "You're very kind," Mrs. Miller said. "I'm sorry to act like such a fool, only this wicked child. . . ."

"Sure honey," consoled the woman. "Now, you better take it easy."

Mrs. Miller rested her head in the crook of her arm; she was quiet enough to be asleep. The woman turned a radio dial; a piano and a husky voice filled the silence and the woman, tapping her foot, kept excellent time. "Maybe we oughta go up too," she said.

"I don't want to see her again. I don't want to be anywhere near her."

"Uh huh, but what you shoulda done, you shoulda called a cop."

Presently they heard the man on the stairs. He strode into the room frowning and scratching the back of his neck. "Nobody there," he said, honestly embarrassed. "She musta beat it."

"Harry, you're a jerk," announced the woman. "We been sitting here the whole time and we woulda seen . . ." she stopped abruptly, for the man's glance was sharp.

"I looked all over," he said, "and there just ain't nobody there. Nobody, understand?"

"Tell me," said Mrs. Miller, rising, "tell me, did you see a large box? Or a doll?"

"No, ma'am, I didn't."

And the woman, as if delivering a verdict, said, "Well, for cryinoutloud. . . ."

Mrs. Miller entered her apartment softly; she walked to the center of the room and stood quite still. No, in a sense it had not changed: the roses, the cakes, and the cherries were in place. But this was an empty room, emptier than if the furnishings and familiars were not present, lifeless and petrified as a funeral parlor. The sofa loomed before her with a new strangeness: its vacancy had a meaning that would have been less penetrating and terrible had Miriam been curled on it. She gazed fixedly at the space where she remembered setting the box and, for a moment, the hassock spun desperately. And she looked through the window; surely the river was real, surely snow was falling—but then, one could not be certain witness to anything: Miriam, so vividly there— and yet, where was she? Where, where?

As though moving in a dream, she sank to a chair. The room was losing shape; it was dark and getting darker and there was nothing to be done about it; she could not lift her hand to light a lamp.

Suddenly, closing her eyes, she felt an upward surge, like a diver emerging from some deeper, greener depth. In times of terror or immense distress, there are moments when the mind waits, as though for a revelation, while a skein of calm is woven over thought; it is like a sleep, or a supernatural trance; and during this lull one is aware of a force of quiet reasoning: well, what if she had never really known a girl named Miriam? that she had been foolishly frightened on the street? In the end, like everything else, it was of no importance. For the only thing she had lost to Miriam was her identity, but now she knew she had found again the person who lived in this room, who cooked her own meals, who owned a canary, who was someone she could trust and believe in: Mrs. H. T. Miller.

Listening in contentment, she became aware of a double sound: a bureau drawer opening and closing; she seemed to hear it long after completion—opening and closing. Then gradually, the harshness of it was replaced by the murmur of a silk dress and this, delicately faint, was moving nearer and swelling in intensity till the walls trembled with the vibration and the room was caving under a wave of whispers. Mrs. Miller stiffened and opened her eyes to a dull, direct stare.

"Hello," said Miriam.

The Headless Hawk

THEY *are of those that rebel against the light; they know not the ways thereof, nor abide in the paths thereof. In the dark they dig through houses, which they had marked for themselves in the daytime: they know not the light. For the morning is to them as the shadow of death: if one know them, they are in the terrors of the shadow of death.*

—JOB *24: 13, 16, 17*

VINCENT switched off the lights in the gallery. Outside, after locking the door, he smoothed the brim of an elegant Panama, and started toward Third Avenue, his umbrella-cane tap-tap-tapping along the pavement. A promise of rain had darkened the day since dawn, and a sky of bloated clouds blurred the five o'clock sun; it was hot, though, humid as tropical mist, and voices, sounding along the gray July street, sounding muffled and strange, carried a fretful undertone. Vincent felt as though he moved below the sea. Buses, cruising crosstown through Fifty-seventh Street, seemed like green-bellied fish, and faces loomed and rocked like wave-riding masks. He studied each passer-by, hunting one, and presently he saw her, a girl in a green raincoat. She was standing on the downtown corner of Fifty-seventh and Third, just standing there smoking a cigarette, and giving somehow the impression she hummed a tune. The raincoat was transparent. She wore dark slacks, no socks, a pair of huaraches, a man's white shirt. Her hair was fawn-colored, and cut like a boy's. When she noticed Vincent crossing toward her, she dropped the cigarette and hurried down the block to the doorway of an antique store.

Vincent slowed his step. He pulled out a handkerchief and dabbed his forehead; if only he could get away, go up to the Cape, lie in the sun. He bought an afternoon paper, and fumbled his change. It rolled in the gutter, dropped silently out of sight down a sewer grating. "Ain't but a nickel, bub," said the newsdealer, for Vincent, though actually unaware of his loss, looked heartbroken. And it was like that often now, never quite in contact, never sure whether a step would take him backward or forward, up or down. Very casually, with the handle of the umbrella hooked over an arm, and his eyes concentrated on the paper's headlines—but what did the damn thing say?—he continued downtown. A swarthy woman carrying a shopping bag jostled him, glared, muttered in coarsely vehement Italian. The ragged cut of her voice seemed to come through layers of wool. As he approached the antique store where the girl in the green raincoat waited, he walked slower still, counting one, two, three, four, five, six—at six he halted before the window.

The window was like a corner of an attic; a lifetime's discardings rose in a pyramid of no particular worth: vacant picture frames, a lavender wig, Gothic shaving mugs, beaded lamps. There was an oriental mask suspended on a ceiling cord, and wind from an electric fan whirring inside the shop revolved it slowly round and round. Vincent, by degrees, lifted his gaze, and looked at the girl directly. She was hovering in the doorway so that he saw her greenness distorted wavy through double glass; the elevated pounded overhead and the window trembled. Her image spread like a reflection on silverware, then gradually hardened again: she was watching him.

He hung an Old Gold between his lips, rummaged for a match and, finding none, sighed. The girl stepped from the doorway. She held out a cheap little lighter; as the flame pulsed up, her eyes, pale, shallow, cat-green fixed him with alarming intensity. Her eyes had an astonished, a shocked look, as though, having at one time witnessed a terrible incident, they'd locked wide open. Carefree bangs fringed her forehead; this boy haircut emphasized the childish and rather poetic quality of her narrow, hollow-cheeked face. It was the kind of face one sometimes sees in paintings of medieval youths.

Letting the smoke pour out his nose, Vincent, knowing it was useless to ask, wondered, as always, what she was living on and where. He flipped away the cigarette, for he had not wanted it to begin with, and then, pivoting, crossed rapidly under the El; as he approached the curb he heard a crash of brakes, and suddenly, as if cotton plugs had been blasted from his ears, city noises crowded in. A cab driver hollered: "Fa crissake, sistuh, get the lead outa yuh pants!" but the girl did not even bother turning her head; trance-eyed, undisturbed as a sleepwalker, and staring straight at Vincent, who watched dumbly, she moved across the street. A colored boy wearing a jazzy purple suit took her elbow. "You sick, Miss?" he said, guiding her forward, and she did not answer. "You look mighty funny, Miss. If you sick, I . . ." then, following the direction of her eyes, he released his hold. There was something here which made him all still inside. "Uh—yeah," he muttered, backing off with a grinning display of tartar-coated teeth.

So Vincent began walking in earnest, and his umbrella tapped code-like block after block. His shirt was soaked through with itchy sweat, and the noises, now so harsh, banged in his head: a trick car horn hooting "My Country, 'Tis of Thee," electric spray of sparks crackling bluely off thundering rails, whiskey laughter hiccuping through gaunt doors of beer-stale bars where orchid juke machines manufactured U.S.A. music—"I got spurs that jingle jangle jingle. . . ." Occasionally he caught a glimpse of her, once mirrored in the window of Paul's Seafood Palace where scarlet lobsters basked on a beach of flaked ice. She followed close with her hands shoved into the pockets of her raincoat. The brassy lights of a movie marquee blinked, and he remembered how she loved movies: murder films, spy chillers, Wild West shows. He turned into a side street leading toward the East River; it was quiet here, hushed like Sunday: a sailor-stroller munching an Eskimo Pie, energetic twins skipping rope, an old velvet lady with gardenia-white hair lifting aside lace curtains and peering listlessly into rain-dark space—a city landscape in July. And behind him the soft insistent slap of sandals. Traffic lights on Second Avenue turned red; at the corner a bearded midget, Ruby the Popcorn Man, wailed, "Hot buttered popcorn, big bag, yah?" Vincent shook his head, and the midget looked very put out, then: "Yuh see?" he jeered, pushing a shovel inside the candlelit cage where bursting kernels bounced like crazy moths. "Yuh see, de girlie knows popcorn's nourishin'." She bought a dime's worth, and it was in a green sack matching her raincoat, matching her eyes.

This is my neighborhood, my street, the house with the gateway is where I live. To remind himself of this was necessary, inasmuch as he'd substituted for a sense of reality a knowledge of time, and place. He glanced gratefully at sourfaced, faded ladies, at the pipe-puffing males squatting on the surrounding steps of brownstone stoops. Nine pale little girls shrieked round a corner flower cart begging daisies to pin in their hair, but the peddler said, "Shoo!" and, fleeing like beads of a broken bracelet, they circled in the street, the wild ones leaping with laughter, and the shy ones, silent and isolated, lifting summer-wilted faces skyward: the rain, would it never come?

Vincent, who lived in a basement apartment, descended several steps and took out his keycase; then, pausing behind the hallway door, he looked back through a peephole in the paneling. The girl was waiting on the sidewalk above; she leaned against a brownstone banister, and her arms fell limp—and popcorn spilled snow-like round her feet. A grimy little boy crept slyly up to pick among it like a squirrel.

2

For Vincent it was a holiday. No one had come by the gallery all morning, which, considering the arctic weather, was not unusual. He sat at his desk devouring tangerines, and enjoying immensely a Thurber story in an old *New Yorker*. Laughing loudly, he did not hear the girl enter, see her cross the dark carpet, notice her at all, in fact, until the telephone rang. "Garland Gallery, hello." She was odd, most certainly, that indecent haircut, those depthless eyes— "Oh, Paul. *Comme ci, comme ça* and you?"—and dressed like a freak: no coat, just a lumberjack's shirt, navy-blue slacks and—was it a joke? —pink ankle socks, a pair of huaraches. "The ballet? Who's dancing? Oh, her!" Under an arm she carried a flat parcel wrapped in sheets of funny-paper—"Look, Paul, what say I call back? There's someone here . . ." and, anchoring the receiver, assuming a commercial smile, he stood up. "Yes?"

Her lips, crusty with chap, trembled with unrealized words as though she had possibly a defect of speech, and her eyes rolled in their sockets like loose marbles. It was the kind of disturbed shyness one associates with children. "I've a picture," she said. "You buy pictures?"

At this, Vincent's smile became fixed. "We exhibit."

"I painted it myself," she said, and her voice, hoarse and slurred, was Southern. "My picture—I painted it. A lady told me there were places around here that bought pictures."

Vincent said, "Yes, of course, but the truth is"— and he made a helpless gesture—"the truth is I've no authority whatever. Mr. Garland—this is his gallery, you know—*is* out of town." Standing there on the expanse of fine carpet, her body sagging sideways with the weight of her package, she looked like a sad rag doll. "Maybe," he began, "maybe Henry Krueger up the street at Sixty-five . . ." but she was not listening.

"I did it myself," she insisted softly. "Tuesdays and Thursdays were our painting days, and a whole year I worked. The others, they kept messing it up, and Mr. Destronelli . . ." Suddenly, as though aware of an indiscretion, she stopped and bit her lip. Her eyes narrowed. "He's not a friend of yours?"

"Who?" said Vincent, confused.

"Mr. Destronelli."

He shook his head, and wondered why it was that eccentricity always excited in him such curious admiration. It was the feeling he'd had as a child toward carnival freaks. And it was true that about those whom he'd loved there was always a little something wrong, broken. Strange, though, that this quality, having stimulated an attraction, should, in his case, regularly end it by destroying it. "Of course I haven't any authority," he repeated, sweeping tangerine hulls into a wastebasket, "but, if you like, I suppose I could look at your work."

A pause; then, kneeling on the floor, she commenced stripping off the funny-paper wrapping. It originally had been, Vincent noticed, part of the New Orleans *Times-Picayune*. "From the South, aren't you?" he said. She did not look up, but he saw her shoulders stiffen. "No," she said. Smiling, he considered a moment, decided it would be tactless to challenge so transparent a lie. Or could she have misunderstood? And all at once he felt an intense longing to touch her head, finger the boyish hair. He shoved his hands in his pockets and glanced at the window. It was spangled with February frost, and some passer-by had scratched on the glass an obscenity. "There," she said.

A headless figure in a monklike robe reclined complacently on top a tacky vaudeville trunk; in one hand she held a fuming blue candle, in the other a miniature gold cage, and her severed head lay bleeding at her feet:

it was the girl's, this head, but here her hair was long, very long, and a snowball kitten with crystal spitfire eyes playfully pawed, as it would a spool of yarn, the sprawling ends. The wings of a hawk, headless, scarlet-breasted copper-clawed, curtained the background like a nightfall sky. It was a crude painting, the hard pure colors molded with male brutality, and, while there was no technical merit evident, it had that power often seen in something deeply felt, though primitively conveyed. Vincent reacted as he did when occasionally a phrase of music surprised a note of inward recognition, or a cluster of words in a poem revealed to him a secret concerning himself: he felt a powerful chill of pleasure run down his spine. "Mr. Garland is in Florida," he said cautiously, "but I think he should see it; you couldn't leave it for, say, a week?"

"I had a ring and I sold it," she said, and he had the feeling she was talking in a trance. "It was a nice ring, a wedding ring—not mine—with writing on it. I had an overcoat, too." She twisted one of her shirt buttons, pulled till it popped off and rolled on the carpet like a pearl eye. "I don't want much—fifty dollars; is that unfair?"

"Too much," said Vincent, more curtly than he intended. Now he wanted her painting, not for the gallery, but for himself. There are certain works of art which excite more interest in their creators than in what they have created, usually because in this kind of work one is able to identify something which has until that instant seemed a private inexpressible perception, and you wonder: who is this that knows me, and how? "I'll give thirty."

For a moment she gaped at him stupidly, and then, sucking her breath, held out her hand, palm up. This directness, too innocent to be offensive, caught him off guard. Somewhat embarrassed, he said, "I'm most awfully afraid I'll have to mail a check. Could you . . . ?" The telephone interrupted, and, as he went to answer, she followed, her hand outstretched, a frantic look pinching her face. "Oh, Paul, may I call back? Oh, I see. Well, hold on a sec." Cupping the mouthpiece against his shoulder, he pushed a pad and pencil across the desk. "Here, write your name and address."

But she shook her head, the dazed, anxious expression deepening.

"Check," said Vincent, "I have to mail a check. Please, your name and address." He grinned encouragingly when at last she began to write.

"Sorry, Paul . . . Whose party? Why, the little bitch, she didn't invite . . . Hey!" he called, for the girl was moving toward the door. "Please, hey!" Cold air chilled the gallery, and the door slammed with a glassy rattle. Hellohellohello. Vincent did not answer; he stood puzzling over the curious information she'd left printed on his pad: D.J.—Y.W.C.A. Hellohellohello.

It hung above his mantel, the painting, and on those nights when he could not sleep he would pour a glass of whiskey and talk to the headless hawk, tell it the stuff of his life: he was, he said, a poet who had never written poetry, a painter who had never painted, a lover who had never loved (absolutely)—someone, in short, without direction, and quite headless. Oh, it wasn't that he hadn't tried—good beginnings, always, bad endings, always. Vincent, white, male, age 36, college graduate: a man in the sea, fifty miles from shore; a victim, born to be murdered, either by himself or another; an actor unemployed. It was there, all of it, in the painting, everything disconnected and cockeyed, and who was she that she should know so much? Inquiries, those he'd made had led nowhere; not another dealer knew of her, and to search for a D.J. living in, presumably, a Y.W.C.A. seemed absurd. Then, too, he'd quite expected she would reappear, but February passed, and March. One evening, crossing the square which fronts the Plaza, he had a queer thing happen. The archaic hansom drivers who line that location were lighting their carriage lamps, for it was dusk, and lamplight traced through moving leaves. A hansom pulled from the curb and rolled past in the twilight. There was a single occupant, and this passenger, whose face he could not see, was a girl with chopped fawn-colored hair. So he settled on a bench, and whiled away time talking with a soldier, and a fairy colored boy who quoted poetry, and a man out airing a dachshund: night characters with whom he waited—but the carriage, with the one for whom he waited, never came back. Again he saw her (or supposed he did) descending subway stairs, and this time lost her in the tiled tunnels of painted arrows and Spearmint machines. It was as if her face were imposed upon his mind; he could no more dispossess it than could, for example, a dead man rid his legendary eyes of the last image seen. Around the middle of April he went up to Connecticut to spend a weekend with his married sister; keyed-up, caustic, he wasn't, as she complained, at all like himself. "What is it, Vinny darling—if you need money . . ." "Oh, shut up!" he said. "Must be love," teased his brother-in-law. "Come on, Vinny, 'fess up; what's she like?" And all this so annoyed him he caught the next train home. From a booth in Grand Central he called to apologize, but a sick nervousness hummed inside him, and he hung up while the operator was still trying to make a connection. He wanted a drink. At the Commodore Bar he spent an hour or so downing four daiquiris—it was Saturday, it was nine, there was nothing to do unless he did it alone, he was feeling sad for himself. Now in the park behind the Public Library sweethearts moved whisperingly under trees, and drinking-fountain water bubbled softly, like their voices, but for all the white April evening meant to him, Vincent, drunk a little and wandering, might as well have been old, like the old bench-sitters rasping phlegm.

In the country, spring is a time of small happenings happening quietly, hyacinth shoots thrusting in a garden, willows burning with a sudden frosty fire of green, lengthening afternoons of long flowing dusk, and midnight rain opening lilac; but in the city there is the fanfare of organ-grinders, and odors, undiluted by winter wind, clog the air; windows long closed go up, and conversation, drifting beyond a room, collides with the jangle of a peddler's bell. It is the crazy season of toy balloons and roller skates, of courtyard baritones and men of freakish enterprise, like the one who jumped up now like a jack-in-the-box. He was old, he had a telescope and a sign: 25¢ See the Moon! See the Stars! 25¢ No stars could penetrate a city's glare, but Vincent saw the moon, a round, shadowed whiteness, and then a blaze of electric bulbs: Four Roses, Bing Cro—— he was moving through caramel-scented staleness, swimming through oceans of cheese-pale faces, neon, and darkness. Above the blasting of a jukebox, bulletfire boomed, a cardboard duck fell plop, and somebody screeched: "Yay Iggy!" It was a Broadway funhouse, a penny arcade, and jammed from wall to wall with Saturday splurgers. He watched a penny movie (*What The Bootblack Saw*), and had his fortune told by a wax witch leering behind glass: "Yours is an affectionate nature" . . . but he read no further, for up near the jukebox there was an attractive commotion. A crowd of kids, clapping in time to jazz music, had formed a circle around two dancers. These dancers were both colored, both girls. They swayed together slow and easy, like lovers, rocked and stamped and rolled serious savage eyes, their muscles rhythmically attuned to the ripple of a clarinet, the rising harangue of a drum. Vincent's gaze traveled round the audience, and when he saw her a bright shiver went through him, for something of the dance's violence was reflected in her face. Standing there beside a tall ugly boy, it was as if she were the sleeper and the Negroes a dream. Trumpet-drum-piano, bawling on behind a black girl's froggy voice, wailed toward a rocking finale. The clapping ended, the dancers parted. She was alone now; though Vincent's instinct was to leave before she noticed, he advanced, and, as one would gently waken a sleeper, lightly touched her shoulder. "Hello," he said, his voice too loud. Turning, she stared at him, and her eyes were clear-blank. First terror, then puzzlement replaced the dead lost look. She took a step backward, and, just as the jukebox commenced hollering again, he seized her wrist: "You re-

member me," he prompted, "the gallery? Your painting?"
She blinked, let the lids sink sleepily over those eyes, and
he could feel the slow relaxing of tension in her arm.
She was thinner than he recalled, prettier, too, and her
hair, grown out somewhat, hung in casual disorder. A
little Christmas ribbon dangled sadly from a stray lock.
He started to say, "Can I buy you a drink?" but she
leaned against him, her head resting on his chest like a
child's, and he said: "Will you come home with me?" She
lifted her face; the answer, when it came, was a breath,
a whisper: "Please," she said.

Vincent stripped off his clothes, arranged them
neatly in the closet, and admired his nakedness before a
mirrored door. He was not so handsome as he supposed,
but handsome all the same. For his moderate height he
was excellently proportioned; his hair was dark yellow,
and his delicate, rather snub-nosed face had a fine,
ruddy coloring. The rumble of running water broke the
quiet; she was in the bathroom preparing to bathe. He
dressed in loose-fitting flannel pajamas, lit a cigarette,
said, "Everything all right?" The water went off, a long
silence, then: "Yes, thank you." On the way home in a
cab he'd made an attempt at conversation, but she had
said nothing, not even when they entered the apartment
—and this last offended him, for, taking rather female
pride in his quarters, he'd expected a complimentary remark. It was one enormously high-ceilinged room, a bath
and kitchenette, a backyard garden. In the furnishings
he'd combined modern with antique and produced a distinguished result. Decorating the walls were a trio of
Toulouse-Lautrec prints, a framed circus poster, D. J.'s
painting, photographs of Rilke, Nijinsky and Duse. A
candelabra of lean blue candles burned on a desk; the
room, washed in their delirious light, wavered. French
doors led into the yard. He never used it much, for it was
a place impossible to keep clean. There were a few
dead tulip stalks dark in the moonshine, a puny heaven
tree, and an old weather-worn chair left by the last ten-

ant. He paced back and forth over the cold flagstones, hoping that in the cool air the drugged drunk sensation he felt would wear off. Nearby a piano was being badly mauled, and in a window above there was a child's face. He was thumbing a blade of grass when her shadow fell long across the yard. She was in the doorway. "You mustn't come out," he said, moving toward her. "It's turned a little cold."

There was about her now an appealing softness; she seemed somehow less angular, less out of tune with the average, and Vincent, offering a glass of sherry, was delighted at the delicacy with which she touched it to her lips. She was wearing his terry-cloth robe; it was by yards too large. Her feet were bare, and she tucked them up beside her on the couch. "It's like Glass Hill, the candlelight," she said, and smiled. "My Granny lived at Glass Hill. We had lovely times, sometimes; do you know what she used to say? She used to say, 'Candles are magic wands; light one and the world is a story book.' "

"What a dreary old lady she must've been," said Vincent, quite drunk. "We should probably have hated each other."

"Granny would've loved you," she said. "She loved any kind of man, every man she ever met, even Mr. Destronelli."

"Destronelli?" It was a name he'd heard before.

Her eyes slid slyly sideways, and this look seemed to say: There must be no subterfuge between us, we who understand each other have no need of it. "Oh, you know," she said with a conviction that, under more commonplace circumstances, would have been surprising. It was, however, as if he'd abandoned temporarily the faculty of surprise. "Everybody knows him."

He curved an arm around her, and brought her nearer. "Not me, I don't," he said, kissing her mouth, neck; she was not responsive especially, but he said—and his voice had gone adolescently shaky—"Never met Mr.

Whoozits." He slipped a hand inside her robe, loosening it away from her shoulders. Above one breast she had a birthmark, small and star-shaped. He glanced at the mirrored door where uncertain light rippled their reflections, made them pale and incomplete. She was smiling. "Mr. Whoozits," he said, "what does he look like?" The suggestion of a smile faded, a small monkeylike frown flickered on her face. She looked above the mantel at her painting, and he realized that this was the first notice she'd shown it; she appeared to study in the picture a particular object, but whether hawk or head he could not say. "Well," she said quietly, pressing closer to him, "he looks like you, like me, like most anybody."

It was raining; in the wet noon light two nubs of candle still burned, and at an open window gray curtains tossed forlornly. Vincent extricated his arm; it was numb from the weight of her body. Careful not to make a noise, he eased out of bed, blew out the candles, tiptoed into the bathroom, and doused his face with cold water. On the way to the kitchenette he flexed his arms, feeling, as he hadn't for a long time, an intensely male pleasure in his strength, a healthy wholeness of person. He made and put on a tray orange juice, raisin-bread toast, a pot of tea; then, so inexpertly that everything on the tray rattled, he brought the breakfast in and placed it on a table beside the bed.

She had not moved; her ruffled hair spread fanwise across the pillow, and one hand rested in the hollow where his head had lain. He leaned over and kissed her lips, and her eyelids, blue with sleep, trembled. "Yes, yes, I'm awake," she murmured, and rain, lifting in the wind, sprayed against the window like surf. He somehow knew that with her there would be none of the usual artifice: no avoidance of eyes, no shame-faced, accusing pause. She raised herself on her elbow; she looked at him, Vincent thought, as if he were her husband, and, handing her the orange juice, he smiled his gratitude.

"What is today?"

"Sunday," he told her, bundling under the quilt, and settling the tray across his legs.

"But there are no church bells," she said. "And it's raining."

Vincent divided a piece of toast. "You don't mind that, do you? Rain—such a peaceful sound." He poured tea. "Sugar? Cream?"

She disregarded this, and said, "Today is Sunday what? What month, I mean?"

"Where have you been living, in the subway?" he said, grinning. And it puzzled him to think she was serious. "Oh, April . . . April something-or-other."

"April," she repeated. "Have I been here long?"

"Only since last night."

"Oh."

Vincent stirred his tea, the spoon tinkling in the cup like a bell. Toast crumbs spilled among the sheets, and he thought of the *Tribune* and the *Times* waiting outside the door, but they, this morning, held no charms; it was best lying here beside her in the warm bed, sipping tea, listening to the rain. Odd, when you stopped to consider, certainly very odd. She did not know his name, nor he hers. And so he said, "I still owe you thirty dollars, do you realize that? Your own fault, of course—leaving such a damn fool address. And D.J., what is that supposed to mean?"

"I don't think I'd better tell you my name," she said. "I could make up one easy enough: Dorothy Jordan, Delilah Johnson; see? There are all kinds of names I could make up, and if it wasn't for him I'd tell you right."

Vincent lowered the tray to the floor. He rolled over on his side, and, facing her, his heartbeat quickened. "Who's him?" Though her expression was calm, anger muddied her voice when she said, "If you don't know him, then tell me, why am I here?"

Silence, and outside the rain seemed suddenly suspended. A ship's horn moaned in the river. Holding her close, he combed his fingers through her hair, and, wanting so much to be believed, said, "Because I love you."

She closed her eyes. "What became of them?"

"Who?"

"The others you've said that to."

It commenced again, the rain spattering grayly at the window, falling on hushed Sunday streets; listening, Vincent remembered. He remembered his cousin, Lucille, poor, beautiful, stupid Lucille who sat all day embroidering silk flowers on scraps of linen. And Allen T. Baker—there was the winter they'd spent in Havana, the house they'd lived in, crumbling rooms of rose-colored rock; poor Allen, he'd thought it was to be forever. Gordon too. Gordon, with the kinky yellow hair, and a head full of old Elizabethan ballads. Was it true he'd shot himself? And Connie Silver, the deaf girl, the one who had wanted to be an actress—what had become of her? Or Helen, Louise, Laura? "There was just one," he said, and to his own ears this had a truthful ring. "Only one, and she's dead."

Tenderly, as if in sympathy, she touched his cheek "I suppose he killed her," she said, her eyes so close he could see the outline of his face imprisoned in their greenness. "He killed Miss Hall, you know. The dearest woman in the world, Miss Hall, and so pretty your breath went away. I had piano lessons with her, and when she played the piano, when she said hello and when she said good-bye—it was like my heart would stop." Her voice had taken on an impersonal tone, as though she were talking of matters belonging to another age, and in which she was not concerned directly. "It was the end of summer when she married him—September, I think. She went to Atlanta, and they were married there, and she never came back. It was just that sudden." She snapped her fingers. "Just like that. I saw a picture of him in the paper. Sometimes I think if she'd known how much I loved her—why are there some you can't ever tell?—I think maybe she wouldn't have married; maybe it would've all been different, like I wanted it." She turned her face into the pillow, and if she cried there was no sound.

On May twentieth she was eighteen; it seemed incredible—Vincent had thought her many years older. He wanted to introduce her at a surprise party, but had finally to admit that this was an unsuitable plan. First off, though the subject was always there on the tip of his tongue, not once had he ever mentioned D.J. to any of his friends; secondly, he could visualize discouragingly well the entertainment provided them at meeting a girl about whom, while they openly shared an apartment, he knew nothing, not even her name. Still the birthday called for some kind of treat. Dinner and the theatre were hopeless. She hadn't, through no fault of his, a dress of any sort. He'd given her forty-odd dollars to buy clothes, and here is what she spent it on: a leather windbreaker, a set of military brushes, a raincoat, a cigarette lighter. Also, her suitcase, which she'd brought to the apartment, had contained nothing but hotel soap, a pair of scissors she used for pruning her hair, two Bibles, and an appalling color-tinted photograph. The photograph showed a simpering middle-aged woman with dumpy features. There was an inscription: Best Wishes and Good Luck from Martha Lovejoy Hall.

Because she could not cook they had their meals out; his salary and the limitations of her wardrobe confined them mostly to the Automat—her favorite: the macaroni was so delicious!—or one of the bar-grills along Third. And so the birthday dinner was eaten in an Automat. She'd scrubbed her face until the skin shone red, trimmed and shampooed her hair, and with the messy skill of a six-year-old playing grownup, varnished her nails. She wore the leather windbreaker, and on it pinned a sheaf of violets he'd given her; it must have looked amusing, for two rowdy girls sharing their table giggled frantically. Vincent said if they didn't shut up . . .

"Oh, yeah, who you think you are?"

"Superman. Jerk thinks he's superman."

It was too much, and Vincent lost his temper. He shoved back from the table, upsetting a ketchup jar. "Let's get the hell out of here," he said, but D.J., who had paid the fracas no attention whatever, went right on spooning blackberry cobbler; furious as he was, he waited quietly until she finished, for he respected her remoteness, and yet wondered in what period of time she lived. It was futile, he'd discovered, to question her past; still, she seemed only now and then aware of the present, and it was likely the future didn't mean much to her. Her mind was like a mirror reflecting blue space in a barren room.

"What would you like now?" he said, as they came into the street. "We could ride in a cab through the park."

She wiped off with her jacket-cuff flecks of blackberry staining the corners of her mouth, and said, "I want to go to a picture show."

The movies. Again. In the last month he'd seen so many films, snatches of Hollywood dialogue rumbled in his dreams. One Saturday at her insistence they'd bought tickets to three different theatres, cheap places where smells of latrine disinfectant poisoned the air. And each morning before leaving for work he left on the mantel fifty cents—rain or shine, she went to a picture show. But Vincent was sensitive enough to see why; there had been in his own life a certain time of limbo when he'd gone to movies every day, often sitting through several repeats of the same film; it was in its way like religion, for there, watching the shifting patterns of black and white, he knew a release of conscience similar to the kind a man must find confessing to his father.

"Handcuffs," she said, referring to an incident in *The Thirty-Nine Steps,* which they'd seen at the Beverly in a program of Hitchcock revivals. "That blond woman and the man handcuffed together—well, it made me think of something else." She stepped into a pair of his pajamas, pinned the corsage of violets to the edge of her pillow, and folded up on the bed. "People getting caught like that, locked together."

Vincent yawned. "Uh huh," he said, and turned off the lights. "Again, happy birthday, darling, it *was* a happy birthday?"

She said, "Once I was in this place, and there were two girls dancing; they were so free—there was just them and nobody else, and it was beautiful like a sunset." She was silent a long while; then, her slow Southern voice dragging over the words: "It was mighty nice of you to bring me violets."

"Glad—like them," he answered sleepily.

"It's a shame they have to die."

"Yes, well, good night."

"Good night."

Close-up. Oh, but John, it isn't for my sake after all we've the children to consider a divorce would ruin their lives! Fadeout. The screen trembles; rattle of drums, flourish trumpets: R.K.O. PRESENTS . . .

Here is a hall without exit, a tunnel without end. Overhead, chandeliers sparkle, and wind-bent candles float on currents of air. Before him is an old man rocking in a rocking chair, an old man with yellow-dyed hair, powdered cheeks, kewpie-doll lips: Vincent recognizes Vincent. Go away, screams Vincent, the young and handsome, but Vincent, the old and horrid, creeps forward on all fours, and climbs spiderlike onto his back. Threats, pleas, blows, nothing will dislodge him. And so he races with his shadow, his rider jogging up and down. A serpent of lightning blazes, and all at once the tunnel seethes with men wearing white tie and tails, women costumed in brocaded gowns. He is humiliated; how gauche they must think him appearing at so elegant a gathering carrying on his back, like Sinbad, a sordid old man. The guests stand about in petrified pairs, and there is no conversation. He notices then that many are also saddled with malevolent semblances of themselves, outward embodiments of inner decay. Just beside him a lizard-like man rides an albino-eyed Negro. A man is coming toward him, the host; short, florid, bald, he steps lightly, precisely in glacé shoes; one arm, held stiffly crooked, supports a massive headless hawk whose talons, latched to the wrist, draw blood. The hawk's wings unfurl as its master struts by. On a pedestal there is perched an old-time phonograph. Winding the handle, the host supplies a record: a tinny worn-out waltz vibrates the morning-glory horn. He lifts a hand, and in a soprano voice announces: "Attention! The dancing will commence." The host with his hawk weaves in and out as round and round they dip, they turn. The walls widen, the ceiling grows tall. A girl glides into Vincent's arms, and a cracked, cruel imitation of his voice says: "Lucille, how divine; that exquisite scent, is it violet?" This is Cousin Lucille, and then, as they circle the room, her face changes. Now he waltzes with another. "Why, Connie, Connie Silver! How marvelous to see you," shrieks the voice, for Connie is quite deaf. Suddenly a gentleman with a bullet-bashed head cuts in: "Gordon forgive me, I never meant . . ." but they are gone, Gordon and Connie, dancing together. Again, a new partner. It is D.J., and she too has a figure barnacled to her back, an enchanting auburn-haired child; like an emblem of innocence, the child cuddles to her chest a snowball kitten. "I am heavier than I look," says the child, and the terrible voice retorts, "But I am heaviest of all." The instant their hands meet he begins to feel the weight upon him diminish; the old Vincent is fading. His feet lift off the floor, he floats upward from her embrace. The victrola grinds away loud as ever, but he is rising high, and the white receding faces gleam below like mushrooms on a dark meadow.

The host releases his hawk, sends it soaring. Vincent thinks, no matter, it is a blind thing, and the wicked are safe among the blind. But the hawk wheels above him, swoops down, claws foremost; at last he knows there is to be no freedom.

And the blackness of the room filled his eyes. One arm lolled over the bed's edge, his pillow had fallen to the floor. Instinctively he reached out, asking mother-comfort of the girl beside him. Sheets smooth and cold; emptiness, and the tawdry fragrance of drying violets. He snapped up straight: "You, where are you?"

The French doors were open. An ashy trace of moon swayed on the threshold, for it was not yet light, and in the kitchen the refrigerator purred like a giant cat. A stack of paper rustled on the desk. Vincent called again, softly this time, as if he wished himself unheard. Rising, he stumbled forward on dizzy legs, and looked into the yard. She was there, leaning, half-kneeling, against the heaven tree. "What?" and she whirled around. He could not see her well, only a dark substantial shape. She came closer. A finger pressed her lips.

"What is it?" he whispered.

She rose on tiptoe, and her breath tingled in his ear. "I warn you, go inside."

"Stop this foolishness," he said in a normal voice. "Out here barefooted, you'll catch . . ." but she clamped a hand over his mouth.

"I saw him," she whispered. "He's here."

Vincent knocked her hand away. It was hard not to slap her. "Him! Him! Him! What's the matter with you? Are you—"he tried too late to prevent the word—"crazy?" There, the acknowledgment of something he'd known, but had not allowed his conscious mind to crystallize. And he thought: Why should this make a difference? A man cannot be held to account for those he loves. Untrue. Feeble-witted Lucille weaving mosaics on silk, embroidering his name on scarves; Connie, in her hushed deaf world, listening for his footstep, a sound she would surely hear; Allen T. Baker thumbing his photograph, still needing love, but old now, and lost —all betrayed. And he'd betrayed himself with talents unexploited, voyages never taken, promises unfulfilled. There had seemed nothing left him until—oh, why in his lovers must he always find the broken image of himself? Now, as he looked at her in the aging dawn, his heart was cold with the death of love.

She moved away, and under the tree. "Leave me here," she said, her eyes scanning tenement windows. "Only a moment."

Vincent waited, waited. On all sides windows looked down like the doors of dreams, and overhead, four flights up, a family's laundry whipped a washline. The setting moon was like the early moon of dusk, a vaporish cartwheel, and the sky, draining of dark, was washed with gray. Sunrise wind shook the leaves of the heaven tree, and in the paling light the yard assumed a pattern, objects a position, and from the roofs came the throaty morning rumble of pigeons. A light went on. Another.

And at last she lowered her head; whatever she was looking for, she had not found it. Or, he wondered as she turned to him with tilted lips, had she?

"Well, you're home kinda early, aren't you, Mr. Waters?" It was Mrs. Brennan, the super's bow-legged wife. "And, well, Mr. Waters—lovely weather, ain't it? —you and me got sumpin' to talk about."

"Mrs. Brennan"—how hard it was to breathe, to speak; the words grated his hurting throat, sounded loud as thunderclaps—"I'm rather ill, so if you don't mind . . ." and he tried to brush past her.

"Say, that's a pity. Ptomaine, must be ptomaine. Yessir, I tell you a person can't be too careful. It's them Jews, you know. They run all them delicatessens. Uh uh, none of that Jew food for me." She stepped before the gate, blocking his path, and pointed an admonishing finger: "Trouble with you, Mr. Waters, is you don't lead no kinda *normal* life."

A knot of pain was set like a malignant jewel in the core of his head; each aching motion made jeweled pinpoints of color flare out. The super's wife babbled on, but there were blank moments when, fortunately, he could not hear at all. It was like a radio—the volume turned low, then full blast. "Now I know she's a decent Christian lady, Mr. Waters, or else what would a gentle-

man like you be doing with—hm. Still, the fact is, Mr.
Cooper don't tell lies, and he's a real calm man, besides.
Been gas meter man for this district I don't know how
long." A truck rolled down the street spraying water,
and her voice, submerged below its roar, came up again
like a shark. "Mr. Cooper had every reason to believe
she meant to kill him—well, you can imagine, her
standin' there with them scissors, and shoutin'. She called
him an Eyetalian name. Now all you got to do is look at
Mr. Cooper to know he ain't no Eyetalian. Well, you can
see, Mr. Waters, such carryings-on are bound to give
the house a bad . . ."

Brittle sunshine plundering the depths of his eyes
made tears, and the super's wife, wagging her finger,
seemed to break into separate pieces: a nose, a chin, a
red, red eye. "Mr. Destronelli," he said. "Excuse me,
Mrs. Brennan, I mean excuse me." She thinks I'm drunk,
and I'm sick, and can't she see I'm sick? "My guest is
leaving. She's leaving today, and she won't be back."

"Well, now, you don't say," said Mrs. Brennan,
clucking her tongue. "Looks like she needs a rest, poor
little thing. So pale, sorta. Course I don't want no more
to do with them Eyetalians than the next one, but imagine thinking Mr. Cooper was an Eyetalian. Why, he's
white as you or me." She tapped his shoulder solicitously.
"Sorry you feel so sick, Mr. Waters; ptomaine, I tell you.
A person can't be too care . . ."

The hall smelled of cooking and incinerator ashes.
There was a stairway which he never used, his apartment being on the first floor, straight ahead. A match
snapped fire, and Vincent, groping his way, saw a small
boy—he was not more than three or four—squatting under the stairwell; he was playing with a big box of
kitchen matches, and Vincent's presence appeared not to
interest him. He simply struck another match. Vincent
could not make his mind work well enough to phrase a
reprimand, and as he waited there, tongue-tied, a door,
his door, opened.

Hide. For if she saw him she would know something was wrong, suspect something. And if she spoke, if their eyes met, then he would never be able to go through with it. So he pressed into a dark corner behind the little boy, and the little boy said, "Whatcha doin', Mister?" She was coming—he heard the slap of her sandals, the green whisper of her raincoat. "Whatcha doin', Mister?" Quickly, his heart banging in his chest, Vincent stooped and, squeezing the child against him, pressed his hand over its mouth so it could not make a sound. He did not see her pass; it was later, after the front door clicked, that he realized she was gone. The little boy sank back on the floor. "Whatcha doin', Mister?"

Four aspirins, one right after the other, and he came back into the room; the bed had not been tidied for a week, a spilt ash tray messed the floor, odds and ends of clothing decorated improbable places, lampshades and such. But tomorrow, if he felt better, there would be a general cleaning; perhaps he'd have the walls repainted maybe fix up the yard. Tomorrow he could begin thinking about his friends again, accept invitations, entertain. And yet this prospect, tasted in advance, was without flavor: all he'd known before seemed to him now sterile and spurious. Footsteps in the hall; could she return this soon, the movie over, the afternoon gone? Fever can make time pass so queerly, and for an instant he felt as though his bones were floating loose inside him. Clop-clop, a child's sloppy shoefall, the footsteps passed up the stairs, and Vincent moved, floated toward the mirrored closet. He longed to hurry, knowing he must, but the air seemed thick with gummy fluid. He brought her suitcase from the closet, and put it on the bed, a sad cheap suitcase with rusty locks and a warped hide. He eyed it with guilt. Where would she go? How would she live? When he'd broken with Connie, Gordon, all the others, there had been about it at least a certain dignity. Really, though—and he'd thought it out—there was no other way. So he gathered her belongings. Miss Martha Lovejoy Hall peeked out from under the leather wind-

breaker, her music-teacher's face smiling an oblique re-
proach. Vincent turned her over, face down, and tucked
in the frame an envelope containing twenty dollars. That
would buy a ticket back to Glass Hill, or wherever it
was she came from. Now he tried to close the case, and,
too weak with fever, collapsed on the bed. Quick yellow
wings glided through the window. A butterfly. He'd
never seen a butterfly in this city, and it was like a floating mysterious flower, like a sign of some sort, and he
watched with a kind of horror as it waltzed in the air.
Outside, somewhere, the razzledazzle of a beggar's grind-
organ started up; it sounded like a broken-down pianola,
and it played *La Marseillaise*. The butterfly lighted on
her painting, crept across crystal eyes, and flattened its
wings like a ribbon bow over the loose head. He fished
about in the suitcase until he found her scissors. He first
purposed to slash the butterfly's wings, but it spiraled to
the ceiling and hung there like a star. The scissors
stabbed the hawk's heart, ate through canvas like a
ravening steel mouth, scraps of picture flaking the floor
like cuttings of stiff hair. He went on his knees, pushed
the pieces into a pile, put them in the suitcase, and
slammed the lid shut. He was crying. And through the
tears the butterfly magnified on the ceiling, huge as a
bird, and there were more: a flock of lilting, winking
yellow; whispering lonesomely, like surf sucking a shore.
The wind from their wings blew the room into space.
He heaved forward, the suitcase banging his leg, and
threw open the door. A match flared. The little boy
said: "Whatcha doin', Mister?" And Vincent, setting the
suitcase in the hall, grinned sheepishly. He closed the
door like a thief, bolted the safety lock and, pulling up a
chair, tilted it under the knob. In the still room there was
only the subtlety of shifting sunlight and a crawling butterfly; it drifted downward like a tricky scrap of crayon
paper, and landed on a candlestick. *Sometimes he is not
a man at all*—she'd told him that, huddling here on the
bed, talking swiftly in the minutes before dawn—*sometimes he is something very different: a hawk, a child,*

a butterfly. And then she'd said: *At the place where they took me there were hundreds of old ladies, and young men, and one of the young men said he was a pirate, and one of the old ladies—she was near ninety —used to make me feel her stomach.* "Feel," *she'd say,* "feel how strong he kicks?" *This old lady took painting class, too, and her paintings looked like crazy quilts. And naturally he was in this place. Mr. Destronelli. Only he called himself Gum. Doctor Gum. Oh, he didn't fool me, even though he wore a gray wig, and made himself up to look real old and kind, I knew. And then one day I left, ran clear away, and hid under a lilac bush, and a man came along in a little red car, and he had a little mouse-haired mustache, and little cruel eyes. But it was him. And when I told him who he was he made me get out of his car. And then another man, that was in Philadelphia, picked me up in a café and took me into an alley. He talked Italian, and had tattoo pictures all over. But it was him. And the next man, he was the one who painted his toenails, sat down beside me in a movie because he thought I was a boy, and when he found out I wasn't he didn't get mad but let me live in his room, and cooked pretty things for me to eat. But he wore a silver locket and one day I looked inside and there was a picture of Miss Hall. So I knew it was him, so I had this feeling she was dead, so I knew he was going to murder me. And he will. He will.*" Dusk, and nightfall, and the fibers of sound called silence wove a shiny blue mask. Waking, he peered through eyeslits, heard the frenzied pulsebeat of his watch, the scratch of a key in a lock. Somewhere in this hour of dusk a murderer separates himself from shadow and with a rope follows the flash of silk legs up doomed stairs. And here the dreamer staring through his mask dreams of deceit. Without investigating he knows the suitcase is missing. that she has come, that she has gone; why, then, does he feel so little the pleasure of safcty, and only cheated, and small—small as the night when he searched the moon through an old man's telescope?

3

Like fragments of an old letter, scattered popcorn lay trampled flat, and she, leaning back in a watchman's attitude, allowed her gaze to hunt among it, as if deciphering here and there a word, an answer. Her eyes shifted discreetly to the man mounting the steps, Vincent. There was about him the freshness of a shower, shave, cologne, but dreary blue circled his eyes, and the crisp seersucker into which he'd changed had been made for a heavier man: a long month of penumonia, and wakeful burning nights had lightened his weight a dozen pounds, and more. Each morning, evening, meeting her here at his gate, or near the gallery, or outside the restaurant where he lunched, a nameless disorder took hold, a paralysis of time and identity. The wordless pantomime of her pursuit contracted his heart, and there were coma-like days when she seemed not one, but all, a multiple person, and her shadow in the street every shadow, following and followed. And once they'd been alone together in an automatic elevator, and he'd screamed: "I am not him! Only me, only me!" But she smiled as she'd smiled telling of the man with painted toenails, because after all, she knew.

It was suppertime, and, not knowing where to eat, he paused under a street lamp that, blooming abruptly, fanned complex light over stone; while he waited there came a clap of thunder, and all along the street every face but two, his and the girl's, tilted upward. A blast of river breeze tossed the children's laughter as they, linking arms, pranced like carousel ponies, and carried the mama's voice who, leaning from a window, howled: rain, Rachel, rain—gonna rain gonna rain! And the gladiola, ivy-filled flower cart jerked crazily as the peddler, one eye slanted skyward, raced for shelter. A potted geranium fell off, and the little girls gathered the blooms and tucked them behind their ears. The blending spatter of running feet and raindrops tinkled on the xylophone sidewalks—the slamming of doors, the lowering of windows, then nothing but silence, and rain. Presently, with slow scraping steps, she came below the lamp to stand beside him, and it was as if the sky were a thunder-cracked mirror, for the rain fell between them like a curtain of splintered glass.

Shut a Final Door

WALTER, listen to me: if everyone dislikes you, works against you, don't believe they do so arbitrarily; you create these situations for yourself."

Anna had said that, and, though his healthier side told him she intended nothing malicious (if Anna was not a friend, then who was?), he'd despised her for it, had gone around telling everybody how much he despised Anna, what a bitch she was. That woman! he said, don't trust that Anna. This plain-spoken act of hers —nothing but a cover-up for all her repressed hostility; terrible liar, too, can't believe a word she says: dangerous, my God! And naturally all he said went back to Anna, so that when he called about a play-opening they'd planned attending together she told him: "Sorry, Walter, I can't afford you any longer. I understand you very well, and I have a certain amount of sympathy. It's very compulsive, your malice, and you aren't too much to blame, but I don't want ever to see you again because I'm not so well myself that I can afford it." But why? And what had he done? Well, sure, he'd gossiped about her, but it wasn't as though he'd meant it, and after all, as he said to Jimmy Bergman (now there was a two-face if ever there was one), what was the use of having friends if you couldn't discuss them objectively?

He said you said they said we said round and round. Round and round, like the paddle-bladed ceiling-fan wheeling above; turning and turning, stirring stale air ineffectively, it made a watch-tick sound, counted seconds in the silence. Walter inched to a cooler part of the bed and closed his eyes against the dark little room. At seven that evening he'd arrived in New Orleans, at seven-thirty he'd registered in this hotel, an anonymous, side-street place. It was August, and it was as though bonfires burned in the red night sky, and the unnatural Southern landscape, observed so assiduously from the train, and which, trying to sublimate all else, he retraced in memory, intensified a feeling of having traveled to the end, the falling off.

But why he was here in this stifling hotel in this faraway town he could not say. There was a window in the room, but he could not seem to get it open, and he was afraid to call the bellboy (what queer eyes that kid had!), and he was afraid to leave the hotel, for what if he got lost? and if he got lost, even a little, then he would be lost altogether. He was hungry; he hadn't eaten since breakfast, so he found some peanut-butter crackers left over from a package he'd bought in Saratoga, and washed them down with a finger of Four Roses, the last. It made him sick. He vomited in the wastebasket, collapsed back on the bed, and cried until the pillow was wet. After a while he just lay there in the hot room, shivering, just lay there and watched the slow-turning fan; there was no beginning to its action, and no end; it was a circle.

An eye, the earth, the rings of a tree, everything is a circle, and all circles, Walter said, have a center. It was crazy for Anna to say what had happened was his own doing. If there was anything wrong with him really, then it had been made so by circumstances beyond his control, by, say, his churchly mother, or his father, an insurance official in Hartford, or his older sister, Cecile, who'd married a man forty years her senior. "I just wanted to get out of the house." That was her excuse,

and, to tell the truth, Walter had thought it reasonable
enough.

But he did not know where to begin thinking about
himself, did not know where to find the center. The first
telephone call? No that had been only three days ago
and, properly speaking, was the end, not the beginning.
Well, he could start with Irving, for Irving was the first
person he'd known in New York.

Now Irving was a sweet little Jewish boy with a remarkable talent for chess and not much else: he had
silky hair, and pink baby cheeks, and looked about sixteen. Actually he was twenty-three, Walter's age, and
they'd met at a bar in the Village. Walter was alone and
very lonesome in New York, and so when this sweet
little Irving was friendly he decided maybe it would be a
good idea to be friendly, too—because you never can
tell. Irving knew a great many people, and everyone was
very fond of him, and he introduced Walter to all his
friends.

And there was Margaret. Margaret was more or less
Irving's girl friend. She was only so-so looking (her eyes
bulged, there was always a little lipstick on her teeth,
she dressed like a child of ten), but she had a hectic
brightness which Walter found attractive. He could not
understand why she bothered with Irving at all. "Why
do you?" he said, on one of the long walks they'd begun
taking together in Central Park.

"Irving is sweet," she said, "and he loves me very
purely, and who knows: I might just as well marry him."

"A damn fool thing to do," he said. "Irving could
never be your husband because he's really your little
brother. Irving is everyone's little brother."

Margaret was too bright not to see the truth in this.
So one day when Walter asked if he might not make love
to her she said, all right, she didn't mind if he did. They
made love often after that.

Eventually Irving heard about it, and one Monday
there was a nasty scene in, curiously enough, the same
bar where they'd met. There had been that evening a

party in honor of Kurt Kuhnhardt (Kuhnhardt Advertising), Margaret's boss, and she and Walter had gone together, afterwards stopping by this bar for a nightcap. Except for Irving and a couple of girls in slacks the place was empty. Irving was sitting at the bar, his cheeks quite pink, his eyes rather glazed. He looked like a little boy playing grownup, for his legs were too short to reach the stool's footrest; they dangled doll-like. The instant Margaret recognized him she tried to turn around and walk out, but Walter wouldn't let her. And anyway, Irving had seen them: never taking his eyes from them, he put down his whiskey, slowly climbed off the stool, and, with a kind of sad, ersatz toughness, strutted forward.

"Irving, dear," said Margaret, and stopped, for he'd given her a terrible look.

His chin was trembling. "You go away," he said, and it was as though he were denouncing some childhood tormentor, "I hate you." Then, almost in slow motion, he swung out and, as if he clutched a knife, struck Walter's chest. It was not much of a blow, and when Walter did nothing but smile, Irving slumped against a jukebox, screaming: "Fight me, you damned coward; come on, and I'll kill you, I swear before God I will." So that was how they left him.

Walking home, Margaret began to cry in a soft tired way. "He'll never be sweet again," she said.

And Walter said, "I don't know what you mean."

"Oh, yes, you do," she told him, her voice a whisper "Yes, you do; the two of us, we've taught him how to hate. Somehow I don't think he ever knew before."

Walter had been in New York now four months. His original capital of five hundred dollars had fallen to fifteen, and Margaret lent him money to pay his January rent at the Brevoort. Why, she wanted to know, didn't he move some place cheaper? Well, he told her, it was better to have a good address. And what about a job? When was he going to start working? Or was he? Sure, he said, sure, as a matter of fact he thought about it a good deal. But he didn't intend fooling around with just any little jerkwater thing that came along. He wanted something good, something with a future, something in, say, advertising. All right, said Margaret, maybe she could help him; at any rate, she'd speak with her boss, Mr. Kuhnhardt.

2

The K.K.A., so called, was a middle-sized agency, but, as such things go, very good, the best. Kurt Kuhnhardt, who'd founded it in 1925, was a curious man with a curious reputation: a lean, fastidious German, a bachelor he lived in an elegant black house on Sutton Place, a house interestingly furnished with, among other things, three Picassos, a superb music-box, South Sea Island masks, and a burly Danish youngster, the houseboy. He invited occasionally some one of his staff in to dinner, whoever was favorite at the moment, for he was continually selecting protégés. It was a dangerous position, these alliances being, as they were, whimsical and uncertain: the protégé found himself checking the want ads when, just the evening previous, he'd dined most enjoyably with his benefactor. During his second week at the K.K.A., Walter, who had been hired as Margaret's assistant received a memorandum from Mr. Kuhnhardt asking him to lunch, and this, of course, excited him unspeakably.

"Kill-joy?" said Margaret, straightening his tie, plucking lint off a lapel. "Nothing of the sort. It's just that—well, Kuhnhardt's wonderful to work for so long as you don't get too involved—or you're likely not to be working—period."

Walter knew what she was up to; she didn't fool him a minute; he felt like telling her so, too, but restrained himself; it wasn't time yet. One of these days, though, he was going to have to get rid of her, and soon. It was degrading, his working for Margaret. And besides, the tendency from now on would be to keep him down. But nobody could do that, he thought looking into Mr.

Kuhnhardt's sea-blue eyes, nobody could keep Walter down.

"You're an idiot," Margaret told him. "My God, I've seen these little friendships of K. K.'s a dozen times, and they don't mean a damn. He used to palsy-walsy around with the switchboard operator. All K. K. wants is someone to play the fool. Take my word, Walter, there aren't any short cuts: what matters is how you do your job."

He said: "And have you complaints on that score? I'm doing as well as could be expected."

"It depends on what you mean by expected," she said.

One Saturday not long afterwards he made a date to meet her in Grand Central. They were going up to Hartford to spend the afternoon with his family, and for this she'd bought a new dress, new hat, and shoes. But he did not show up. Instead, he drove out on Long Island with Mr. Kuhnhardt, and was the most awed of three hundred guests at Rosa Cooper's debut ball. Rosa Cooper (nee Kuppermann) was heiress to the Cooper Dairy Products: a dark, plump, pleasant child with an unnatural British accent, the result of four years at Miss Jewett's. She wrote a letter to a friend named Anna Stimson, who subsequently showed it to Walter: "Met the divinest man. Danced with him six times, a divine dancer. He is an Advertising Executive, and is terribly divinely good-looking. We have a date—dinner and the theatre!"

Margaret did not mention the episode, nor did Walter. It was as though nothing had happened, except that now, unless there was office business to discuss, they never spoke, never saw each other. One afternoon, knowing she would not be at home, he went to her apartment and used a passkey given him long ago; there were things he'd left here, clothes, some books, his pipe; rummaging around collecting all this he discovered a photograph of himself scrawled red with lipstick: it gave him for an instant the sensation of falling in a dream. He also came across the only gift he'd ever given her, a bottle of L'Heure Bleue, still unopened. He sat down on the bed, and, smoking a cigarette, stroked his hand over the cool pillow, remembering the way her head had lain there, remembering, too, how they used to lie here Sunday mornings reading the funnies aloud, Barney Google and Dick Tracy and Joe Palooka.

He looked at the radio, a little green box; they'd always made love to music, any kind, jazz, symphonies, choir programs: it had been their signal, for whenever she'd wanted him, she'd said, "Shall we listen to the radio, darling?" Anyway, it was finished, and he hated her, and that was what he needed to remember. He found the bottle of perfume again, and put it in his pocket: Rosa might like a surprise.

In the office the next day he stopped by the water cooler and Margaret was standing there. She smiled at him fixedly, and said: "Well, I didn't know you were a thief." It was the first overt disclosure of the hostility between them. And suddenly it occurred to Walter he hadn't in all the office a single ally. Kuhnhardt? He could never count on him. And everyone else was an enemy: Jackson, Einstein, Fischer, Porter, Capehart, Ritter, Villa, Byrd. Oh, sure, they were all smart enough not to tell him point-blank, not so long as K. K.'s enthusiasm continued.

Well, dislike was at least positive, and the one thing he could not tolerate was vague relations, possibly because his own feelings were so indecisive, ambiguous. He was never certain whether he liked X or not. He needed X's love, but was incapable of loving. He could never be sincere with X, never tell him more than fifty percent of the truth. On the other hand, it was impossible for him to permit X these same imperfections: somewhere along the line Walter was sure he'd be betrayed. He was afraid of X, terrified. Once in high school he'd plagiarized a poem, and printed it in the school magazine; he could not forget its final line, *All our acts are acts of fear*. And when his teacher caught him out, had anything ever seemed to him more unjust?

3

He spent most of the early summer weekends at Rosa Cooper's Long Island place. The house was, as a rule, well staffed with hearty Yale and Princeton undergraduates, which was irritating, for they were the sort of boys who, around Hartford, made green birds fly in his stomach, and seldom allowed him to meet them on their own ground. As for Rosa herself, she was a darling; everyone said so, even Walter.

But darlings are rarely serious, and Rosa was not serious about Walter. He didn't mind too much. He was able on these weekends to make a good many contacts: Taylor Ovington, Joyce Randolph (the starlet), E. L. McEvoy, a dozen or so people whose names cast considerable glare in his address book. One evening he went with Anna Stimson to see a film featuring the Randolph girl, and before they were scarcely seated everyone for aisles around knew she was a Friend of his, knew she drank too much, was immoral, and not nearly so pretty as Hollywood made her out to be. Anna told him he was an adolescent female. "You're a man in only one respect, sweetie," she said.

It was through Rosa that he'd met Anna Stimson. An editor on a fashion magazine, she was almost six feet tall, wore black suits, affected a monocle, a walking cane, and pounds of jingling Mexican silver. She'd been married twice, once to Buck Strong, the horse-opera idol, and she had a child, a fourteen-year-old son who'd had to be put away in what she called a "corrective academy."

"He was a nasty child," she said. "He liked to take potshots out the window with a .22, and throw things, and steal from Woolworth's: awful brat, just like you."

Anna was good to him, though, and in her less depressed, less malevolent moments listened kindly while he groaned out his problems, while he explained why he was the way he was. All his life some cheat had been dealing him the wrong cards. Attributing to Anna every vice but stupidity, he liked to use her as a kind of confessor: there was nothing he could tell her of which she might legitimately disapprove. He would say: "I've told Kuhnhardt a lot of lies about Margaret; I suppose that's pretty rotten, but she would do the same for me; and anyway my idea is not for him to fire her, but maybe transfer her to the Chicago office."

Or, "I was in a bookshop, and a man was standing there and we began talking: a middle-aged man, rather nice, very intelligent. When I went outside he followed, a little ways behind: I crossed the street, he crossed the street, I walked fast, he walked fast. This kept up six or seven blocks, and when I finally figured out what was going on I felt tickled, I felt like kidding him on. So I stopped at the corner and hailed a cab; then I turned around and gave this guy a long, long look, and he came rushing up, all smiles. And I jumped in the cab, and slammed the door and leaned out the window and laughed out loud: the look on his face, it was awful, it was like Christ. I can't forget it. And tell me, Anna, why did I do this crazy thing? It was like paying back all the people who've ever hurt me, but it was something else, too." He would tell Anna these stories, go home and go to sleep. His dreams were clear blue.

Now the problem of love concerned him, mainly because he did not consider it a problem. Nevertheless, he was conscious of being unloved. This knowledge was like an extra heart beating inside him. But there was no one. Anna, perhaps. Did Anna love him? "Oh," said Anna, "when was anything ever what it seemed to be? Now it's a tadpole, now it's a frog. It looks like gold but you put it on your finger and it leaves a green ring. Take my second husband: he looked like a nice guy, and turned out to be just another heel. Look around this very room: why, you couldn't burn incense in that fireplace, and those mirrors, they give space, they tell a lie. Nothing, Walter, is ever what it seems to be. Christmas trees are cellophane, and snow is only soap chips. Flying around inside us is something called the Soul, and when you die you're never dead; yes, and when we're alive we're never alive. And so you want to know if I love you? Don't be dumb, Walter, we're not even friends. . . ."

4

Listen, the fan: turning wheels of whisper: he said you said they said we said round and round fast and slow while time recalled itself in endless chatter. Old broken fan breaking silence: August the third the third the third!

August the third, a Friday, and it was there, right in Winchell's column, his own name: "Big shot Ad exec Walter Ranney and dairy heiress Rosa Cooper are telling intimates to start buying rice." Walter himself had given the item to a friend of a friend of Winchell's. He showed it to the counter boy at the Whelan's where he ate breakfast. "That's me," he said, "I'm the guy," and the look on the boy's face was good for his digestion.

It was late when he reached the office that morning, and as he walked down the aisle of desks a small gratifying flurry among the typists preceded him. No one said anything, however. Around eleven, after a pleasant hour of doing nothing but feel exhilarated, he went to the drugstore downstairs for a cup of coffee. Three men from the office, Jackson, Ritter and Byrd, were there, and when Walter came in Jackson poked Byrd, and Byrd poked Ritter, and all of them turned around. "Whatcha say, big shot?" said Jackson, a pink man prematurely bald, and the other two laughed. Acting as if he hadn't heard, Walter stepped quickly into a phone booth. "Bastards," he said, pretending to dial a number. And finally, after waiting a long while for them to leave, he made a real call. "Rosa, hello, did I wake you up?"

"No."

"Say, did you see Winchell?"

"Yes."

Walter laughed. "Where do you suppose he gets that stuff?"

Silence.

"What's the matter? You sound kind of funny."

"Do I?"

"Are you mad or something?"

"Just disappointed."

"About what?"

Silence. And then: "It was a cheap thing to do, Walter, pretty cheap."

"I don't know what you mean."

"Good-bye, Walter."

On the way out he paid the cashier for a cup of coffee he'd forgotten to have. There was a barbershop in the building. He said he wanted a shave; no—make it a haircut; no—a manicure; and suddenly, seeing himself in the mirror, where his face reflected as pale almost as the barber's bib, he knew he did not know what he wanted. Rosa had been right, he was cheap. He'd always been willing to confess his faults, for, by admitting them, it was as if he made them no longer to exist. He went back upstairs, and sat at his desk, and felt as though he were bleeding inside, and wished very much to believe in God. A pigeon strutted on the ledge outside his window. For some time he watched the shimmering sunlit feathers, the wobbly sedateness of its movements; then, before realizing it, he'd picked up and thrown a glass paperweight: the pigeon climbed calmly upward, the paperweight careened like a giant raindrop: suppose, he thought, listening for a faraway scream, suppose it hits someone, kills them? But there was nothing. Only the ticking fingers of typists, a knocking at the door! "Hey, Ranney, K. K. wants to see you."

"I'm sorry," said Mr. Kuhnhardt, doodling with a gold pen. "And I'll write a letter for you, Walter. Any time."

Now in the elevator the enemy, all submerging with him, crushed Walter between them; Margaret was there wearing a blue hair-ribbon. She looked at him, and her face was different from other faces, not vacant as theirs were, and sterile: here still was compassion. But as she looked at him, she looked through him, too. This is my dream: he must not allow himself to believe otherwise; and yet under his own arm he carried the dream's contradiction, a manila envelope stuffed with all the personals saved from his desk. When the elevator emptied into the lobby, he knew he must speak with Margaret, ask her to forgive him, beg her protection, but she was slipping swiftly toward an exit, losing herself among the enemy. I love you, he said, running after her, I love you, he said, saying nothing.

"Margaret! Margaret!"

She turned around. The blue hair-ribbon matched her eyes, and her eyes, gazing up at him, softened, became rather friendly. Or pitying.

"Please," he said, "I thought we could have a drink together, go over to Benny's, maybe. We used to like Benny's, remember?"

She shook her head. "I've got a date, and I'm late already."

"Oh."

"Yes—well, I'm late," she said, and began to run. He stood watching as she raced down the street, her ribbon streaming, shining in the darkening summer light. And then she was gone.

His apartment, a one-room walk-up near Gramercy Park, needed an airing, a cleaning, but Walter, after pouring a drink, said to hell with it and stretched out on the couch. What was the use? No matter what you did or how hard you tried, it all came finally to zero; everyday everywhere everyone was being cheated, and who was there to blame? It was strange, though; lying here sipping whiskey in the dusk-graying room he felt calmer than he had for God knows how long. It was like the time he'd failed algebra and felt so relieved, so free: failure was definite, a certainty, and there is always peace in certainties. Now he would leave New York, take a vacation trip; he had a few hundred dollars, enough to last until fall.

And, wondering where he should go, he all at once saw, as if a film had commenced running in his head, silk caps, cherry-colored and lemon, and little, wise-faced men wearing exquisite polka-dot shirts. Closing his eyes, he was suddenly five years old, and it was delicious remembering the cheers, the hot dogs, his father's big pair of binoculars. Saratoga! Shadows masked his face in the sinking light. He turned on a lamp, fixed another drink, put a rumba record on the phonograph, and began to dance, the soles of his shoes whispering on the carpet: he'd often thought that with a little training he could've been a professional.

Just as the music ended, the telephone rang. He simply stood there, afraid somehow to answer, and the lamplight, the furniture, everything in the room went quite dead. When at last he thought it had stopped, it commenced again; louder, it seemed, and more insistent. He tripped over a footstool, picked up the receiver, dropped and recovered it, said: "Yes?"

Long-distance: a call from some town in Pennsylvania, the name of which he didn't catch. Following a series of spasmic rattlings, a voice, dry and sexless and altogether unlike any he'd ever heard before, came through: "Hello, Walter."

"Who is this?"

No answer from the other end, only a sound of strong orderly breathing; the connection was so good it seemed as though whoever it was was standing beside him with lips pressed against his ear. "I don't like jokes. Who is this?"

"Oh, you know me, Walter. You've known me a long time." A click, and nothing.

5

It was night and raining when the train reached Saratoga. He'd slept most of the trip, sweating in the hot dampness of the car, and dreamed of an old castle where only old turkeys lived, and dreamed a dream involving his father, Kurt Kuhnhardt, someone no-faced, Margaret and Rosa, Anna Stimson, and a queer fat lady with diamond eyes. He was standing on a long, deserted street; except for an approaching procession of slow, black, funeral-like cars there was no sign of life. Still, he knew, eyes unseen observed his nakedness from every window, and he hailed frantically the first of the limousines; it stopped and a man, his father, invitingly held open the door. Daddy, he yelled, running forward, and the door slammed shut, mashing off his fingers, and his father, with a great belly-laugh, leaned out the window to toss an enormous wreath of roses. In the second car was Margaret, in the third the lady with the diamond eyes (wasn't this Miss Casey, his old algebra teacher?), in the fourth Mr. Kuhnhardt and a new protégé, the no-faced creature. Each door opened, each closed, all laughed, all threw roses. The procession rolled smoothly away down the silent street. And with a terrible scream Walter fell among the mountain of roses: thorns tore wounds, and a sudden rain, a gray cloudburst, shattered the blooms, and washed pale blood bleeding over the leaves.

By the fixed stare of a woman sitting opposite, he realized at once he'd yelled aloud in his sleep. He smiled at her sheepishly, and she looked away with, he imagined, some embarrassment. She was a cripple; on her left foot she wore a giant shoe. Later, in the Saratoga station, he helped with her luggage, and they shared a taxi; there was no conversation: each sat in his corner looking at the rain, the blurred lights. In New York a few hours before he'd withdrawn from the bank all his savings, locked the door of his apartment, and left no messages; furthermore, there was in this town not a soul who knew him. It was a good feeling.

The hotel was filled: not to mention the racing crowd, there was, the desk clerk told him, a medical convention. No, sorry, he didn't know of a room anywhere. Maybe tomorrow.

So Walter found the bar. As long as he was going to stay up all night he might as well do it drunk. The bar, very large, very hot and noisy, was brilliant with summer-season grotesques: sagging silver-fox ladies, and little stunted jockeys, and pale loud-voiced men wearing cheap fantastic checks. After a couple of drinks, though, the noise seemed faraway. Then, glancing around, he saw the cripple. She was alone at a table where she sat primly sipping a crème de menthe. They exchanged a smile. Rising, Walter went to join her. "It's not like we were strangers," she said, as he sat down. "Here for the races, I suppose?"

"No," he said, "just a rest. And you?"

She pursed her lips. "Maybe you noticed I've got a clubfoot. Oh, sure now, don't look surprised: you noticed, everybody does. Well, see," she said, twisting the straw in her glass, "see, my doctor's going to give a talk at this convention, going to talk about me and my foot on account of I'm pretty special. Gee, I'm scared. I mean I'm going to have to show off my foot."

Walter said he was sorry, and she said, oh, there was nothing to be sorry about; after all, she was getting a little vacation out of it, wasn't she? "And I haven't been out of the city in six years. It was six years ago I spent a week at the Bear Mountain Inn." Her cheeks were red, rather mottled, and her eyes, set too closely together, were lavender-colored, intense: they seemed never to blink. She wore a gold band on her wedding finger; play-acting, to be sure: it would not have fooled anybody.

"I'm a domestic," she said, answering a question.

"And there's nothing wrong with that. It's honest and I like it. The people I work for have the cutest kid, Ronnie. I'm better to him than his mother, and he loves me more; he's told me so. That one, she stays drunk all the time."

It was depressing to listen to, but Walter, afraid suddenly to be alone, stayed and drank and talked in the way he'd once talked to Anna Stimson. Shh! she said at one point, for his voice had risen too high, and a good many people were staring. Walter said the hell with them, he didn't care; it was as if his brain were made of glass, and all the whiskey he'd drunk had turned into a hammer; he could feel the shattered pieces rattling in his head, distorting focus, falsifying shape; the cripple, for instance, seemed not one person, but several: Irving, his mother, a man named Bonaparte, Margaret, all those and others: more and more he came to understand experience is a circle of which no moment can be isolated, forgotten.

6

The bar was closing. They went Dutch on the check and, while waiting for change, neither spoke. Watching him with her unblinking lavender eyes, she seemed quite controlled, but there was going on inside, he could tell, some subtle agitation. When the waiter returned they divided the change, and she said: "If you want to, you can come to my room." A rash-like blush covered her face. "I mean, you said you didn't have any place to sleep . . ." Walter reached out and took her hand: the smile she gave him was touchingly shy.

Reeking with dime-store perfume, she came out of the bathroom wearing only a sleazy flesh-colored kimono, and the monstrous black shoe. It was then that he realized he could never go through with it. And he'd never felt so sorry for himself: not even Anna Stimson would ever have forgiven him this. "Don't look," she said, and there was a trembling in her voice, "I'm funny about anybody seeing my foot."

He turned to the window, where pressing elm leaves rustled in the rain, and lightning, too far off for sound, winked whitely. "All right," she said. Walter did not move.

"All right," she repeated anxiously. "Shall I put out the light? I mean, maybe you like to get ready—in the dark."

He came to the edge of the bed, and, bending down, kissed her cheek. "I think you're so very sweet, but . . ."

The telephone interrupted. She looked at him dumbly. "Jesus God," she said, and covered the mouthpiece with her hand, "it's long-distance! I'll bet it's about Ronnie! I'll bet he's sick, or—hello—what?—Ranney? Gee, no. You've got the wrong . . ."

"Wait," said Walter, taking the receiver. "This is me, this is Walter Ranney."

"Hello, Walter."

The voice, dull and sexless and remote, went straight to the pit of his stomach. The room seemed to seesaw, to buckle. A mustache of sweat sprouted on his upper lip. "Who is this?" he said so slowly the words did not connect coherently.

"Oh, you know me, Walter. You've known me a long time." Then silence: whoever it was had hung up.

"Gee," said the woman, "now how do you suppose they knew you were in my room? I mean—say, was it bad news? You look kind of . . ."

Walter fell across her, clutching her to him, pressing his wet cheek against hers. "Hold me," he said, discovering he could still cry. "Hold me, please."

"Poor little boy," she said, patting his back. "My poor little boy: we're awfully alone in this world, aren't we?" And presently he went to sleep in her arms.

But he had not slept since, nor could he now, not even listening to the lazy lull of the fan; in its turning he could hear train wheels: Saratoga to New York, New York to New Orleans. And New Orleans he'd chosen for no special reason, except that it was a town of strangers, and a long way off. Four spinning fan blades, wheels and voices, round and round; and after all, as he saw it now, there was to this network of malice no ending, none whatever.

Water flushed down wall pipes, steps passed overhead, keys jangled in the hall, a news commentator rumbled somewhere beyond, next door a little girl said, why? Why? WHY? Yet in the room there was a sense of silence. His feet shining in the transom-light looked like amputated stone: the gleaming toenails were ten small mirrors, all reflecting greenly. Sitting up, he rubbed sweat off with a towel; now more than anything the heat frightened him, for it made him know tangibly his own helplessness. He threw the towel across the room, where, landing on a lampshade, it swung back and forth. At this moment the telephone rang. And rang. And it was ringing so loud he was sure all the hotel could hear. An army would be pounding at his door. So he pushed his face into the pillow, covered his ears with his hands, and thought: think of nothing things, think of wind.

Children on Their Birthdays

(*This Story is for Andrew Lyndon*)

YESTERDAY AFTERNOON the six-o'clock bus ran over Miss Bobbit. I'm not sure what there is to be said about it; after all, she was only ten years old, still I know no one of us in this town will forget her. For one thing, nothing she ever did was ordinary, not from the first time that we saw her, and that was a year ago. Miss Bobbit and her mother, they arrived on that same six-o'clock bus, the one that comes through from Mobile. It happened to be my cousin Billy Bob's birthday, and so most of the children in town were here at our house. We were sprawled on the front porch having tutti-frutti and devil cake when the bus stormed around Deadman's Curve. It was the summer that never rained; rusted dryness coated everything; sometimes when a car passed on the road, raised dust would hang in the still air an hour or more. Aunt El said if they didn't pave the highway soon she was going to move down to the seacoast; but she'd said that for such a long time. Anway, we were sitting on the porch, tutti-frutti melting on our plates, when suddenly, just as we were wishing that something would happen, something did; for out of the red road dust appeared Miss Bobbit. A wiry little girl in a starched, lemon-colored party dress, she sassed along with a grown-up mince, one hand on her hip, the other supporting a spinsterish umbrella. Her mother, lugging two cardboard valises and a wind-up victrola, trailed in the background. She was a gaunt shaggy woman with silent eyes and a hungry smile.

All the children on the porch had grown so still that when a cone of wasps started humming the girls did not set up their usual holler. Their attention was too fixed upon the approach of Miss Bobbit and her mother, who had by now reached the gate. "Begging your pardon," called Miss Bobbit in a voice that was at once silky and childlike, like a pretty piece of ribbon, and immaculately exact, like a movie-star or a schoolmarm, "but might we speak with the grown-up persons of the house?" This, of course, meant Aunt El; and, at least to some degree, myself. But Billy Bob and all the other boys, no one of whom was over thirteen, followed down to the gate after us. From their faces you would have thought they'd never seen a girl before. Certainly not like Miss Bobbit. As Aunt El said, whoever heard tell of a child wearing makeup? Tangee gave her lips an orange glow, her hair, rather like a costume wig, was a mass of rosy curls, and her eyes had a knowing, penciled tilt; even so, she had a skinny dignity, she was a lady, and, what is more, she looked you in the eye with manlike directness. "I'm Miss Lily Jane Bobbit, Miss Bobbit from Memphis, Tennessee," she said solemnly. The boys looked down at their toes, and, on the porch, Cora McCall, who Billy Bob was courting at the time, led the girls into a fanfare of giggles. *"Country* children," said Miss Bobbit with an understanding smile, and gave her parasol a saucy whirl. "My mother," and this homely woman allowed an abrupt nod to acknowledge herself, "my mother and I have taken rooms here. Would you be so kind as to point out the house? It belongs to a Mrs. Sawyer." Why, sure, said Aunt El, that's Mrs. Sawyer's, right there across the street. The only boarding house around here, it is an old tall dark place with about two dozen lightning rods scattered on the roof: Mrs. Sawyer is scared to death in a thunderstorm.

Coloring like an apple, Billy Bob said, please ma'am, it being such a hot day and all, wouldn't they rest a spell and have some tutti-frutti? and Aunt El said yes, by all means, but Miss Bobbit shook her head. "Very fattening, tutti-frutti; but *merci* you kindly," and they started across the road, the mother half-dragging her parcels in the dust. Then, and with an earnest expression, Miss Bobbit turned back; the sunflower yellow of her eyes darkened, and she rolled them slightly sideways, as if trying to remember a poem. "My mother has a disorder of the tongue, so it is necessary that I speak for her," she announced rapidly and heaved a sigh. "My mother is a very fine seamstress; she has made dresses for the society of many cities and towns, including Memphis and Tallahassee. No doubt you have noticed and admired the dress I am wearing. Every stitch of it was hand-sewn by my mother. My mother can copy any pattern, and just recently she won a twenty-five-dollar prize from the *Ladies' Home Journal*. My mother can also crochet, knit and embroider. If you want any kind of sewing done, please come to my mother. Please advise your friends and family. Thank you." And then, with a rustle and a swish, she was gone.

Cora McCall and the girls pulled their hair-ribbons nervously, suspiciously, and looked very put out and prune-faced. I'm *Miss* Bobbit, said Cora, twisting her face into an evil imitation, and I'm Princess Elizabeth, that's who I am, ha, ha, ha. Furthermore, said Cora, that dress was just as tacky as could be; personally, Cora said, all my clothes come from Atlanta; plus a pair of shoes from New York, which is not even to mention my silver turquoise ring all the way from Mexico City, Mexico. Aunt El said they ought not to behave that way about a fellow child, a stranger in the town, but the girls went on like a huddle of witches, and certain boys, the sillier ones that liked to be with the girls, joined in and said things that made Aunt El go red and declare she was going to send them all home and tell their daddies, to boot. But before she could carry forward this threat Miss Bobbit herself intervened by traipsing across the Sawyer porch, costumed in a new and startling manner.

The older boys, like Billy Bob and Preacher Star, who had sat quiet while the girls razzed Miss Bobbit, and who had watched the house into which she'd disappeared with misty, ambitious faces, they now straightened up and ambled down to the gate. Cora McCall sniffed and poked out her lower lip, but the rest of us went and sat on the steps. Miss Bobbit paid us no mind whatever. The Sawyer yard is dark with mulberry trees and it is planted with grass and sweet shrub. Sometimes after a rain you can smell the sweet shrub all the way into our house; and in the center of this yard there is a sundial which Mrs. Sawyer installed in 1912 as a memorial to her Boston bull, Sunny, who died after having lapped up a bucket of paint. Miss Bobbit pranced into the yard toting the victrola, which she put on the sundial; she wound it up, and started a record playing, and it played the Court of Luxemborg. By now it was almost nightfall, a firefly hour, blue as milkglass; and birds like arrows swooped together and swept into the folds of trees. Before storms, leaves and flowers appear to burn with a private light, color, and Miss Bobbit, got up in a little white skirt like a powderpuff and with strips of gold-glittering tinsel ribboning her hair, seemed, set against the darkening all around, to contain this illuminated quality. She held her arms arched over her head, her hands lily-limp, and stood straight up on the tips of her toes. She stood that way for a good long while, and Aunt El said it was right smart of her. Then she began to waltz around and around, and around and around she went until Aunt El said, why, she was plain dizzy from the sight. She stopped only when it was time to rewind the victrola; and when the moon came rolling down the ridge, and the last supper bell had sounded, and all the children had gone home, and the night iris was beginning to bloom, Miss Bobbit was still there in the dark turning like a top.

We did not see her again for some time. Preacher Star came every morning to our house and stayed straight through to supper. Preacher is a rail-thin boy with a butchy shock of red hair; he has eleven brothers and sisters, and even they are afraid of him, for he has a terrible temper, and is famous in these parts for his green-eyed meanness: last fourth of July he whipped Ollie Overton so bad that Ollie's family had to send him to the hospital in Pensacola; and there was another time he bit off half a mule's ear, chewed it and spit it on the ground. Before Billy Bob got his growth, Preacher played the devil with him, too. He used to drop cockleburrs down his collar, and rub pepper in his eyes, and tear up his homework. But now they are the biggest friends in town: talk alike, walk alike; and occasionally they disappear together for whole days, Lord knows where to. But during these days when Miss Bobbit did not appear they stayed close to the house. They would stand around in the yard trying to slingshot sparrows off telephone poles; or sometimes Billy Bob would play his ukulele, and they would sing so loud Uncle Billy Bob, who is Judge for this county, claimed he could hear them all the way to the courthouse: *send me a letter, send it by mail, send it in care of the Birming-ham jail*. Miss Bobbit did not hear them; at least she never poked her head out the door. Then one day Mrs. Sawyer, coming over to borrow a cup of sugar, rattled on a good deal about her new boarders. You know, she said, squinting her chicken-bright eyes, the husband was a crook, uh huh, the child told me herself. Hasn't an ounce of shame, not a mite. Said her daddy was the dearest daddy and the sweetest singing man in the whole of Tennessee. . . . And I said, honey, where is he? and just as off-hand as you please she says, Oh, he's in the penitentiary and we don't hear from him no more. Say, now, does that make your blood run cold? Uh huh, and I been thinking, her mama, I been thinking she's some kinda foreigner: never says a word, and sometimes it looks like she don't understand what nobody says to her. And you know, they eat everything *raw*. *Raw* eggs, *raw* turnips, carrots—no meat whatsoever. For reasons of health, the child says, but ho! she's been straight out on the bed running a fever since last Tuesday.

That same afternoon Aunt El went out to water her roses, only to discover them gone. These were special roses, ones she'd planned to send to the flower show in Mobile, and so naturally she got a little hysterical. She rang up the Sheriff, and said, listen here, Sheriff, you come over here right fast. I mean somebody's got off with all my Lady Anne's that I've devoted myself to heart and soul since early spring. When the Sheriff's car pulled up outside our house, all the neighbors along the street came out on their porches, and Mrs. Sawyer, layers of cold cream whitening her face, trotted across the road. Oh shoot, she said, very disappointed to find no one had been murdered, oh shoot, she said, nobody's stole them roses. Your Billy Bob brought them roses over and left them for little Bobbit. Aunt El did not say one word. She just marched over to the peach tree, and cut herself a switch. Ohhh, Billy Bob, she stalked along the street calling his name, and then she found him down at Speedy's garage where he and Preacher were watching Speedy take a motor apart. She simply lifted him by the hair and, switching blueblazes, towed him home. But she couldn't make him say he was sorry and she couldn't make him cry. And when she was finished with him he ran into the backyard and climbed high into the tower of a pecan tree and swore he wasn't ever going to come down. Then his daddy stood at the window and called to him: Son, we aren't mad with you, so come down and eat your supper. But Billy Bob wouldn't budge. Aunt El went and leaned against the tree. She spoke in a voice soft as the gathering light. I'm sorry, son, she said, I didn't mean whipping you so hard like that. I've fixed a nice supper, son, potato salad and boiled ham and deviled eggs. Go away, said Billy Bob, I don't want no supper, and I hate you like all-fire. His daddy said he ought not to talk like that to his mother, and she began to cry. She stood there under the tree and cried, raising the hem of her skirt to dab at her eyes. I don't hate you, son. . . . If I didn't love you I wouldn't whip you. The pecan leaves began to rattle;

Billy Bob slid slowly to the ground, and Aunt El, rushing her fingers through his hair, pulled him against her. Aw, Ma, he said, Aw, Ma.

After supper Billy Bob came and flung himself on the foot of my bed. He smelled all sour and sweet, the way boys do, and I felt very sorry for him, especially because he looked so worried. His eyes were almost shut with worry. You're s'posed to send sick folks flowers, he said righteously. About this time we heard the victrola, a lilting faraway sound, and a night moth flew through the window, drifting in the air delicate as the music. But it was dark now, and we couldn't tell if Miss Bobbit was dancing. Billy Bob, as though he were in pain, doubled up on the bed like a jackknife; but his face was suddenly clear, his grubby boy-eyes twitching like candles. She's so cute, he whispered, she's the cutest dickens I ever saw, gee, to hell with it, I don't care, I'd pick all the roses in China.

Preacher would have picked all the roses in China, too. He was as crazy about her as Billy Bob. But Miss Bobbit did not notice them. The sole communication we had with her was a note to Aunt El thanking her for the flowers. Day after day she sat on her porch, always dressed to beat the band, and doing a piece of embroidery, or combing curls in her hair, or reading a Webster's dictionary—formal, but friendly enough; if you said good-day to her she said good-day to you. Even so, the boys never could seem to get up the nerve to go over and talk with her, and most of the time she simply looked through them, even when they tomcatted up and down the street trying to get her eye. They wrestled, played Tarzan, did foolheaded bicycle tricks. It was a sorry business. A great many girls in town strolled by the Sawyer house two and three times within an hour just on the chance of getting a look. Some of the girls who did this were: Cora McCall, Mary Murphy Jones, Janice Ackerman. Miss Bobbit did not show any interest in them either. Cora would not speak to Billy Bob any more. The same was true with Janice and Preacher. As a matter of fact, Janice wrote Preacher a letter in red ink on lace-trimmed paper in which she told him he was vile beyond all human beings and words, that she considered their engagement broken, that he could have back the stuffed squirrel he'd given her. Preacher, saying he wanted to act nice, stopped her the next time she passed our house, and said, well, hell, she could keep that old squirrel if she wanted to. Afterwards, he couldn't understand why Janice ran away bawling the way she did.

Then one day the boys were being crazier than usual; Billy Bob was sagging around in his daddy's World War khakis, and Preacher, stripped to the waist, had a naked woman drawn on his chest with one of Aunt El's old lipsticks. They looked like perfect fools, but Miss Bobbit, reclining in a swing, merely yawned. It was noon, and there was no one passing in the street, except a colored girl, baby-fat and sugar-plum shaped, who hummed along carrying a pail of blackberries. But the boys, teasing at her like gnats, joined hands and wouldn't let her go by, not until she paid a tariff. I ain't studyin' no tariff, she said, what kinda tariff you talkin' about, mister? A party in the barn, said Preacher, between clenched teeth, mighty nice party in the barn. And she, with a sulky shrug, said, huh, she intended studyin' no barn parties. Whereupon Billy Bob capsized her berry pail, and when she, with despairing, piglike shrieks, bent down in futile gestures of rescue, Preacher, who can be mean as the devil, gave her behind a kick which sent her sprawling jellylike among the blackberries and the dust. Miss Bobbit came tearing across the road, her finger wagging like a metronome; like a schoolteacher she clapped her hands, stamped her foot, said: "It is a well-known fact that gentlemen are put on the face of this earth for the protection of ladies. Do you suppose boys behave this way in towns like Memphis, New York, London, Hollywood or Paris?" The boys hung back, and shoved their hands in their pockets. Miss Bobbit helped the colored girl to her feet; she dusted her off, dried her eyes, held out a handkerchief and told her to blow. "A pretty pass," she said, "a fine situation when a lady can't walk safely in the public daylight."

Then the two of them went back and sat on Mrs. Sawyer's porch; and for the next year they were never far apart, Miss Bobbit and this baby elephant, whose name was Rosalba Cat. At first, Mrs. Sawyer raised a fuss about Rosalba being so much at her house. She told Aunt El that it went against the grain to have a nigger lolling smack there in plain sight on her front porch. But Miss Bobbit had a certain magic, whatever she did she did it with completeness, and so directly, so solemnly, that there was nothing to do but accept it. For instance, the tradespeople in town used to snicker when they called her *Miss* Bobbit; but by and by she was Miss Bobbit, and they gave her stiff little bows as she whirled by spinning her parasol. Miss Bobbit told everyone that Rosalba was her sister, which caused a good many jokes; but like most of her ideas, it gradually seemed natural, and when we would overhear them calling each other Sister Rosalba and Sister Bobbit none of us cracked a smile. But Sister Rosalba and Sister Bobbit did some queer things. There was the business about the dogs. Now there are a great many dogs in this town, rat terriers, bird dogs, blood-hounds; they trail along the forlorn noon-hot streets in sleepy herds of six to a dozen, all waiting only for dark and the moon, when straight through the lonesome hours you can hear them howling: someone is dying, someone is dead. Miss Bobbit complained to the Sheriff; she said that certain of the dogs always planted themselves under her window, and that she was a light sleeper to begin with; what is more, and as Sister Rosalba said, she did not believe they were dogs at all, but some kind of devil. Naturally the Sheriff did nothing; and so she took the matter into her own hands. One morning, after an especially loud night, she was seen stalking through the town with Rosalba at her side, Rosalba carrying a flower basket filled with rocks; whenever they saw a dog they paused while Miss Bobbit scrutinized him. Sometimes she would shake her head, but more often she said, "Yes, that's one

of them, Sister Rosalba," and Sister Rosalba, with ferocious aim, would take a rock from her basket and crack
the dog between the eyes.

Another thing that happened concerns Mr. Henderson. Mr. Henderson has a back room in the Sawyer
house; a tough runt of a man who formerly was a wildcat
oil prospector in Oklahoma, he is about seventy years old
and, like a lot of old men, obsessed by functions of the
body. Also, he is a terrible drunk. One time he had been
drunk for two weeks; whenever he heard Miss Bobbit
and Sister Rosalba moving around the house, he would
charge to the top of the stairs and bellow down to Mrs.
Sawyer that there were midgets in the walls trying to get
at his supply of toilet paper. They've already stolen fifteen cents' worth, he said. One evening, when the two
girls were sitting under a tree in the yard, Mr. Henderson,
sporting nothing more than a nightshirt, stamped out
after them. Steal all my toilet paper, will you? he hollered,
I'll show you midgets. . . . Somebody come help me,
else these midget bitches are liable to make off with every
sheet in town. It was Billy Bob and Preacher who caught
Mr. Henderson and held him until some grown men arrived and began to tie him up. Miss Bobbit, who had
behaved with admirable calm, told the men they did not
know how to tie a proper knot, and undertook to do so
herself. She did such a good job that all the circulation
stopped in Mr. Henderson's hands and feet and it was a
month before he could walk again.

It was shortly afterwards that Miss Bobbit paid us
a call. She came on Sunday and I was there alone, the
family having gone to church. "The odors of a church are
so offensive," she said, leaning forward and with her
hands folded primly before her. "I don't want you to
think I'm a heathen, Mr. C.; I've had enough experience
to know that there is a God and that there is a Devil. But
the way to tame the Devil is not to go down there to
church and listen to what a sinful mean fool he is. No,
love the Devil like you love Jesus: because he is a powerful man, and will do you a good turn if he knows you trust

him. He has frequently done me good turns, like at dancing school in Memphis. . . . I always called in the Devil to help me get the biggest part in our annual show. That is common sense; you see, I knew Jesus wouldn't have any truck with dancing. Now, as a matter of fact, I have called in the Devil just recently. He is the only one who can help me get out of this town. Not that I live here, not exactly. I think always about somewhere else, somewhere else where everything is dancing, like people dancing in the streets, and everything is pretty, like children on their birthdays. My precious papa said I live in the sky, but if he'd lived more in the sky he'd be rich like he wanted to be. The trouble with my papa was he did not love the Devil, he let the Devil love him. But I am very smart in that respect; I know the next best thing is very often the best. It was the next best thing for us to move to this town; and since I can't pursue my career here, the next best thing for me is to start a little business on the side. Which is what I have done. I am sole subscription agent in this county for an impressive list of magazines, including *Reader's Digest, Popular Mechanics, Dime Detective* and *Child's Life*. To be sure, Mr. C., I'm not here to sell you anything. But I have a thought in mind. I was thinking those two boys that are always hanging around here, it occurred to me that they are men, after all. Do you suppose they would make a pair of likely assistants?"

Billy Bob and Preacher worked hard for Miss Bobbit, and for Sister Rosalba, too. Sister Rosalba carried a line of cosmetics called Dewdrop, and it was part of the boys' job to deliver purchases to her customers. Billy Bob used to be so tired in the evening he could hardly chew his supper. Aunt El said it was a shame and a pity, and finally one day when Billy Bob came down with a touch of sunstroke she said, all right, that settled it, Billy Bob would just have to quit Miss Bobbit. But Billy Bob cussed her out until his daddy had to lock him in his room; whereupon he said he was going to kill himself. Some cook we'd had told him once that if you ate a mess of collards all slopped over with molasses it would kill you sure as shooting; and so that is what he did. I'm dying, he said, rolling back and forth on his bed, I'm dying and nobody cares.

Miss Bobbit came over and told him to hush up. "There's nothing wrong with you, boy," she said. "All you've got is a stomach ache." Then she did something that shocked Aunt El very much: she stripped the covers off Billy Bob and rubbed him down with alchohol from head to toe. When Aunt El told her she did not think that was a nice thing for a little girl to do, Miss Bobbit replied: "I don't know whether it's nice or not, but it's certainly very refreshing." After which Aunt El did all she could to keep Billy Bob from going back to work for her, but his daddy said to leave him alone, they would have to let the boy lead his own life.

Miss Bobbit was very honest about money. She paid Billy Bob and Preacher their exact commission, and she would never let them treat her, as they often tried to do, at the drugstore or to the picture show. "You'd better save your money," she told them. "That is, if you want to go to college. Because neither one of you has got the brains to win a scholarship, not even a football scholarship." But it was over money that Billy Bob and Preacher had a big falling out; that was not the real reason, of course: the real reason was that they had grown cross-eyed jealous over Miss Bobbit. So one day, and he had the gall to do this right in front of Billy Bob, Preacher said to Miss Bobbit that she'd better check her accounts carefully because he had more than a suspicion that Billy Bob wasn't turning over to her *all* the money he collected. That's a damned lie, said Billy Bob, and with a clean left hook he knocked Preacher off the Sawyer porch and jumped after him into a bed of nasturtiums. But once Preacher got a hold on him, Billy Bob didn't stand a chance. Preacher even rubbed dirt in his eyes. During all this, Mrs. Sawyer, leaning out an upper-story window, screamed like an eagle, and Sister Rosalba, fatly cheerful, ambiguously shouted, Kill him! Kill him! Kill him! Only Miss Bobbit seemed to know what she was doing. She plugged in the lawn hose, and gave the boys a close-up, blinding bath. Gasping, Preacher staggered to his feet. Oh, honey, he said, shaking himself like a wet dog, honey, you've got to decide. "Decide *what?*" said Miss Bobbit, right away in a huff. Oh, honey, wheezed Preacher, you don't want us boys killing each other. You got to decide who is your real true sweetheart. "Sweetheart, my eye," said Miss Bobbit. "I should've known better than to get myself involved with a lot of country children. What sort of businessman are you going to make? Now, you listen here, Preacher Star: I don't want a sweetheart, and if I did, it wouldn't be you. As a matter of fact, you don't even get up when a lady enters the room."

Preacher spit on the ground and swaggered over to Billy Bob. Come on, he said, just as though nothing had happened, she's a hard one, she is, she don't want nothing but to make trouble between two good friends. For a moment it looked as if Billy Bob was going to join him in a peaceful togetherness; but suddenly, coming to his senses, he drew back and made a gesture. The boys regarded each other a full minute, all the closeness between them turning an ugly color: you can't hate so much unless you love, too. And Preacher's face showed all of this. But there was nothing for him to do except go away. Oh, yes, Preacher, you looked so lost that day that for the first time I really liked you, so skinny and mean and lost going down the road all by yourself.

They did not make it up, Preacher and Billy Bob; and it was not because they didn't want to, it was only that there did not seem to be any straight way for their friendship to happen again. But they couldn't get rid of this friendship: each was always aware of what the other was up to; and when Preacher found himself a new buddy, Billy Bob moped around for days, picking things up, dropping them again, or doing sudden wild things, like purposely poking his finger in the electric fan. Sometimes in the evenings Preacher would pause by the gate and talk with Aunt El. It was only to torment Billy Bob,

I suppose, but he stayed friendly with all of us, and at Christmas time he gave us a huge box of shelled peanuts. He left a present for Billy Bob, too. It turned out to be a book of Sherlock Holmes; and on the flyleaf there was scribbled, "Friends Like Ivy On the Wall Must Fall." That's the corniest thing I ever saw, Billy Bob said. Jesus, what a dope he is! But then, and though it was a cold winter day, he went in the backyard and climbed up into the pecan tree, crouching there all afternoon in the blue December branches.

But most of the time he was happy, because Miss Bobbit was there, and she was always sweet to him now. She and Sister Rosalba treated him like a man; that is to say, they allowed him to do everything for them. On the other hand, they let him win at three-handed bridge, they never questioned his lies, nor discouraged his ambitions. It was a happy while. However, trouble started again when school began. Miss Bobbit refused to go. "It's ridiculous," she said, when one day the principal, Mr. Copland, came around to investigate, "really ridiculous; I can read and write and there are *some* people in this town who have every reason to know that I can count money. No, Mr. Copland, consider for a moment and you will see neither of us has the time nor energy. After all, it would only be a matter of whose spirit broke first, yours or mine. And besides, what is there for you to teach me? Now, if you knew anything about dancing, that would be another matter; but under the circumstances, yes, Mr. Copland, under the circumstances, I suggest we forget the whole thing." Mr. Copland was perfectly willing to. But the rest of the town thought she ought to be whipped. Horace Deasley wrote a piece in the paper which was titled "A Tragic Situation." It was, in his opinion, a tragic situation when a small girl could defy what he, for some reason, termed the Constitution of the United States. The article ended with a question: *Can she get away with it?* She did; and so did Sister Rosalba. Only she was colored, so no one cared. Billy Bob was not as lucky. It was school for him, all right; but

he might as well have stayed home for the good it did
him. On his first report card he got three F's, a record of
some sort. But he is a smart boy. I guess he just couldn't
live through those hours without Miss Bobbit; away from
her he always seemed half-asleep. He was always in a
fight, too; either his eye was black, or his lip was split, or
his walk had a limp. He never talked about these fights,
but Miss Bobbit was shrewd enough to guess the reason
why. "You are a dear, I know, I know. And I appreciate
you, Billy Bob. Only don't fight with people because of
me. Of course they say mean things about me. But do
you know why that is, Billy Bob? It's a compliment, kind
of. Because deep down they think I'm absolutely wonderful."

   And she was right: if you are not admired no one
will take the trouble to disapprove. But actually we had
no idea of how wonderful she was until there appeared
the man known as Manny Fox. This happened late in
February. The first news we had of Manny Fox was a
series of jovial placards posted up in the stores around
town: Manny Fox Presents the Fan Dancer Without the
Fan; then, in smaller print: Also, Sensational Amateur
Program Featuring Your Own Neighbors—First Prize, A
Genuine Hollywood Screen Test. All this was to take
place the following Thursday. The tickets were priced at
one dollar each, which around here is a lot of money; but
it is not often that we get any kind of flesh entertainment,
so everybody shelled out their money and made a great
todo over the whole thing. The drugstore cowboys talked
dirty all week, mostly about the fan dancer without the
fan, who turned out to be Mrs. Manny Fox. They stayed
down the highway at the Chucklewood Tourist Camp;
but they were in town all day, driving around in an old
Packard which had Manny Fox's full name stenciled on
all four doors. His wife was a deadpan pimento-tongued
redhead with wet lips and moist eyelids; she was quite
large actually, but compared to Manny Fox she seemed
rather frail, for he was a fat cigar of a man.

   They made the pool hall their headquarters, and

every afternoon you could find them there, drinking beer and joking with the town loafs. As it developed, Manny Fox's business affairs were not restricted to theatrics. He also ran a kind of employment bureau: slowly he let it be known that for a fee of $150 he could get for any adventurous boys in the county high-class jobs working on fruit ships sailing from New Orleans to South America. The chance of a lifetime, he called it. There are not two boys around here who readily lay their hands on so much as five dollars; nevertheless, a good dozen managed to raise the money. Ada Willingham took all she'd saved to buy an angel tombstone for her husband and gave it to her son, and Acey Trump's papa sold an option on his cotton crop.

But the night of the show! That was a night when all was forgotten: mortgages, and the dishes in the kitchen sink. Aunt El said you'd think we were going to the opera, everybody so dressed up, so pink and sweet-smelling. The Odeon had not been so full since the night they gave away the matched set of sterling silver. Practically everybody had a relative in the show, so there was a lot of nervousness to contend with. Miss Bobbit was the only contestant we knew real well. Billy Bob couldn't sit still; he kept telling us over and over that we mustn't applaud for anybody but Miss Bobbit; Aunt El said that would be very rude, which sent Billy Bob off into a state again; and when his father bought us all bags of popcorn he wouldn't touch his because it would make his hands greasy, and please, another thing, we mustn't be noisy and eat ours while Miss Bobbit was performing. That she was to be a contestant had come as a last-minute surprise. It was logical enough, and there were signs that should've told us; the fact, for instance, that she had not set foot outside the Sawyer house in how many days? And the victrola going half the night, her shadow whirling on the window shade, and the secret, stuffed look on Sister Rosalba's face whenever asked after Sister Bobbit's health. So there was her name on the program, listed second, in fact, though she did not appear for a long while. First came Manny Fox, greased and leering, who told a lot of peculiar jokes, clapping his hands, ha, ha. Aunt El said if he told another joke like that she was going to walk straight out: he did, and she didn't. Before Miss Bobbit came on there were eleven contestants, including Eustacia Bernstein, who imitated movie stars so that they all sounded like Eustacia, and there was an extraordinary Mr. Buster Riley, a jug-eared old wool-hat from way in the back country who played "Waltzing Matilda" on a saw. Up to that point, he was the hit of the show; not that there was any marked difference in the various receptions, for everybody applauded generously, everybody, that is, except Preacher Star. He was sitting two rows ahead of us, greeting each act with a donkey-loud boo. Aunt El said she was never going to speak to him again. The only person he ever applauded was Miss Bobbit. No doubt the Devil was on her side, but she deserved it. Out she came, tossing her hips, her curls, rolling her eyes. You could tell right away it wasn't going to be one of her classical numbers. She tapped across the stage, daintily holding up the sides of a cloud-blue skirt. That's the cutest thing I ever saw, said Billy Bob, smacking his thigh, and Aunt El had to agree that Miss Bobbit looked real sweet. When she started to twirl the whole audience broke into spontaneous applause; so she did it all over again, hissing, "Faster, faster," at poor Miss Adelaide, who was at the piano doing her Sunday-school best. "I was born in China, and raised in Jay-pan . . ." We had never heard her sing before, and she had a rowdy sandpaper voice. ". . . if you don't like my peaches, stay away from my can, o-ho o-ho!" Aunt El gasped; she gasped again when Miss Bobbit, with a bump, up-ended her skirt to display blue-lace underwear, thereby collecting most of the whistles the boys had been saving for the fan dancer without the fan, which was just as well, as it later turned out, for that lady, to the tune of "An Apple for the Teacher" and cries of gyp gyp, did her routine attired in a bathing suit. But showing off her bottom was not Miss Bobbit's final triumph. Miss Adelaide commenced an ominous thundering in the darker keys, at which point Sister Rosalba, carrying a lighted Roman candle, rushed onstage and handed it to Miss Bobbit, who was in the midst of a full split; she made it, too, and just as she did the Roman candle burst into fiery balls of red, white and blue, and we all had to stand up because she was singing "The Star Spangled Banner" at the top of her lungs. Aunt El said afterwards that it was one of the most gorgeous things she'd ever seen on the American stage.

Well, she surely did deserve a Hollywood screen test and, inasmuch as she won the contest, it looked as though she were going to get it. Manny Fox said she was: honey, he said, you're real star stuff. Only he skipped town the next day, leaving nothing but hearty promises. Watch the mails, my friends, you'll all be hearing from me. That is what he said to the boys whose money he'd taken, and that is what he said to Miss Bobbit. There are three deliveries daily, and this sizable group gathered at the post office for all of them, a jolly crowd growing gradually joyless. How their hands trembled when a letter slid into their mailbox. A terrible hush came over them as the days passed. They all knew what the other was thinking, but no one could bring himself to say it, not even Miss Bobbit. Postmistress Patterson said it plainly, however: the man's a crook, she said, I knew he was a crook to begin with, and if I have to look at your faces one more day I'll shoot myself.

Finally, at the end of two weeks, it was Miss Bobbit who broke the spell. Her eyes had grown more vacant than anyone had ever supposed they might, but one day, after the last mail was up, all her old sizzle came back. "O.K., boys, it's lynch law now," she said, and proceeded to herd the whole troupe home with her. This was the first meeting of the Manny Fox Hangman's Club, an organization which, in a more social form, endures to this day, though Manny Fox has long since been caught and, so to say, hung. Credit for this went quite properly to Miss Bobbit. Within a week she'd written over three hundred descriptions of Manny Fox and dispatched them to Sheriffs throughout the South; she also wrote letters to papers in the larger cities, and these attracted wide attention. As a result, four of the robbed boys were offered good-paying jobs by the United Fruit Company, and late this spring, when Manny Fox was arrested in Uphigh, Arkansas, where he was pulling the same old dodge, Miss Bobbit was presented with a Good Deed Merit award from the Sunbeam Girls of America. For some reason, she made a point of letting the world know that this did not exactly thrill her. "I do not approve of the organization," she said. "All that rowdy bugle blowing. It's neither good-hearted nor truly feminine. And anyway, what is a good deed? Don't let anybody fool you, a good deed is something you do because you want something in return." It would be reassuring to report she was wrong, and that her just reward, when at last it came, was given out of kindness and love. However, this is not the case. About a week ago the boys involved in the swindle all received from Manny Fox checks covering their losses, and Miss Bobbit, with clodhopping determination, stalked into a meeting of the Hangman's Club, which is now an excuse for drinking beer and playing poker every Thursday night. "Look, boys," she said, laying it on the line, "none of you ever thought to see that money again, but now that you have, you ought to invest it in something practical—like me." The proposition was that they should pool their money and finance her trip to Hollywood; in return, they would get ten percent of her life's earnings which, after she was a star, and that would not be very long, would make them all rich men. "At least," as she said, "in this part of the country." Not one of the boys wanted to do it: but when Miss Bobbit looked at you, what was there to say?

Since Monday, it has been raining buoyant summer rain shot through with sun, but dark at night and full of sound, full of dripping leaves, watery chimings, sleepless scuttlings. Billy Bob is wide-awake, dry-eyed, though everything he does is a little frozen and his tongue is as

stiff as a bell tongue. It has not been easy for him, Miss
Bobbit's going. Because she'd meant more than that.
Than what? Than being thirteen years old and crazy in
love. She was the queer things in him, like the pecan
tree and liking books and caring enough about people to
let them hurt him. She was the things he was afraid to
show anyone else. And in the dark the music trickled
through the rain: won't there be nights when we will
hear it just as though it were really there? And afternoons when the shadows will be all at once confused,
and she will pass before us, unfurling across the lawn
like a pretty piece of ribbon? She laughed to Billy Bob;
she held his hand, she even kissed him. "I'm not going
to die," she said. "You'll come out there, and we'll climb
a mountain, and we'll all live there together, you and
me and Sister Rosalba." But Billy Bob knew it would
never happen that way, and so when the music came
through the dark he would stuff the pillow over his head.

Only there was a strange smile about yesterday, and
that was the day she was leaving. Around noon the sun
came out, bringing with it into the air all the sweetness
of wisteria. Aunt El's yellow Lady Anne's were blooming
again, and she did something wonderful, she told Billy
Bob he could pick them and give them to Miss Bobbit
for good-bye. All afternoon Miss Bobbit sat on the porch
surrounded by people who stopped by to wish her well.
She looked as though she were going to Communion,
dressed in white and with a white parasol. Sister Rosalba
had given her a handkerchief, but she had to borrow it
back because she couldn't stop blubbering. Another little
girl brought a baked chicken, presumably to be eaten on
the bus; the only trouble was she'd forgotten to take
out the insides before cooking it. Miss Bobbit's mother
said that was all right by her, chicken was chicken;
which is memorable because it is the single opinion she
ever voiced. There was only one sour note. For hours
Preacher Star had been hanging around down at the
corner, sometimes standing at the curb tossing a coin,
and sometimes hiding behind a tree, as if he didn't want

anyone to see him. It made everybody nervous. About twenty minutes before bus time he sauntered up and leaned against our gate. Billy Bob was still in the garden picking roses; by now he had enough for a bonfire, and their smell was as heavy as wind. Preacher stared at him until he lifted his head. As they looked at each other the rain began again, falling fine as sea spray and colored by a rainbow. Without a word, Preacher went over and started helping Billy Bob separate the roses into two giant bouquets: together they carried them to the curb. Across the street there were bumblebees of talk, but when Miss Bobbit saw them, two boys whose flower-masked faces were like yellow moons, she rushed down the steps, her arms outstretched. You could see what was going to happen; and we called out, our voices like lightning in the rain, but Miss Bobbit, running toward those moons of roses, did not seem to hear. That is when the six-o'clock bus ran over her.

Master Misery

HER HIGH HEELS, clacking across the marble foyer, made
her think of ice cubes rattling in a glass, and the flowers,
those autumn chrysanthemums in the urn at the entrance,
if touched they would shatter, splinter, she was sure,
into frozen dust; yet the house was warm, even somewhat overheated, but cold, and Sylvia shivered, but
cold, like the snowy swollen wastes of the secretary's
face: Miss Mozart, who dressed all in white, as though
she were a nurse. Perhaps she really was; that, of
course, could be the answer. Mr. Revercomb, you are
mad, and this is your nurse; she thought about it for a
moment; well, no. And now the butler brought her
scarf. His beauty touched her: slender, so gentle, a
Negro with freckled skin and reddish, unreflecting eyes.
As he opened the door, Miss Mozart appeared, her
starched uniform rustling dryly in the hall. "We hope
you will return," she said, and handed Sylvia a sealed envelope. "Mr. Revercomb was most particularly pleased."

Outside, dusk was falling like blue flakes, and
Sylvia walked crosstown along the November streets
until she reached the lonely upper reaches of Fifth
Avenue. It occurred to her then that she might walk
home through the park: an act of defiance almost, for
Henry and Estelle, always insistent upon their city
wisdom, had said over and again, Sylvia, you have no

idea how dangerous it is, walking in the park after dark; look what happened to Myrtle Calisher. This isn't Easton, honey. That was the other thing they said. And said. God, she was sick of it. Still, and aside from a few of the other typists at SnugFare, an underwear company for which she worked, who else in New York did she know? Oh, it would be all right if only she did not have to live with them, if she could afford somewhere a small room of her own; but there in that chintz-cramped apartment she sometimes felt she would choke them both. And why had she come to New York? For whatever reason, and it was indeed becoming vague, a principal cause of leaving Easton had been to rid herself of Henry and Estelle; or rather, their counterparts, though in point of fact Estelle was actually from Easton, a town north of Cincinnati. She and Sylvia had grown up together. The real trouble with Henry and Estelle was that they were so excruciatingly married. Nambypamby, bootsytotsy, and everything had a name: the telephone was Tinkling Tillie, the sofa, Our Nelle, the bed, Big Bear; yes, and what about those His-Her towels, those He-She pillows? Enough to drive you loony. "Loony!" she said aloud, the quiet park erasing her voice. It was lovely now, and she was right to have walked here, with wind moving through the leaves, and globe lamps, freshly aglow, kindling the chalk drawings of children, pink birds, blue arrows, green hearts. But suddenly, like a pair of obscene words, there appeared on the path two boys: pimple-faced, grinning, they loomed in the dusk like menacing flames, and Sylvia, passing them, felt a burning all through her, quite as though she'd brushed fire. They turned and followed her past a deserted playground, one of them bump-bumping a stick along an iron fence, the other whistling: these two sounds accumulated around her like the gathering roar of an oncoming engine, and when one of the boys, with a laugh, called, "Hey, whatsa hurry?" her mouth twisted for breath. Don't, she thought, thinking to throw down her purse and run. At that moment, however, a man walking a dog came up a sidepath, and she followed at his heels to the exit. Wouldn't they feel gratified, Henry and Estelle, wouldn't they we-told-you-so if she were to tell them? and, what is more, Estelle would write it home and the next thing you knew it would be all over Easton that she'd been raped in Central Park. She spent the rest of the way home despising New York: anonymity, its virtuous terror; and the speaking drainpipe, all-night light, ceaseless footfall, subway corridor, numbered door (3C).

"Shh, honey," Estelle said, sidling out of the kitchen, "Bootsy's doing his homework." Sure enough, Henry, a law student at Columbia, was hunched over his books in the living room, and Sylvia, at Estelle's request, took off her shoes before tiptoeing through. Once inside her room, she threw herself on the bed and put her hands over her eyes. Had today really happened? Miss Mozart and Mr. Revercomb, were they really in the tall house on Seventy-eighth Street?

"So, honey, what happened today?" Estelle had entered without knocking.

Sylvia sat up on her elbow. "Nothing. Except that I typed ninety-seven letters."

"About what, honey?" asked Estelle, using Sylvia's hairbrush.

"Oh, hell, what do you suppose? SnugFare, the shorts that safely support our leaders of Science and Industry."

"Gee, honey, don't sound so cross. I don't know what's wrong with you sometimes. You sound so cross. Ouch! Why don't you get a new brush? This one's just knotted with hair . . . ."

"Mostly yours."

"What did you say?"

"Skip it."

"Oh, I thought you said something. Anyway, like I was saying, I wish you didn't have to go to that office and come home every day feeling cross and out of sorts. Personally, and I said this to Bootsy just last night and he agreed with me one hundred percent, I said, Bootsy, I think Sylvia ought to get married: a girl high-strung like that needs her tensions relaxed. There's no earthly reason why you shouldn't. I mean maybe you're not pretty in the ordinary sense, but you have beautiful eyes, and an intelligent, really sincere look. In fact you're the sort of girl any professional man would be lucky to get. And I should think you would want to . . . Look what a different person I am since I married Henry. Doesn't it make you lonesome seeing how happy we are? I'm here to tell you, honey, that there is nothing like lying in bed at night with a man's arms around you and . . ."

"Estelle! For Christ's sake!" Sylvia sat bolt upright in bed, anger on her cheeks like rouge. But after a moment she bit her lip and lowered her eyelids. "I'm sorry," she said, "I didn't mean to shout. Only I wish you wouldn't talk like that."

"It's all right," said Estelle, smiling in a dumb, puzzled way. Then she went over and gave Sylvia a kiss. "I understand, honey. It's just that you're plain worn out. And I'll bet you haven't had anything to eat either. Come on in the kitchen and I'll scramble you some eggs."

When Estelle set the eggs before her, Sylvia felt quite ashamed; after all, Estelle was trying to be nice; and so then, as though to make it all up, she said: "Somthing did happen today."

Estelle sat down across from her with a cup of coffee, and Sylvia went on: "I don't know how to tell about it. It's so very odd. But—well, I had lunch at the Automat today, and I had to share the table with these three men. I might as well have been invisible because they talked about the most personal things. One of the men said his girl friend was going to have a baby and he didn't know where he was going to get the money to do anything about it. So one of the other men asked him why didn't he sell something. He said he didn't have anything to sell. Whereupon the third man (he was rather delicate and didn't look as if he belonged with the others) said yes, there was something he could sell: *dreams*. Even I laughed, but the man shook his head and said very seriously: no, it was perfectly true, his wife's aunt, Miss Mozart, worked for a rich man who bought dreams, regular night-time dreams—from anybody. And he wrote down the man's name and address and gave it to his friend; but the man simply left it lying on the table. It was too crazy for him, he said."

"Me, too," Estelle put in a little righteously.

"I don't know," said Sylvia, lighting a cigarette. "But I couldn't get it out of my head. The name written on the paper was A. F. Revercomb and the address was on East Seventy-eighth Street. I only glanced at it for a moment, but it was . . . I don't know, I couldn't seem to forget it. It was beginning to give me a headache. So I left the office early . . ."

Slowly, and with emphasis, Estelle put down her coffee cup. "Honey, listen, you don't mean you went to see him, this Revercomb nut?"

"I didn't mean to," she said, immediately embarrassed. To try and tell about it she now realized was a mistake. Estelle had no imagination, she would never understand. So her eyes narrowed, the way they always did when she composed a lie. "And, as a matter of fact, I didn't," she said flatly. "I started to; but then I realized how silly it was, and went for a walk instead."

"That was sensible of you," said Estelle as she began stacking dishes in the kitchen sink. "Imagine what might have happened. Buying dreams! Whoever heard? Uh uh, honey, this sure isn't Easton."

Before retiring, Sylvia took a Seconal, something she seldom did; but she knew otherwise she would never rest, not with her mind so nimble and somersaulting; then, too, she felt a curious sadness, a sense of loss, as though she'd been the victim of some real or even moral theft, as though, in fact, the boys encountered in the park had snatched (abruptly she switched on the light) her purse. The envelope Miss Mozart had handed her: it was in the purse, and until now she had forgotten it. She tore it open. Inside there was a blue note folded around a bill; on the note there was written: *In payment of one dream, $5*. And now she believed it; it was true, and she had sold Mr. Revercomb a dream. Could it be really so simple as that? She laughed a little as she turned off the light again. If she were to sell a dream only twice a week, think of what she could do: a place somewhere all her own, she thought, deepening toward sleep; ease, like firelight, wavered over her, and there came the moment of twilit lantern slides, deeply deeper. His lips, his arms: telescoped, descending; and distastefully she kicked away the blanket. Were these cold man-arms the arms Estelle had spoken of? Mr. Revercomb's lips brushed her ear as he leaned far into her sleep. Tell me? he whispered.

It was a week before she saw him again, a Sunday afternoon in early December. She'd left the apartment intending to see a movie, but somehow, and as though it had happened without her knowledge, she found herself on Madison Avenue, two blocks from Mr. Revercomb's. It was a cold, silver-skied day, with winds sharp and catching as hollyhock; in store windows icicles of Christmas tinsel twinkled amid mounds of sequined snow: all to Sylvia's distress, for she hated holidays, those times when one is most alone. In one window she saw a spectacle which made her stop still. It was a life-sized, mechanical Santa Claus; slapping his stomach he rocked back and forth in a frenzy of electrical mirth. You could hear beyond the thick glass his squeaky uproarious laughter. The longer she watched the more evil he seemed, until, finally, with a shudder, she turned and made her way into the street of Mr. Revercomb's house. It was, from the outside, an ordinary town house, perhaps a trifle less polished, less imposing than some others, but relatively grand all the same. Winter-withered ivy writhed about the leaded windowpanes and trailed in octopus ropes over the door; at the sides of the door were two small stone lions with blind, chipped eyes. Sylvia took a breath, then rang the bell. Mr. Revercomb's pale and charming Negro recognized her with a courteous smile.

On the previous visit, the parlor in which she had awaited her audience with Mr. Revercomb had been empty except for herself. This time there were others present, women of several appearances, and an excessively nervous, gnat-eyed young man. Had this group been what it resembled, namely, patients in a doctor's anteroom, he would have seemed either an expectant father or a victim of St. Vitus. Sylvia was seated next to him, and his fidgety eyes unbuttoned her rapidly: whatever he saw apparently intrigued him very little, and Sylvia was grateful when he went back to his twitchy preoccupations. Gradually, though, she became conscious of how interested in her the assemblage seemed; in the dim, doubtful light of the plant-filled room their gazes were more rigid than the chairs upon which they sat; one woman was particularly relentless. Ordinarily, her face would have had a soft commonplace sweetness, but now, watching Sylvia, it was ugly with distrust, jealousy. As though trying to tame some creature which might suddenly spring full-fanged, she sat stroking a flea-bitten neck fur, her stare continuing its assault until the earthquake footstep of Miss Mozart was heard in the hall. Immediately, and like frightened students, the group, separating into their individual identities, came to attention. "You, Mr. Pocker," accused Miss Mozart, "you're next!" And Mr. Pocker, wringing his hands, jittering his eyes, followed after her. In the dusk-room the gathering settled again like sun motes.

It began then to rain; melting window reflections quivered on the walls, and Mr. Revercomb's young butler, seeping through the room, stirred a fire in the grate, set tea things upon a table. Sylvia, nearest the fire, felt drowsy with warmth and the noise of rain; her head tilted sideways, she closed her eyes, neither asleep nor really awake. For a long while only the crystal swingings of a clock scratched the polished silence of Mr. Revercomb's house. And then, abruptly, there was an enormous commotion in the hall, capsizing the room into a fury of sound: a bull-deep voice, vulgar as red, roared out: "Stop Oreilly? The ballet butler and who else?" The owner of this voice, a tub-shaped, brick-colored little man, shoved his way to the parlor threshold, where he stood drunkenly seesawing from foot to foot. "Well, well, well," he said, his gin-hoarse voice descending the scale, "and all these ladies before me? But Oreilly is a gentleman, Oreilly waits his turn."

"Not here, he doesn't," said Miss Mozart, stealing up behind him and seizing him sternly by the collar. His face went even redder and his eyes bubbled out: "You're choking me," he gasped, but Miss Mozart whose green-pale hands were as strong as oak roots, jerked his tie still tighter, and propelled him toward the door, which presently slammed with shattering effect: a tea cup tinkled, and dry dahlia leaves tumbled from their heights. The lady with the fur slipped an aspirin into her mouth. "Dis*gusting*," she said, and the others, all except Sylvia, laughed delicately, admiringly, as Miss Mozart strode past dusting her hands.

It was raining thick and darkly when Sylvia left Mr. Revercomb's. She looked around the desolate street for a taxi; there was nothing, however, and no one; yes, someone, the drunk man who had caused the disturbance. Like a lonely city child, he was leaning against a parked car and bouncing a rubber ball up and down. "Lookit, kid," he said to Sylvia, "lookit, I just found this ball. Do you suppose that means good luck?" Sylvia smiled at him; for all his bravado, she thought him rather harmless, and there was a quality in his face, some grinning sadness suggesting a clown minus makeup. Juggling his ball, he skipped along after her as she headed toward Madison Avenue. "I'll bet I made a fool of myself in there," he said. "When I do things like that I just want to sit down and cry." Standing so long in the rain seemed to have sobered him considerably. "But she ought not to have choked me that way; damn, she's too rough. I've known some rough women: my sister Berenice could brand the wildest bull; but that other one, she's the roughest of the lot. Mark Oreilly's word, she's going to end up in the electric chair," he said, and smacked his lips. "They've got no cause to treat me like that. It's every bit his fault anyhow. I didn't have an awful lot to begin with, but then he took it every bit, and now I've got *niente,* kid, *niente."*

"That's too bad," said Sylvia, though she did not know what she was being sympathetic about. "Are you a clown, Mr. Oreilly?"

"Was,'' he said.

By this time they had reached the avenue, but Sylvia did not even look for a taxi; she wanted to walk on in the rain with the man who had been a clown. "When I was a little girl I only liked clown dolls," she told him. "My room at home was like a circus."

"I've been other things besides a clown. I have sold insurance also."

"Oh?" said Sylvia, disappointed. "And what do you do now?"

Oreilly chuckled and threw his ball especially high; after the catch his head still remained tilted upward. "I watch the sky," he said. "There I am with my suitcase traveling through the blue. It's where you travel when you've got no place else to go. But what do I do on this planet? I have stolen, begged, and sold my dreams—all for purposes of whiskey. A man cannot travel in the blue without a bottle. Which brings us to a point: how'd you take it, baby, if I asked for the loan of a dollar?"

"I'd take it fine," Sylvia replied, and paused, uncertain of what she'd say next. They wandered along so slowly, the stiff rain enclosing them like an insulating pressure; it was as though she were walking with a childhood doll, one grown miraculous and capable; she

reached and held his hand: dear clown traveling in the
blue. "But I haven't got a dollar. All I've got is seventy
cents."

"No hard feelings," said Oreilly. "But honest, is
that the kind of money he's paying nowadays?"

Sylvia knew whom he meant. "No, no—as a matter of fact, I didn't sell him a dream." She made no attempt to explain; she didn't understand it herself.
Confronting the graying invisibility of Mr. Revercomb
(impeccable, exact as a scale, surrounded in a cologne
of clinical odors; flat gray eyes planted like seed in the
anonymity of his face and sealed within steel-dull
lenses) she could not remember a dream, and so she
told of two thieves who had chased her through the park
and in and out among the swings of a playground. "Stop,
he said for me to stop; there are dreams and dreams, he
said, but that is not a real one, that is one you are making
up. Now how do you suppose he knew that? So I told
him another dream; it was about him, of how he held
me in the night with balloons rising and moons falling all
around. He said he was not interested in dreams concerning himself." Miss Mozart, who transcribed the
dreams in shorthand, was told to call the next person. "I
don't think I will go back there again," she said.

"You will," said Oreilly. "Look at me, even I go
back, and he has long since finished with me, Master
Misery."

"Master Misery? Why do you call him that?"

They had reached the corner where the maniacal
Santa Claus rocked and bellowed. His laughter echoed
in the rainy squeaking street, and a shadow of him
swayed in the rainbow lights of the pavement. Oreilly,
turning his back upon the Santa Claus, smiled and said:
"I call him Master Misery on account of that's who he is.
Master Misery. Only maybe you call him something else;
anyway, he is the same fellow, and you must've known
him. All mothers tell their kids about him: he lives in
hollows of trees, he comes down chimneys late at night,
he lurks in graveyards and you can hear his step in the

attic. The sonofabitch, he is a thief and a threat: he will take everything you have and end by leaving you nothing, not even a dream. Boo!" he shouted, and laughed louder than Santa Claus. "Now do you know who he is?"

Sylvia nodded. "I know who he is. My family called him something else. But I can't remember what. It was so long ago."

"But you remember him?"

"Yes, I remember him."

"Then call him Master Misery," he said, and, bouncing his ball, walked away from her. "Master Misery," his voice trailed to a mere moth of sound, "Mas-ter Mis-er-y . . ."

It was hard to look at Estelle, for she was in front of a window, and the window was filled with windy sun, which hurt Sylvia's eyes, and the glass rattled, which hurt her head. Also, Estelle was lecturing. Her nasal voice sounded as though her throat were a depository for rusty blades. "I wish you could see yourself," she was saying. Or was that something she'd said a long while back? Never mind. "I don't know what's happened to you: I'll bet you don't weigh a hundred pounds, I can see every bone and vein, and your hair! you look like a poodle."

Sylvia passed a hand over her forehead. "What time is it, Estelle?"

"It's four," she said, interrupting herself long enough to look at her watch. "But where is your watch?"

"I sold it," said Sylvia, too tired to lie. It did not matter. She had sold so many things, including her beaver coat and gold mesh evening bag.

Estelle shook her head. "I give up, honey, I plain give up. And that was the watch your mother gave you for graduation. It's a shame," she said, and made an old-maid noise with her mouth, "a pity and a shame. I'll never understand why you left us. That is your business, I'm sure; only how could you have left us for this . . . this . . . ?"

"Dump," supplied Sylvia, using the word advisedly. It was a furnished room in the East Sixties between Second and Third Avenues. Large enough for a daybed and a splintery old bureau with a mirror like a cataracted eye, it had one window, which looked out on a vast vacant lot (you could hear the tough afternoon voices of desperate running boys) and in the distance, like an exclamation point for the skyline, there was the black smokestack of a factory. This smokestack occurred frequently in her dreams; it never failed to arouse Miss Mozart: "Phallic, phallic," she would mutter, glancing up from her shorthand. The floor of the room was a garbage pail of books begun but never finished, antique newspapers, even orange hulls, fruit cores, underwear, a spilled powder box.

Estelle kicked her way through this trash, and sat down on the daybed. "Honey, you don't know, but I've been worried crazy. I mean I've got pride and all that and if you don't like me, well, o.k.; but you've got no right to stay away like this and not let me hear from you in over a month. So today I said to Bootsy, Bootsy, I've got a feeling something terrible has happened to Sylvia. You can imagine how I felt when I called your office and they told me you hadn't worked there for the last four weeks. What happened, were you fired?"

"Yes, I was fired." Sylvia began to sit up. "Please, Estelle—I've got to get ready; I've got an appointment."

"Be still. You're not going anywhere till I know what's wrong. The landlady downstairs told me you were found sleepwalking. . . ."

"What do you mean talking to her? Why are you spying on me?"

Estelle's eyes puckered, as though she were going to cry. She put her hand over Sylvia's and petted it gently. "Tell me, honey, is it because of a man?"

"It's because of a man, yes," said Sylvia, laughter at the edge of her voice.

"You should have come to me before," Estelle sighed. "I know about men. That is nothing for you to be ashamed of. A man can have a way with a woman that kind of makes her forget everything else. If Henry wasn't the fine upstanding potential lawyer that he is, why, I would still love him, and do things for him that before I knew what it was like to be with a man would have seemed shocking and horrible. But honey, this fellow you're mixed up with, he's taking advantage of you."

"It's not that kind of relationship," said Sylvia, getting up and locating a pair of stockings in the furor of her bureau drawers. "It hasn't got anything to do with love. Forget about it. In fact, go home and forget about me altogether."

Estelle looked at her narrowly. "You scare me, Sylvia; you really scare me." Sylvia laughed and went on getting dressed. "Do you remember a long time ago when I said you ought to get married?"

"Uh huh. And now you listen." Sylvia turned around; there was a row of hairpins spaced across her mouth; she extracted them one at a time all the while she talked. "You talk about getting married as though it were the answer absolute; very well, up to a point I agree. Sure, I want to be loved; who the hell doesn't? But even if I was willing to compromise, where is the man I'm going to marry? Believe me, he must've fallen down a manhole. I mean it seriously when I say there are no men in New York—and even if there were, how do you meet them? Every man I ever met here who seemed the slightest bit attractive was either married, too poor to get married, or queer. And anyway, this is no place to fall in love; this is where you ought to come when you want to get over being in love. Sure, I suppose I could marry somebody; but do I want that? Do I?"

Estelle shrugged. "Then what do you want?"

"More than is coming to me." She poked the last hairpin into place, and smoothed her eyebrows before the mirror. "I have an appointment, Estelle, and it is time for you to go now."

"I can't leave you like this," said Estelle, her hand

waving helplessly around the room. "Sylvia, you were my childhood friend."

"That is just the point: we're not children any more; at least, I'm not. No, I want you to go home, and I don't want you to come here again. I just want you to forget about me."

Estelle fluttered at her eyes with a handkerchief, and by the time she reached the door she was weeping quite loudly. Sylvia could not afford remorse: having been mean, there was nothing to be but meaner. "Go on," she said, following Estelle into the hall, "and write home any damn nonsense about me you want to!" Letting out a wail that brought other roomers to their doors, Estelle fled down the stairs.

After this Sylvia went back into her room and sucked a piece of sugar to take the sour taste out of her mouth: it was her grandmother's remedy for bad tempers. Then she got down on her knees and pulled from under the bed a cigar box she kept hidden there. When you opened the box it played a homemade and somewhat disorganized version of "Oh How I Hate to Get up in the Morning." Her brother had made the music-box and given it to her on her fourteenth birthday. Eating the sugar, she'd thought of her grandmother, and hearing the tune she thought of her brother; the rooms of the house where they had lived rotated before her, all dark and she like a light moving among them: up the stairs, down, out and through, spring sweet and lilac shadows in the air and the creaking of a porch swing. All gone, she thought, calling their names, and now I am absolutely alone. The music stopped. But it went on in her head; she could hear it bugling above the child-cries of the vacant lot. And it interfered with her reading. She was reading a little diary-like book she kept inside the box. In this book she wrote down the essentials of her dreams; they were endless now, and it was so hard to remember. Today she would tell Mr. Revercomb about the three blind children. He would like that. The prices he paid varied, and she was sure this was at least a ten-dollar dream. The cigar-box anthem followed her down the stairs and through the streets and she longed for it to go away.

In the store where the Santa Claus had been there was a new and equally unnerving exhibit. Even when she was late to Mr. Revercomb's, as now, Sylvia was compelled to pause by the window. A plaster girl with intense glass eyes sat astride a bicycle pedaling at the maddest pace; though its wheel spokes spun hypnotically, the bicycle of course never budged: all that effort and the poor girl going nowhere. It was a pitifully human situation, and one that Sylvia could so exactly identify with herself that she always felt a real pang. The music-box rewound in her head: the tune, her brother, the house, a high-school dance, the house, the tune! Couldn't Mr. Revercomb hear it? His penetrating gaze carried such dull suspicion. But he seemed pleased with her dream, and, when she left, Miss Mozart gave her an envelope containing ten dollars.

"I had a ten-dollar dream," she told Oreilly, and Oreilly, rubbing his hands together, said, "Fine! Fine! But that's just my luck, baby—you should've got here sooner 'cause I went and did a terrible thing. I walked into a liquor store up the street, snatched a quart and ran." Sylvia didn't believe him until he produced from his pinned-together overcoat a bottle of bourbon, already half gone. "You're going to get in trouble some day," she said, "and then what would happen to me? I don't know what I would do without you." Oreilly laughed and poured a shot of the whiskey into a water glass. They were sitting in an all-night cafeteria, a great glaring food depot alive with blue mirrors and raw murals. Although to Sylvia it seemed a sordid place, they met there frequently for dinner; but even if she could have afforded it she did not know where else they could go, for together they presented a curious aspect: a young girl and a doddering, drunken man. Even here people often stared at them; if they stared long enough, Oreilly would stiffen with dignity and say: "Hello, hot lips, I remember you from way back. Still working in the men's room?" But usually they were left to themselves, and sometimes they would sit talking until two and three in the morning.

"It's a good thing the rest of Master Misery's crowd don't know he gave you that ten bucks. One of them would say you stole the dream. I had that happen once. Eaten up, all of em, never saw such a bunch of sharks, worse than actors or clowns or businessmen. Crazy, if you think about it: you worry whether you're going to go to sleep, if you're going to have a dream, if you're going to remember the dream. Round and round. So you get a couple of bucks, so you rush to the nearest liquor store—or the nearest sleeping-pill machine. And first thing you know, you're roaming your way up outhouse alley. Why, baby, you know what it's like? It's just like life."

"No, Oreilly, that's what it isn't like. It hasn't anything to do with life. It has more to do with being dead. I feel as though everything were being taken from me, as though some thief were stealing me down to the bone. Oreilly, I tell you I haven't an ambition, and there used to be so much. I don't understand it and I don't know what to do."

He grinned. "And you say it isn't like life? Who understands life and who knows what to do?"

"Be serious," she said. "Be serious and put away that whiskey and eat your soup before it gets stone cold." She lighted a cigarette, and the smoke, smarting her eyes, intensified her frown. "If only I knew what he wanted with those dreams, all typed and filed. What does he do with them? You're right when you say he is Master Misery. . . . He can't be simply some silly quack; it can't be so meaningless as that. But why does he want dreams? Help me, Oreilly, think, think: what does it mean?"

Squinting one eye, Oreilly poured himself another drink; the clownlike twist of his mouth hardened into a line of scholarly straightness. "That is a million-dollar question, kid. Why don't you ask something easy, like how to cure the common cold? Yes, kid, what does it mean? I have thought about it a good deal. I have thought about it in the process of making love to a woman, and I have thought about it in the middle of a poker game." He tossed the drink down his throat and shuddered. "Now a sound can start a dream; the noise of one car passing in the night can drop a hundred sleepers into the deep parts of themselves. It's funny to think of that one car racing through the dark, trailing so many dreams. Sex, a sudden change of light, a pickle, these are little keys that can open up our insides, too. But most dreams begin because there are furies inside of us that blow open all the doors. I don't believe in Jesus Christ, but I do believe in people's souls; and I figure it this way, baby: dreams are the mind of the soul and the secret truth about us. Now Master Misery, maybe he hasn't got a soul, so bit by bit he borrows yours, steals it like he would steal your dolls or the chicken wing off your plate. Hundreds of souls have passed through him and gone into a filing case."

"Oreilly, be serious," she said again, annoyed because she thought he was making more jokes. "And look, your soup is . . ." She stopped abruptly, startled by Oreilly's peculiar expression. He was looking toward the entrance. Three men were there, two policemen and a civilian wearing a clerk's cloth jacket. The clerk was pointing toward their table. Oreilly's eyes circled the room with trapped despair; he sighed then, and leaned back in his seat, ostentatiously pouring himself another drink. "Good evening, gentlemen," he said, when the official party confronted him, "will you join us for a drink?"

"You can't arrest him," cried Sylvia, "you can't arrest a clown!" She threw her ten-dollar bill at them, but the policemen did not pay any attention, and she began to pound the table. All the customers in the place were staring, and the manager came running up, wringing his hands. The police said for Oreilly to get to his feet.

"Certainly," Oreilly said, "though I do think it shocking you have to trouble yourselves with such petty crimes as mine when everywhere there are master thieves afoot. For instance, this pretty child," he stepped between the officers and pointed to Sylvia, "she is the recent victim of a major theft: poor baby, she has had her soul stolen."

For two days following Oreilly's arrest Sylvia did not leave her room: sun on the window, then dark. By the third day she had run out of cigarettes, so she ventured as far as the corner delicatessen. She bought a package of cupcakes, a can of sardines, a newspaper and cigarettes. In all this time she'd not eaten and it was a light, delicious, sharpening sensation; but the climb back up the stairs, the relief of closing the door, these so exhausted her she could not quite make the daybed. She slid down to the floor and did not move until it was day again. She thought afterwards that she'd been there about twenty minutes. Turning on the radio as loud as it would go, she dragged a chair up to the window and opened the newspaper on her lap: *Lana Denies, Russia Rejects, Miners Conciliate:* of all things this was saddest, that life goes on: if one leaves one's lover, life should stop for him, and if one disappears from the world, then the world should stop, too: and it never did. And that was the real reason for most people getting up in the morning: not because it would matter but because it wouldn't. But if Mr. Revercomb succeeded finally in collecting all the dreams out of every head, perhaps— the idea slipped, became entangled with radio and newspaper. *Falling Temperatures.* A snowstorm moving across Colorado, across the West, falling upon all the small towns, yellowing every light, filling every footfall, falling now and here: but how quickly it had come, the snowstorm: the roofs, the vacant lot, the distance deep in white and deepening, like sleep. She looked at the paper and she looked at the snow. But it must have been snowing all day. It could not have just started. There was no sound of traffic; in the swirling wastes of the vacant lot children circled a bonfire; a car, buried at the curb, winked its headlights: help! help! silent, like the heart's distress. She crumbled a cupcake and sprinkled it on the windowsill: north-birds would come to keep her company. And she left the window open for them; snow-wind scattered flakes that dissolved on the floor like April-fool jewels. *Presents Life Can Be Beautiful:* turn down that radio! The witch of the woods was tapping at her door: Yes, Mrs. Halloran, she said, and turned off the radio altogether. Snow-quiet, sleep-silent, only the fun-fire faraway songsinging of childen; and the room was blue with cold, colder than the cold of fairytales: lie down my heart among the igloo flowers of snow. Mr. Revercomb, why do you wait upon the threshold? Ah, do come inside, it is so cold out there.

But her moment of waking was warm and held. The window was closed, and a man's arms were around her. He was singing to her, his voice gentle but jaunty: *cherryberry, moneyberry, happyberry pie, but the best old pie is a loveberry pie* . . .

"Oreilly, is it—is it really you?"

He squeezed her. "Baby's awake now. And how does she feel?"

"I had thought I was dead," she said, and happiness winged around inside her like a bird lamed but still flying. She tried to hug him and she was too weak. "I love you, Oreilly; you are my only friend and I was so frightened. I thought I would never see you again." She paused, remembering. "But why aren't you in jail?"

Oreilly's face got all tickled and pink. "I was never in jail," he said mysteriously. "But first, let's have something to eat. I brought some things up from the delicatessen this morning."

She had a sudden feeling of floating. "How long have you been here?"

"Since yesterday," he said, fussing around with bundles and paper plates. "You let me in yourself."

"That's impossible. I don't remember it at all."

"I know," he said, leaving it at that. "Here, drink your milk like a good kid and I'll tell you a real wicked story. Oh, it's wild," he promised, slapping his sides gladly and looking more than ever like a clown. "Well, like I said, I never was in jail and this bit of fortune came to me because there I was being hustled down the street by those bindlestiffs when who should I see come swinging along but the gorilla woman: you guessed it, Miss Mozart. Hi, I says to her, off to the barber shop for a shave? It's about time you were put under arrest, she says, and smiles at one of the cops. Do your duty, officer. Oh, I says to her, I'm not under arrest. Me, I'm just on my way to the station house to give them the lowdown on you, you dirty communist. You can imagine what sort of holler she set up then; she grabbed hold of me and the cops grabbed hold of her. Can't say I didn't warn them: careful, boys, I said, she's got hair on her chest. And she sure did lay about her. So I just sort of walked off down the street. Never have believed in standing around watching fistfights the way people do in this city."

Oreilly stayed with her in the room over the weekend. It was like the most beautiful party Sylvia could remember; she'd never laughed so much, for one thing, and no one, certainly no one in her family, had ever made her feel so loved. Oreilly was a fine cook, and he fixed delicious dishes on the little electric stove; once he scooped snow off the windowsill and made sherbet flavored with strawberry syrup. By Sunday she was strong enough to dance. They turned on the radio and she danced until she fell to her knees, windless and laughing. "I'll never be afraid again," she said. "I hardly know what I was afraid of to begin with."

"The same things you'll be afraid of the next time," Oreilly told her quietly. "That is a quality of Master Misery: no one ever knows what he is—not even children, and they know mostly everything."

Sylvia went to the window; an arctic whiteness lay over the city, but the snow had stopped, and the night sky was as clear as ice: there, riding above the river, she saw the first star of evening. "I see the first star," she said, crossing her fingers.

"And what do you wish when you see the first star?"

"I wish to see another star," she said. "At least that is what I usually wish."

"But tonight?"

She sat down on the floor and leaned her head against his knee. "Tonight I wished that I could have back my dreams."

"Don't we all?" Oreilly said, stroking her hair. "But then what would you do? I mean what would you do if you could have them back?"

Sylvia was silent a moment; when she spoke her eyes were gravely distant. "I would go home," she said slowly. "And that is a terrible decision, for it would mean giving up most of my other dreams. But if Mr. Revercomb would let me have them back, then I would go home tomorrow."

Saying nothing, Oreilly went to the closet and brought back her coat. "But why?" she asked as he helped her on with it. "Never mind," he said, "just do what I tell you. We're going to pay Mr. Revercomb a call, and you're going to ask him to give you back your dreams. It's a chance."

Sylvia balked at the door. "Please, Oreilly, don't make me go. I can't, please, I'm afraid."

"I thought you said you'd never be afraid again."

But once in the street he hurried her so quickly against the wind she did not have time to be frightened. It was Sunday, stores were closed and the traffic lights seemed to wink only for them, for there were no moving cars along the snow-deep avenue. Sylvia even forgot where they were going, and chattered of trivial oddments: right here at this corner is where she'd seen Garbo, and over there, that is where the old woman was run over. Presently, however, she stopped, out of breath and overwhelmed with sudden realization. "I can't,

Oreilly," she said, pulling back. "What can I say to him?"

"Make it like a business deal," said Oreilly. "Tell him straight out that you want your dreams, and if he'll give them to you you'll pay back all the money: on the installment plan, naturally. It's simple enough, kid. Why the hell couldn't he give them back? They are all right there in a filing case."

This speech was somehow convincing and, stamping her frozen feet, Sylvia went ahead with a certain courage. "That's the kid," he said. They separated on Third Avenue, Oreilly being of the opinion that Mr. Revercomb's immediate neighborhood was not for the moment precisely safe. He confined himself in a doorway, now and then lighting a match and singing aloud: *but the best old pie is a whiskeyberry pie!* Like a wolf, a long thin dog came padding over the moon-slats under the elevated, and across the street there were the misty shapes of men ganged around a bar: the idea of maybe cadging a drink in there made him groggy.

Just as he had decided on perhaps trying something of the sort, Sylvia appeared. And she was in his arms before he knew that it was really her. "It can't be so bad, sweetheart," he said softly, holding her as best he could. "Don't cry, baby; it's too cold to cry: you'll chap your face." As she strangled for words, her crying evolved into a tremulous, unnatural laugh. The air was filled with the smoke of her laughter. "Do you know what he said?" she gasped. "Do you know what he said when I asked for my dreams?" Her head fell back, and her laughter rose and carried over the street like an abandoned, wildly colored kite. Oreilly had finally to shake her by the shoulders. "He said—I couldn't have them back because—because he'd used them all up."

She was silent then, her face smoothing into an expressionless calm. She put her arm through Oreilly's, and together they moved down the street; but it was as if they were friends pacing a platform, each waiting for the other's train, and when they reached the corner he cleared his throat and said: "I guess I'd better turn off here. It's as likely a spot as any."

Sylvia held on to his sleeve. "But where will you go, Oreilly?"

"Traveling in the blue," he said, trying a smile that didn't work out very well.

She opened her purse. "A man cannot travel in the blue without a bottle," she said, and, kissing him on the cheek, slipped five dollars in his pocket.

"Bless you, baby."

It did not matter that it was the last of her money, that now she would have to walk home, and alone. The pilings of snow were like the white waves of a white sea, and she rode upon them, carried by winds and tides of the moon. I do not know what I want, and perhaps I shall never know, but my only wish from every star will always be another star; and truly I am not afraid, she thought. Two boys came out of a bar and stared at her; in some park some long time ago she'd seen two boys and they might be the same. Truly I am not afraid, she thought, hearing their snowy footsteps following after her: and anyway, there was nothing left to steal.

A Diamond Guitar

THE NEAREST TOWN to the prison farm is twenty miles
away. Many forests of pine trees stand between the farm
and the town, and it is in these forests that the convicts
work; they tap for turpentine. The prison itself is in a
forest. You will find it there at the end of a red rutted
road, barbed wire sprawling like a vine over its walls.
Inside, there live one hundred and nine white men,
ninety-seven Negroes and one Chinese. There are two
sleep houses—great green wooden buildings with tar-
paper roofs. The white men occupy one, the Negroes
and the Chinese the other. In each sleep house there is
one large potbellied stove, but the winters are cold
here, and at night with the pines waving frostily and a
freezing light falling from the moon the men, stretched
on their iron cots, lie awake with the fire colors of the
stove playing in their eyes.

The men whose cots are nearest the stove are the
important men—those who are looked up to or feared.
Mr. Schaeffer is one of these. Mr. Schaeffer—for that is
what he is called, a mark of special respect—is a lanky,
pulled-out man. He has reddish, silvering hair, and his
face is attenuated, religious; there is no flesh to him; you
can see the workings of his bones, and his eyes are a
poor, dull color. He can read and he can write, he can
add a column of figures. When another man receives a
letter, he brings it to Mr. Schaeffer. Most of these letters

are sad and complaining; very often Mr. Schaeffer improvises more cheerful messages and does not read what is written on the page. In the sleep house there are two other men who can read. Even so, one of them brings his letters to Mr. Schaeffer, who obliges by never reading the truth. Mr. Schaeffer himself does not receive mail, not even at Christmas; he seems to have no friends beyond the prison, and actually he has none there—that is, no particular friend. This was not always true.

One winter Sunday some winters ago Mr. Schaeffer was sitting on the steps of the sleep house carving a doll. He is quite talented at this. His dolls are carved in separate sections, then put together with bits of spring wire; the arms and legs move, the head rolls. When he has finished a dozen or so of these dolls, the Captain of the farm takes them into town, and there they are sold in a general store. In this way Mr. Schaeffer earns money for candy and tobacco.

That Sunday, as he sat cutting out the fingers for a little hand, a truck pulled into the prison yard. A young boy, handcuffed to the Captain of the farm, climbed out of the truck and stood blinking at the ghostly winter sun. Mr. Schaeffer only glanced at him. He was then a man of fifty, and seventeen of those years he'd lived at the farm. The arrival of a new prisoner could not arouse him. Sunday is a free day at the farm, and other men who were moping around the yard crowded down to the truck. Afterward, Pick Axe and Goober stopped by to speak with Mr. Schaeffer.

Pick Axe said, "He's a foreigner, the new one is. From Cuba. But with yellow hair."

"A knifer, Cap'n says," said Goober, who was a knifer himself. "Cut up a sailor in Mobile."

"Two sailors," said Pick Axe. "But just a café fight. He didn't hurt them boys none."

"To cut off a man's ear? You call that not hurtin' him? They give him two years, Cap'n says."

Pick Axe said, "He's got a guitar with jewels all over it."

It was getting too dark to work. Mr. Schaeffer fitted the pieces of his doll together and, holding its little hands, set it on his knee. He rolled a cigarette; the pines were blue in the sundown light, and the smoke from his cigarette lingered in the cold, darkening air. He could see the Captain coming across the yard. The new prisoner, a blond young boy, lagged a pace behind. He was carrying a guitar studded with glass diamonds that cast a starry twinkle, and his new uniform was too big for him; it looked like a Halloween suit.

"Somebody for you, Schaeffer," said the Captain, pausing on the steps of the sleep house. The Captain was not a hard man; occasionally he invited Mr. Schaeffer into his office, and they would talk together about things they had read in the newspaper. "Tico Feo," he said as though it were the name of a bird or a song, "this is Mr. Schaeffer. Do like him, and you'll do right."

Mr. Schaeffer glanced up at the boy and smiled. He smiled at him longer than he meant to, for the boy had eyes like strips of sky—blue as the winter evening—and his hair was as gold as the Captain's teeth. He had a fun-loving face, nimble, clever; and, looking at him, Mr. Schaeffer thought of holidays and good times.

"Is like my baby sister," said Tico Feo, touching Mr. Schaeffer's doll. His voice with its Cuban accent was soft and sweet as a banana. "She sit on my knee also."

Mr. Schaeffer was suddenly shy. Bowing to the Captain, he walked off into the shadows of the yard. He stood there whispering the names of the evening stars as they opened in flower above him. The stars were his pleasure, but tonight they did not comfort him; they did not make him remember that what happens to us on earth is lost in the endless shine of eternity. Gazing at them—the stars—he thought of the jeweled guitar and its worldly glitter.

It could be said of Mr. Schaeffer that in his life he'd done only one really bad thing: he'd killed a man. The circumstances of that deed are unimportant, except to say that the man deserved to die and that for it Mr. Schaeffer was sentenced to ninety-nine years and a day. For a long while—for many years, in fact—he had not thought of how it was before he came to the farm. His memory of those times was like a house where no one lives and where the furniture has rotted away. But tonight it was as if lamps had been lighted through all the gloomy dead rooms. It had begun to happen when he saw Tico Feo coming through the dusk with his splendid guitar. Until that moment he had not been lonesome. Now, recognizing his loneliness, he felt alive. He had not wanted to be alive. To be alive was to remember brown rivers where the fish run, and sunlight on a lady's hair.

Mr. Schaeffer hung his head. The glare of the stars had made his eyes water.

The sleep house usually is a glum place, stale with the smell of men and stark in the light of two unshaded electric bulbs. But with the advent of Tico Feo it was as though a tropic occurrence had happened in the cold room, for when Mr. Schaeffer returned from his observance of the stars he came upon a savage and garish scene. Sitting cross-legged on a cot, Tico Feo was picking at his guitar with long swaying fingers and singing a song that sounded as jolly as jingling coins. Though the song was in Spanish, some of the men tried to sing it with him, and Pick Axe and Goober were dancing together. Charlie and Wink were dancing too, but separately. It was nice to hear the men laughing, and when Tico Feo finally put aside his guitar, Mr. Schaeffer was among those who congratulated him.

"You deserve such a fine guitar," he said.

"Is diamond guitar," said Tico Feo, drawing his hand over its vaudeville dazzle. "Once I have a one with rubies. But that one is stole. In Havana my sister work in a, how you say, where make guitar; is how I have this one."

Mr. Schaeffer asked him if he had many sisters, and Tico Feo, grinning, held up four fingers. Then, his blue eyes narrowing greedily, he said, "Please, Mister, you give me doll for my two little sister?"

The next evening Mr. Schaeffer brought him the dolls. After that he was Tico Feo's best friend and they were always together. At all times they considered each other.

Tico Feo was eighteen years old and for two years had worked on a freighter in the Caribbean. As a child he'd gone to school with nuns, and he wore a gold crucifix around his neck. He had a rosary too. The rosary he kept wrapped in a green silk scarf that also held three other treasures: a bottle of Evening in Paris cologne, a pocket mirror and a Rand McNally map of the world. These and the guitar were his only possessions, and he would not allow anyone to touch them. Perhaps he prized his map the most. At night, before the lights were turned off, he would shake out his map and show Mr. Schaeffer the places he'd been—Galveston, Miami, New Orleans, Mobile, Cuba, Haiti, Jamaica, Puerto Rico, the Virgin Islands—and the places he wanted to go to. He wanted to go almost everywhere, especially Madrid, especially the North Pole. This both charmed and frightened Mr. Schaeffer. It hurt him to think of Tico Feo on the seas and in far places. He sometimes looked defensively at his friend and thought, "You are just a lazy dreamer."

It is true that Tico Feo was a lazy fellow. After that first evening he had to be urged even to play his guitar. At daybreak when the guard came to rouse the men, which he did by banging a hammer on the stove, Tico Feo would whimper like a child. Sometimes he pretended to be ill, moaned and rubbed his stomach; but he never got away with this, for the Captain would send him out to work with the rest of the men. He and Mr. Schaeffer were put together on a highway gang. It was hard work, digging at frozen clay and carrying croker sacks filled with broken stone. The guard had always to be shouting at Tico Feo, for he spent most of the time trying to lean on things.

Each noon, when the dinner buckets were passed around, the two friends sat together. There were some good things in Mr. Schaeffer's bucket, as he could afford apples and candy bars from the town. He liked giving these things to his friend, for his friend enjoyed them so much, and he thought, "You are growing; it will be a long time until you are a grown man."

Not all the men liked Tico Feo. Because they were jealous, or for more subtle reasons, some of them told ugly stories about him. Tico Feo himself seemed unaware of this. When the men gathered around him, and he played his guitar and sang his songs, you could see that he felt he was loved. Most of the men did feel a love for him; they waited for and depended upon the hour between supper and lights out. "Tico, play your box," they would say. They did not notice that afterward there was a deeper sadness than there had ever been. Sleep jumped beyond them like a jack rabbit, and their eyes lingered ponderingly on the firelight that creaked behind the grating of the stove. Mr. Schaeffer was the only one who understood their troubled feeling, for he felt it too. It was that his friend had revived the brown rivers where the fish run, and ladies with sunlight in their hair.

Soon Tico Feo was allowed the honor of having a bed near the stove and next to Mr. Schaeffer. Mr. Schaeffer had always known that his friend was a terrible liar. He did not listen for the truth in Tico Feo's tales of adventure, of conquests and encounters with famous people. Rather, he took pleasure in them as plain stories, such as you would read in a magazine, and it warmed him to hear his friend's tropic voice whispering in the dark.

Except that they did not combine their bodies or think to do so, though such things were not unknown at the farm, they were as lovers. Of the seasons, spring is the most shattering: stalks thrusting through the earth's winter-stiffened crust, young leaves cracking out on old left-to-die branches, the falling-asleep wind cruising through all the newborn green. And with Mr. Schaeffer it was the same, a breaking up, a flexing of muscles that had hardened.

It was late January. The friends were sitting on the steps of the sleep house, each with a cigarette in his hand. A moon thin and yellow as a piece of lemon rind curved above them, and under its light, threads of ground frost glistened like silver snail trails. For many days Tico Feo had been drawn into himself—silent as a robber waiting in the shadows. It was no good to say to him, "Tico, play your box." He would only look at you with smooth, under-ether eyes.

"Tell a story," said Mr. Schaeffer, who felt nervous and helpless when he could not reach his friend. "Tell about when you went to the race track in Miami."

"I not ever go to no race track," said Tico Feo, thereby admitting to his wildest lie, one involving hundreds of dollars and a meeting with Bing Crosby. He did not seem to care. He produced a comb and pulled it sulkily through his hair. A few days before this comb had been the cause of a fierce quarrel. One of the men, Wink, claimed that Tico Feo had stolen the comb from him, to which the accused replied by spitting in his face. They had wrestled around until Mr. Schaeffer and another man got them separated. "Is my comb. You tell him!" Tico Feo had demanded of Mr. Schaeffer. But Mr. Schaeffer with quiet firmness had said no, it was not his friend's comb—an answer that seemed to defeat all concerned. "Aw," said Wink, "if he wants it so much, Christ's sake, let the sonofabitch keep it." And later, in a puzzled, uncertain voice, Tico Feo had said, "I thought you was my friend." "I am," Mr. Schaeffer had thought, though he said nothing.

"I not go to no race track, and what I said about the widow woman, that is not true also." He puffed up his cigarette to a furious glow and looked at Mr. Schaeffer with a speculating expression. "Say, you have money, Mister?"

"Maybe twenty dollars," said Mr. Schaeffer hesitantly, afraid of where this was leading.

"Not so good, twenty dollar," Tico said, but without disappointment. "No important, we work our way. In Mobile I have my friend Frederico. He will put us on a boat. There will not be trouble," and it was as though he were saying that the weather had turned colder.

There was a squeezing in Mr. Schaeffer's heart; he could not speak.

"Nobody here can run to catch Tico. He run the fastest."

"Shotguns run faster," said Mr. Schaeffer in a voice hardly alive. "I'm too old," he said, with the knowledge of age churning like nausea inside him.

Tico Feo was not listening. "Then, the world. The world, *el mundo,* my friend." Standing up, he quivered like a young horse; everything seemed to draw close to him—the moon, the callings of screech owls. His breath came quickly and turned to smoke in the air. "Should we go to Madrid? Maybe someone teach me to bullfight. You think so, Mister?"

Mr. Schaeffer was not listening either. "I'm too old," he said. "I'm too damned old."

For the next several weeks Tico Feo kept after him—the world, *el mundo,* my friend; and he wanted to hide. He would shut himself in the toilet and hold his head. Nevertheless, he was excited, tantalized. What if it could come true, the race with Tico across the forests and to the sea? And he imagined himself on a boat, he who had never seen the sea, whose whole life had been land-rooted. During this time one of the convicts died, and in the yard you could hear the coffin being made. As each nail thudded into place, Mr. Schaeffer thought, "This is for me, it is mine."

Tico Feo himself was never in better spirits; he sauntered about with a dancer's snappy, gigolo grace, and had a joke for everyone. In the sleep house after supper his fingers popped at the guitar like firecrackers. He taught the men to cry *olé,* and some of them sailed their caps through the air.

When work on the road was finished, Mr. Schaeffer

and Tico Feo were moved back into the forests. On Valentine's Day they ate their lunch under a pine tree. Mr. Schaeffer had ordered a dozen oranges from the town and he peeled them slowly, the skins unraveling in a spiral; the juicier slices he gave to his friend, who was proud of how far he could spit the seeds—a good ten feet.

It was a cold beautiful day, scraps of sunlight blew about them like butterflies, and Mr. Schaeffer, who liked working with the trees, felt dim and happy. Then Tico Feo said, "That one, he no could catch a fly in his mouth." He meant Armstrong, a hog-jowled man sitting with a shotgun propped between his legs. He was the youngest of the guards and new at the farm.

"I don't know," said Mr. Schaeffer. He'd watched Armstrong and noticed that, like many people who are both heavy and vain, the new guard moved with a skimming lightness. "He might could fool you."

"I fool him, maybe," said Tico Feo, and spit an orange seed in Armstrong's direction. The guard scowled at him, then blew a whistle. It was the signal for work to begin.

Sometime during the afternoon the two friends came together again; that is, they were nailing turpentine buckets onto trees that stood next to each other. At a distance below them a shallow bouncing creek branched through the woods. "In water no smell," said Tico Feo meticulously, as though remembering something he'd heard. "We run in the water; until dark we climb a tree. Yes, Mister?"

Mr. Schaeffer went on hammering, but his hand was shaking, and the hammer came down on his thumb. He looked around dazedly at his friend. His face showed no reflection of pain, and he did not put the thumb in his mouth, the way a man ordinarily might.

Tico Feo's blue eyes seemed to swell like bubbles, and when in a voice quieter than the wind sounds in the pinetops he said, "Tomorrow," these eyes were all that Mr. Schaeffer could see.

"Tomorrow, Mister?"

"Tomorrow," said Mr. Schaeffer.

The first colors of morning fell upon the walls of the sleep house, and Mr. Schaeffer, who had rested little, knew that Tico Feo was awake too. With the weary eyes of a crocodile he observed the movements of his friend in the next cot. Tico Feo was unknotting the scarf that contained his treasures. First he took the pocket mirror. Its jellyfish light trembled on his face. For a while he admired himself with serious delight, and combed and slicked his hair as though he were preparing to step out to a party. Then he hung the rosary about his neck. The cologne he never opened, nor the map. The last thing he did was to tune his guitar. While the other men were dressing, he sat on the edge of his cot and tuned the guitar. It was strange, for he must have known he would never play it again.

Bird shrills followed the men through the smoky morning woods. They walked single file, fifteen men to a group, and a guard bringing up the rear of each line. Mr. Schaeffer was sweating as though it were a hot day, and he could not keep in marching step with his friend, who walked ahead, snapping his fingers and whistling at the birds.

A signal had been set. Tico Feo was to call, "Time out," and pretend to go behind a tree. But Mr. Schaeffer did not know when it would happen.

The guard named Armstrong blew a whistle, and his men dropped from the line and separated to their various stations. Mr. Schaeffer, though going about his work as best he could, took care always to be in a position where he could keep an eye on both Tico Feo and the guard. Armstrong sat on a stump, a chew of tobacco lopsiding his face, and his gun pointing into the sun. He had the tricky eyes of a cardsharp; you could not really tell where he was looking.

Once another man gave the signal. Although Mr. Schaeffer had known at once that it was not the voice of his friend, panic had pulled at his throat like a rope. As the morning wore on there was such a drumming in his ears he was afraid he would not hear the signal when it came.

The sun climbed to the center of the sky. "He is just a lazy dreamer. It will never happen," thought Mr. Schaeffer, daring a moment to believe this. But "First we eat," said Tico Feo with a practical air as they set their dinner pails on the bank above the creek. They ate in silence, almost as though each bore the other a grudge, but at the end of it Mr. Schaeffer felt his friend's hand close over his own and hold it with a tender pressure.

"Mister Armstrong, time out . . ."

Near the creek Mr. Schaeffer had seen a sweet gum tree, and he was thinking it would soon be spring and the sweet gum ready to chew. A razory stone ripped open the palm of his hand as he slid off the slippery embankment into the water. He straightened up and began to run; his legs were long, he kept almost abreast of Tico Feo, and icy geysers sprayed around them. Back and forth through the woods the shouts of men boomed hollowly like voices in a cavern, and there were three shots, all highflying, as though the guard were shooting at a cloud of geese.

Mr. Schaeffer did not see the log that lay across the creek. He thought he was still running, and his legs thrashed about him; it was as though he were a turtle stranded on its back.

While he struggled there, it seemed to him that the face of his friend, suspended above him, was part of the white winter sky—it was so distant, judging. It hung there but an instant, like a hummingbird, yet in that time he'd seen that Tico Feo had not wanted him to make it, had never thought he would, and he remembered once thinking that it would be a long time before his friend was a grown man. When they found him, he was still lying in the ankle-deep water as though it were a summer afternoon and he were idly floating on the stream.

Since then three winters have gone by, and each has been said to be the coldest, the longest. Two recent months of rain washed deeper ruts in the clay road leading to the farm, and it is harder than ever to get there, harder to leave. A pair of searchlights has been added to the walls, and they burn there through the night like the eyes of a giant owl. Otherwise, there have not been many changes. Mr. Schaeffer, for instance, looks much the same, except that there is a thicker frost of white in his hair, and as the result of a broken ankle he walks with a limp. It was the Captain himself who said that Mr. Schaeffer had broken his ankle attempting to capture Tico Feo. There was even a picture of Mr. Schaeffer in the newspaper, and under it this caption: "Tried to Prevent Escape." At the time he was deeply mortified, not because he knew the other men were laughing, but because he thought of Tico Feo seeing it. But he cut it out of the paper anyway, and keeps it in an envelope along with several clippings pertaining to his friend: a spinster woman told the authorities he'd entered her home and kissed her, twice he was reported seen in the Mobile vicinity, finally it was believed that he had left the country.

No one has ever disputed Mr. Schaeffer's claim to the guitar. Several months ago a new prisoner was moved into the sleep house. He was said to be a fine player, and Mr. Schaeffer was persuaded to lend him the guitar. But all the man's tunes came out sour, for it was as though Tico Feo, tuning his guitar that last morning, had put a curse upon it. Now it lies under Mr. Schaeffer's cot, where its glass diamonds are turning yellow; in the night his hand sometimes searches it out, and his fingers drift across the strings: then, the world.

House of Flowers

OTTILIE should have been the happiest girl in Port-au-Prince. As Baby said to her, look at all the things that can be put to your credit. Like what? said Ottilie, for she was vain and preferred compliments to pork or perfume. Like your looks, said Baby: you have a lovely light color, even almost blue eyes, and such a pretty, sweet face—there is no girl on the road with steadier customers, every one of them ready to buy you all the beer you can drink. Ottilie conceded that this was true, and with a smile continued to total her fortunes: I have five silk dresses and a pair of green satin shoes, I have three gold teeth worth thirty thousand francs, maybe Mr. Jamison or someone will give me another bracelet. But, Baby, she sighed, and could not express her discontent.

Baby was her best friend; she had another friend too: Rosita. Baby was like a wheel, round, rolling; junk rings had left green circles on several of her fat fingers, her teeth were dark as burnt tree stumps, and when she laughed you could hear her at sea, at least so the sailors claimed. Rosita, the other friend, was taller than most men, and stronger; at night, with the customers on hand, she minced about, lisping in a silly doll voice, but in the daytime she took spacious, loping strides and spoke out in a military baritone. Both of Ottilie's friends were from the Dominican Republic, and considered it reason enough to feel themselves a cut above the natives of this darker country. It did not concern them that Ottilie was a native. You have brains, Baby told her, and certainly what Baby doted on was a good brain. Ottilie was often afraid that her friends would discover that she could neither read nor write.

The house where they lived and worked was rickety, thin as a steeple, and frosted with fragile, bougainvillaea-vined balconies. Though there was no sign outside, it was called the Champs Elysées. The proprietress, a spinsterish, smothered-looking invalid, ruled from an upstairs room, where she stayed locked away rocking in a rocking chair and drinking ten to twenty Coca-Colas a day. All counted, she had eight ladies working for her; with the exception of Ottilie, no one of them was under thirty. In the evening, when the ladies assembled on the porch, where they chatted and flourished paper fans that beat the air like delirious moths, Ottilie seemed a delightful dreaming child surrounded by older, uglier sisters.

Her mother was dead, her father was a planter who had gone back to France, and she had been brought up in the mountains by a rough peasant family, the sons of whom had each at a young age lain with her in some green and shadowy place. Three years earlier, when she was fourteen, she had come down for the first time to the market in Port-au-Prince. It was a journey of two days and a night, and she'd walked carrying a ten-pound sack of grain; to ease the load she'd let a little of the grain spill out, then a little more, and by the time she had reached the market there was almost none left. Ottilie had cried because she thought of how angry the family would be when she came home without the money for the grain; but these tears were not for long: such a jolly nice man helped her dry them. He bought her a slice of coconut, and took her to see his cousin, who was the proprietress of the Champs Elysées. Ottilie could not believe her good luck; the jukebox music, the satin shoes and joking men were as strange and marvelous as the electric-light bulb in her room, which she never tired of clicking on and off. Soon she had become the most talked-of girl on the road, the proprietress was able to ask double for her, and Ottilie grew vain; she could pose for hours in front of a mirror. It was seldom that she thought of the mountains; and yet, after three years, there was much of the mountains still with her: their winds seemed still to move around her, her hard, high haunches had not softened, nor had the soles of her feet, which were rough as lizard's hide.

When her friends spoke of love, of men they had loved, Ottilie became sulky: How do you feel if you're in love? she asked. Ah, said Rosita with swooning eyes, you feel as though pepper has been sprinkled on your heart, as though tiny fish are swimming in your veins. Ottilie shook her head; if Rosita was telling the truth, then she had never been in love, for she had never felt that way about any of the men who came to the house.

This so troubled her that at last she went to see a *Houngan* who lived in the hills above town. Unlike her friends, Ottilie did not tack Christian pictures on the walls of her room; she did not believe in God, but many gods: of food, light, of death, ruin. The Houngan was in touch with these gods; he kept their secrets on his altar, could hear their voices in the rattle of a gourd, could dispense their power in a potion. Speaking through the gods, the Houngan gave her this message: You must catch a wild bee, he said, and hold it in your closed hand . . . if the bee does not sting, then you will know you have found love.

On the way home she thought of Mr. Jamison. He was a man past fifty, an American connected with an engineering project. The gold bracelets chattering on her wrists were presents from him, and Ottilie, passing a fence snowy with honeysuckle, wondered if after all she was not in love with Mr. Jamison. Black bees festooned the honeysuckle. With a brave thrust of her hand she caught one dozing. Its stab was like a blow that knocked her to her knees; and there she knelt, weeping until it was hard to know whether the bee had stung her hand or her eyes.

It was March, and events were leading toward carnival. At the Champs Elysées the ladies were sewing on their costumes; Ottilie's hands were idle, for she had decided not to wear a costume at all. On rah-rah weekends, when drums sounded at the rising moon, she sat at her window and watched with a wandering mind the little bands of singers dancing and drumming their way along the road; she listened to the whistling and the laughter and felt no desire to join in. Somebody would think you were a thousand years old, said Baby, and Rosita said: Ottilie, why don't you come to the cockfight with us?

She was not speaking of an ordinary cockfight. From all parts of the island contestants had arrived bringing their fiercest birds. Ottilie thought she might as well go, and screwed a pair of pearls into her ears. When they arrived the exhibition was already under way; in a great tent a sea-sized crowd sobbed and shouted, while a second crowd, those who could not get in, thronged on the outskirts. Entry was no problem to the ladies from the Champs Elysées: a policeman friend cut a path for them and made room on a bench by the ring. The country people surrounding them seemed embarrassed to find themselves in such stylish company. They looked shyly at Baby's lacquered nails, the rhinestone combs in Rosita's hair, the glow of Ottilie's pearl earrings. However, the fights were exciting, and the ladies were soon forgotten; Baby was annoyed that this should be so, and her eyes rolled about searching for glances in their direction. Suddenly she nudged Ottilie. Ottilie, she said, you've got an admirer: see that boy over there, he's staring at you like you were something cold to drink.

At first she thought he must be someone she knew, for he was looking at her as though she should recognize him; but how could she know him when she'd never known anyone so beautiful, anyone with such long legs,

little ears? She could see that he was from the mountains: his straw country hat and the worn-out blue of his
thick shirt told her as much. He was a ginger color, his
skin shiny as a lemon, smooth as a guava leaf, and the
tilt of his head was as arrogant as the black and scarlet
bird he held in his hands. Ottilie was used to boldly smiling at men; but now her smile was fragmentary, it clung
to her lips like cake crumbs.

Eventually there was an intermission. The arena
was cleared, and all who could crowded into it to dance
and stamp while an orchestra of drums and strings sang
out carnival tunes. It was then that the young man approached Ottilie; she laughed to see his bird perched like
a parrot on his shoulder. Off with you, said Baby, out-
raged that a peasant should ask Ottilie to dance, and
Rosita rose menacingly to stand between the young man
and her friend. He only smiled, and said: Please, madame, I would like to speak with your daughter. Ottilie
felt herself being lifted, felt her hips meet against his to
the rhythm of music, and she did not mind at all, she let
him lead her into the thickest tangle of dancers. Rosita
said: Did you hear that, he thought I was her mother?
And Baby, consoling her, grimly said: After all, what do
you expect? They're only natives, both of them: when
she comes back we'll just pretend we don't know her.

As it happened, Ottilie did not return to her friends.
Royal, this was the young man's name, Royal Bonaparte, he told her, had not wanted to dance. We must
walk in a quiet place, he said, hold my hand and I will
take you. She thought him strange, but did not feel
strange with him, for the mountains were still with her,
and he was of the 'mountains. With her hands together,
and the iridescent cock swaying on his shoulder, they
left the tent and wandered lazily down a white road,
then along a soft lane where birds of sunlight fluttered
through the greenness of leaning acacia trees.

I have been sad, he said, not looking sad. In my
village Juno is a champion, but the birds here are strong
and ugly, and if I let him fight I would only have a dead

Juno. So I will take him home and say that he won. Ottilie, will you have a dip of snuff?

She sneezed voluptuously. Snuff reminded her of her childhood, and mean as those years had been, nostalgia touched her with its far-reaching wand. Royal, she said, be still a minute, I want to take off my shoes.

Royal himself did not have shoes; his golden feet were slender and airy, and the prints they left were like the track of a delicate animal. He said: How is it that I find you here, in all the world here, where nothing is good, where the rum is bad and the people thieves? Why do I find you here, Ottilie?

Because I must make my way, the same as you, and here there is a place for me. I work in a—oh, kind of hotel.

We have our own place, he said. All the side of a hill, and there at the top of the hill is my cool house. Ottilie, will you come and sit inside it?

Crazy, said Ottilie, teasing him, crazy, and she ran between the trees, and he was after her, his arms out as though he held a net. The bird Juno flared his wings, crowed, flew to the ground. Scratchy leaves and fur of moss thrilled the soles of Ottilie's feet as she lilted through the shade and shadows; abruptly, into a veil of rainbow fern, she fell with a thorn in her heel. She winced when Royal pulled out the thorn; he kissed the place where it had been, his lips moved to her hands, her throat, and it was as though she were among drifting leaves. She breathed the odor of him, the dark, clean smell that was like the roots of things, of geraniums, of heavy trees.

Now that's enough, she pleaded, though she did not feel that this was so: it was only that after an hour of him her heart was about to give out. He was quiet then, his tickly haired head rested above her heart, and shoo she said to the gnats that clustered about his sleeping eyes, shush she said to Juno who pranced around crowing at the sky.

While she lay there, Ottilie saw her old enemy, the

bees. Silently, in a line like ants, the bees were crawling in and out of a broken stump that stood not far from her. She loosened herself from Royal's arms, and smoothed a place on the ground for his head. Her hand was trembling as she lay it in the path of the bees, but the first that came along tumbled onto her palm, and when she closed her fingers it made no move to hurt her. She counted ten, just to be sure, then opened her hand, and the bee, in spiraling arcs, climbed the air with a joyful singing.

The proprietress gave Baby and Rosita a piece of advice: Leave her alone, let her go, a few weeks and she will be back. The proprietress spoke in the calm of defeat: to keep Ottilie with her, she'd offered the best room in the house, a new gold tooth, a Kodak, an electric fan, but Ottilie had not wavered, she had gone right on putting her belongings in a cardboard box. Baby tried to help, but she was crying so much that Ottilie had to stop her: it was bound to be bad luck, all those tears falling on a bride's possessions. And to Rosita she said: Rosita, you ought to be glad for me instead of standing there wringing your hands.

It was only two days after the cockfight that Royal shouldered Ottilie's cardboard box and walked her in the dusk toward the mountains. When it was learned that she was no longer at the Champs Elysées many of the customers took their trade elsewhere; others, though remaining loyal to the old place, complained of a gloom in the atmosphere: some evenings there was hardly anyone to buy the ladies a beer. Gradually it began to be felt that Ottilie after all would not come back; at the end of six months the proprietress said: She must be dead.

Royal's house was like a house of flowers; wisteria sheltered the roof, a curtain of vines shaded the windows, lilies bloomed at the door. From the windows one could see far, faint winkings of the sea, as the house was high up a hill; here the sun burned hot but the shadows were cold. Inside, the house was always dark and cool, and the walls rustled with pasted pink and green newspapers. There was only one room; it contained a stove, a teetering mirror on top a marble table, and a brass bed big enough for three fat men.

But Ottilie did not sleep in this grand bed. She was not allowed even to sit upon it, for it was the property of Royal's grandmother, Old Bonaparte. A charred, lumpy creature, bowlegged as a dwarf and bald as a buzzard, Old Bonparte was much respected for miles around as a maker of spells. There were many who were afraid to have her shadow fall upon them; even Royal was wary of her, and he stuttered when he told her that he'd brought home a wife. Motioning Ottilie to her, the old woman bruised her here and there with vicious little pinches, and informed her grandson that his bride was too skinny: She will die with her first.

Each night the young couple waited to make love until they thought Old Bonaparte had gone to sleep. Sometimes, stretched on the straw moonlit pallet where they slept, Ottilie was sure that Old Bonaparte was awake and watching them. Once she saw a gummy, star-struck eye shining in the dark. There was no use complaining to Royal, he only laughed: What harm was there in an old woman who had seen so much of life wanting to see a little more?

Because she loved Royal, Ottilie put away her grievances and tried not to resent Old Bonaparte. For a long while she was happy; she did not miss her friends or the life in Port-au-Prince; even so, she kept her souvenirs of those days in good repair: with a sewing basket Baby had given her as a wedding gift she mended the silk dresses, the green silk stockings that now she never wore, for there was no place to wear them: only men congregated at the café in the village, at the cockfights. When women wanted to meet they met at the washing stream. But Ottilie was too busy to be lonesome. At daybreak she gathered eucalyptus leaves to start a fire and begin their meals; there were chickens to feed, a goat to be

milked, there was Old Bonaparte's whining for attention. Three and four times a day she filled a bucket of
drinking water and carried it to where Royal worked in
the cane fields a mile below the house. She did not mind
that on these visits he was gruff with her: she knew that
he was showing off before the other men who worked in
the fields, and who grinned at her like split watermelons.
But at night, when she had him home, she'd pull his ears
and pout that he treated her like a dog until, in the dark
of the yard where the fireflies flamed, he would hold her
and whisper something to make her smile.

They had been married about five months when
Royal began doing the things he'd done before his marriage. Other men went to the café in the evenings, stayed
whole Sundays at a cockfight—he couldn't understand
why Ottilie should carry on about it; but she said he had
no right behaving the way he did, and that if he loved
her he wouldn't leave her alone day and night with that
mean old woman. I love you, he said, but a man has to
have his pleasures too. There were nights when he pleas-
ured himself until the moon was in the middle of the
sky; she never knew when he was coming home, and
she would lie fretting on the pallet, imagining she could
not sleep without his arms around her.

But Old Bonaparte was the real torment. She was
about to worry Ottilie out of her mind. If Ottilie was
cooking, the terrible old woman was sure to come poking around the stove, and when she did not like what
there was to eat she would take a mouthful and spit it
on the floor. Every mess she could think of she made:
she wet the bed, insisted on having the goat in the room,
whatever she touched was soon spilled or broken, and
to Royal she complained that a woman who couldn't
keep a nice house for her husband was worthless. She
was underfoot the whole day, and her red, remorseless
eyes were seldom shut; but the worst of it, the thing that
finally made Ottilie threaten to kill her, was the old woman's habit of sneaking up from nowhere and pinching
her so hard you could see the fingernail marks. If you

do that one more time, if you just dare, I'll snatch that knife and cut out your heart! Old Bonaparte knew Ottilie meant it, and though she stopped the pinching, she thought of other jokes: for instance, she made a point of walking all over a certain part of the yard, pretending she did not know that Ottilie had planted a little garden there.

One day two exceptional things happened. A boy came from the village bringing a letter for Ottilie; at the Champs Elysées postcards had once in a while arrived from sailors and other traveling men who had spent pleasant moments with her, but this was the first letter she'd ever received. Since she could not read it, her first impulse was to tear it up: there was no use having it hang around to haunt her. Of course there was a chance that someday she would learn to read; and so she went to hide it in her sewing basket.

When she opened the sewing basket, she made a sinister discovery: there, like a gruesome ball of yarn, was the severed head of a yellow cat. So, the miserable old woman was up to new tricks! She wants to put a spell, thought Ottilie, not in the least frightened. Primly lifting the head by one of its ears, she carried it to the stove and dropped it into a boiling pot: at noon Old Bonaparte sucked her teeth and remarked that the soup Ottilie had made for her was surprisingly tasty.

The next morning, just in time for the midday meal, she found twisting in her basket a small green snake which, chopping fine as sand, she sprinkled into a serving of stew. Each day her ingenuity was tested: there were spiders to bake, a lizard to fry, a buzzard's breast to boil. Old Bonaparte ate several helpings of everything. With a restless glittering her eyes followed Ottilie as she watched for some sign that the spell was taking hold. You don't look well, Ottilie, she said, mixing a little molasses in the vinegar of her voice. You eat like an ant: here now, why don't you have a bowl of this good soup?

Because, answered Ottilie evenly, I don't like buz-

zard in my soup; or spiders in my bread, snakes in the
stew: I have no appetite for such things.

Old Bonaparte understood; with swelling veins and
a stricken, powerless tongue, she rose shakily to her
feet, then crashed across the table. Before nightfall she
was dead.

Royal summoned mourners. They came from the
village, from the neighboring hills and, wailing like dogs
at midnight, laid siege to the house. Old women beat
their heads against the walls, moaning men prostrated
themselves: it was the art of sorrow, and those who best
mimicked grief were much admired. After the funeral
everyone went away, satisfied that they'd done a good
job.

Now the house belonged to Ottilie. Without Old
Bonaparte's prying and her mess to clean she had more
spare time, but she did not know what to do with it. She
sprawled on the great brass bed, she loafed in front of
the mirror; monotony hummed in her head, and to drive
away its fly-buzz sound she would sing the songs she'd
learned from the jukebox at the Champs Elysées. Waiting in the twilight for Royal she would remember that at
this hour her friends in Port-au-Prince were gossiping on
the porch and waiting for the turning headlights of a
car; but when she saw Royal ambling up the path, his
cane cutter swinging at his side like a crescent moon,
she forgot such thoughts and ran with a satisfied heart to
meet him.

One night as they lay half-drowsing, Ottilie felt
suddenly another presence in the room. Then, gleaming
there at the foot of the bed, she saw, as she had seen before, a watching eye; thus she knew what for some time
she had suspected: that Old Bonaparte was dead but
not gone. Once, when she was alone in the house, she'd
heard a laugh, and once again, out in the yard, she'd
seen the goat gazing at someone who was not there and
twinkling his ears as he did whenever the old woman
scratched his skull.

Stop shaking the bed, said Royal, and Ottilie, with

a finger raised at the eye, whisperingly asked him if
he could not see it. When he replied that she was
dreaming, she reached for the eye and screamed at feeling only air. Royal lighted a lamp; he cuddled Ottilie
on his lap and smoothed her hair while she told him of
the discoveries she'd made in her sewing basket, and of
how she had disposed of them. Was it wrong what she'd
done? Royal did not know, it was not for him to say,
but it was his opinion that she would have to be punished;
and why? because the old woman wanted it, because
she would otherwise never leave Ottilie in peace: that
was the way with haunts.

In accordance with this, Royal fetched a rope the
next morning and proposed to tie Ottilie to a tree in the
yard: there she was to remain until dark without food or
water, and anyone passing would know her to be in a
state of disgrace.

But Ottilie crawled under the bed and refused to
come out. I'll run away, she whimpered. Royal, if you
try to tie me to that old tree I'll run away.

Then I'd have to go and get you, said Royal, and
that would be the worse for you.

He gripped her by an ankle and dragged her squeal-
ing from under the bed. All the way to the yard she
caught at things, the door, a vine, the goat's beard, but
none of these would hold her, and Royal was not de-
tained from tying her to the tree. He made three knots
in the rope, and went off to work sucking his hand
where she had bit him. She hollered to him all the bad
words she'd ever heard until he disappeared over the
hill. The goat, Juno and the chickens gathered to stare
at her humiliation; slumping to the ground, Ottilie stuck
out her tongue at them.

Because she was almost asleep, Ottilie thought it
was a dream when, in the company of a child from the
village, Baby and Rosita, wobbling on high heels and
carrying fancy umbrellas, tottered up the path calling
her name. Since they were people in a dream, they

probably would not be surprised to find her tied to a tree.

My God, are you mad? shrieked Baby, keeping her distance as though she feared that indeed this must be the case. Speak to us, Ottilie!

Blinking, giggling, Ottilie said: I'm just happy to see you. Rosita, please untie me so that I can hug you both.

So this is what the brute does, said Rosita, tearing at the ropes. Wait till I see him, beating you and tying you in the yard like a dog.

Oh no, said Ottilie. Royal never beats me. It's just that today I'm being punished.

You wouldn't listen to us, said Baby. And now you see what's come of it. That man has plenty to answer for, she added, brandishing her umbrella.

Ottilie hugged her friends and kissed them. Isn't it a pretty house? she said, leading them toward it. It's like you picked a wagon of flowers and built a house with them: that is what I think. Come in out of the sun. It's cool inside and smells so sweet.

Rosita sniffed as though what she smelled was nothing sweet, and in her well-bottom voice declared that yes, it was better that they stay out of the sun, as it seemed to be affecting Ottilie's head.

It's a mercy that we've come, said Baby, fishing inside an enormous purse. And you can thank Mr. Jamison for that. Madame said you were dead, and when you never answered our letter we thought it must be so. But Mr. Jamison, that's the loveliest man you'll ever know, he hired a car for me and Rosita, your dearest loving friends, to come up here and find out what had happened to our Ottilie. Ottilie, I've got a bottle of rum here in my purse, so get us a glass and we'll all have a round.

The elegant foreign manners and flashing finery of the city ladies had intoxicated their guide, a little boy whose peeking black eyes bobbed at the window. Ottilie was impressed, too, for it was a long time since she'd seen painted lips or smelled bottle perfume, and while

Baby poured the rum she got out her satin shoes, her pearl earrings. Dear, said Rosita when Ottilie had finished dressing up, there's no man alive that wouldn't buy you a whole keg of beer; to think of it, a gorgeous piece like you suffering far away from those who love you.

I haven't been suffering so much, said Ottilie. Just sometimes.

Hush now, said Baby. You don't have to talk about it yet. It's all over anyway. Here, dear, let me see your glass again. A toast to old times, and those to be! Tonight Mr. Jamison is going to buy champagne for everybody: Madame is letting him have it at half-price.

Oh, said Ottilie, envying her friends. Well, she wanted to know, what did people say of her, was she remembered?

Ottilie, you have no idea, said Baby; men nobody ever laid eyes on before have come into the place asking where is Ottilie, because they've heard about you way off in Havana and Miami. As for Mr. Jamison, he doesn't even look at us other girls, just comes and sits on the porch drinking by himself.

Yes, said Ottilie wistfully. He was always sweet to me, Mr. Jamison.

Presently the sun was slanting, and the bottle of rum stood three-quarters empty. A thunderburst of rain had for a moment drenched the hills that now, seen through the windows, shimmered like dragonfly wings, and a breeze, rich with the scent of rained-on flowers, roamed the room rustling the green and pink papers on the walls. Many stories had been told, some of them funny, a few that were sad; it was like any night's talk at the Champs Elysées, and Ottilie was happy to be a part of it again.

But it's getting late, said Baby. And we promised to be back before midnight. Ottilie, can we help you pack?

Although she had not realized that her friends expected her to leave with them, the rum stirring in her made it seem a likely assumption, and with a smile she thought: I told him I would go away. Only, she said aloud, it's not like I would have even a week to enjoy myself: Royal will come right down and get me.

Both her friends laughed at this. You're so silly, said Baby. I'd like to see that Royal when some of our men got through with him.

I wouldn't stand for anybody hurting Royal, said Ottilie. Besides, he'd be even madder when we got home.

Baby said: But, Ottilie, you wouldn't be coming back here with him.

Ottilie giggled, and looked about the room as though she saw something invisible to the others. Why, sure I would, she said.

Rolling her eyes, Baby produced a fan and jerked it in front of her face. That's the craziest thing I've ever heard, she said between hard lips. Isn't that the craziest thing you've ever heard, Rosita?

It's that Ottilie's been through so much, said Rosita. Dear, why don't you lie down on the bed while we pack your things?

Ottilie watched as they commenced piling her possessions. They scooped her combs and pins, they wound up her silk stockings. She took off her pretty clothes, as if she were going to put on something finer still; instead, she slipped back into her old dress; then, working quietly, and as though she were helping her friends, she put everything back where it belonged. Baby stamped her foot when she saw what was happening.

Listen, said Ottilie. If you and Rosita are my friends, please do what I tell you: tie me in the yard just like I was when you came. That way no bee is ever going to sting me.

Stinking drunk, said Baby; but Rosita told her to shut up. I think, said Rosita with a sigh, I think Ottilie is in love. If Royal wanted her back, she would go with him, and this being the way things were they might as well go home and say that Madame was right, that Ottilie was dead.

Yes, said Ottilie, for the drama of it appealed to her. Tell them that I am dead.

So they went into the yard; there, with heaving bosoms and eyes as round as the daytime moon scudding above, Baby said she would have no part in tying Ottilie to the tree, which left Rosita to do it alone. On parting, it was Ottilie who cried the most, though she was glad to see them go, for she knew that as soon as they were gone she would not think of them again. Teetering on their high heels down the dips of the path, they turned to wave, but Ottilie could not wave back, and so she forgot them before they were out of sight.

Chewing eucalyptus leaves to sweeten her breath, she felt the chill of twilight twitch the air. Yellow deepened the daytime moon, and roosting birds sailed into the darkness of the tree. Suddenly, hearing Royal on the path, she threw her legs akimbo, let her neck go limp, lolled her eyes far back into their sockets. Seen from a distance, it would look as though she had come to some violent, pitiful end; and, listening to Royal's footsteps quicken to a run, she happily thought: This will give him a good scare.

A Christmas Memory

IMAGINE A MORNING in late November. A coming of winter morning more than twenty years ago. Consider the kitchen of a spreading old house in a country town. A great black stove is its main feature; but there is also a big round table and a fireplace with two rocking chairs placed in front of it. Just today the fireplace commenced its seasonal roar.

A woman with shorn white hair is standing at the kitchen window. She is wearing tennis shoes and a shapeless gray sweater over a summery calico dress. She is small and sprightly, like a bantam hen; but, due to a long youthful illness, her shoulders are pitifully hunched. Her face is remarkable—not unlike Lincoln's, craggy like that, and tinted by sun and wind; but it is delicate too, finely boned, and her eyes are sherry-colored and timid. "Oh my," she exclaims, her breath smoking the windowpane, "it's fruitcake weather!"

The person to whom she is speaking is myself. I am seven; she is sixty-something. We are cousins, very distant ones, and we have lived together—well, as long as I can remember. Other people inhabit the house, relatives; and though they have power over us, and frequently make us cry, we are not, on the whole, too much aware of them. We are each other's best friend. She calls me Buddy, in memory of a boy who was formerly her best friend. The other Buddy died in the 1880's, when she was still a child. She is still a child.

"I knew it before I got out of bed," she says, turning away from the window with a purposeful excitement in her eyes. "The courthouse bell sounded so cold and clear. And there were no birds singing; they've gone to warmer country, yes indeed. Oh, Buddy, stop stuffing biscuit and fetch our buggy. Help me find my hat. We've thirty cakes to bake."

It's always the same: a morning arrives in November, and my friend, as though officially inaugurating the Christmas time of year that exhilarates her imagination and fuels the blaze of her heart, announces: "It's fruitcake weather! Fetch our buggy. Help me find my hat."

The hat is found, a straw cartwheel corsaged with velvet roses out-of-doors has faded: it once belonged to a more fashionable relative. Together, we guide our buggy, a dilapidated baby carriage, out to the garden and into a grove of pecan trees. The buggy is mine; that is, it was bought for me when I was born. It is made of wicker, rather unraveled, and the wheels wobble like a drunkard's legs. But it is a faithful object; springtimes, we take it to the woods and fill it with flowers, herbs, wild fern for our porch pots; in the summer, we pile it with picnic paraphernalia and sugar-cane fishing poles and roll it down to the edge of a creek; it has its winter uses, too: as a truck for hauling firewood from the yard to the kitchen, as a warm bed for Queenie, our tough little orange and white rat terrier who has survived distemper and two rattlesnake bites. Queenie is trotting beside it now.

Three hours later we are back in the kitchen hulling a heaping buggyload of windfall pecans. Our backs hurt from gathering them: how hard they were to find (the main crop having been shaken off the trees and sold by the orchard's owners, who are not us) among the concealing leaves, the frosted, deceiving grass. Caarackle! A cheery crunch, scraps of miniature thunder sound as the shells collapse and the golden mound of sweet oily ivory meat mounts in the milk-glass bowl. Queenie begs to taste, and now and again my friend sneaks her a mite, though insisting we deprive ourselves. "We mustn't, Buddy. If we start, we won't stop. And there's scarcely enough as there is. For thirty cakes." The kitchen is growing dark. Dusk turns the window into a mirror: our reflections mingle with the rising moon as we work by the fireside in the firelight. At last, when the moon is quite high, we toss the final hull into the fire and, with joined sighs, watch it catch flame. The buggy is empty, the bowl is brimful.

We eat our supper (cold biscuits, bacon, blackberry jam) and discuss tomorrow. Tomorrow the kind of work I like best begins: buying. Cherries and citron, ginger and vanilla and canned Hawaiian pineapple, rinds and raisins and walnuts and whiskey and oh, so much flour, butter, so many eggs, spices, flavorings: why, we'll need a pony to pull the buggy home.

But before these purchases can be made, there is the question of money. Neither of us has any. Except for skinflint sums persons in the house occasionally provide (a dime is considered very big money); or what we earn ourselves from various activities: holding rummage sales, selling buckets of hand-picked blackberries, jars of homemade jam and apple jelly and peach preserves, rounding up flowers for funerals and weddings. Once we won seventy-ninth prize, five dollars, in a national football contest. Not that we know a fool thing about football. It's just that we enter any contest we hear about: at the moment our hopes are centered on the fifty-thousand-dollar Grand Prize being offered to name a new brand of coffee (we suggested "A.M."; and, after some hesitation, for my friend thought it perhaps sacrilegious, the slogan "A.M.! Amen!"). To tell the truth, our only *really* profitable enterprise was the Fun and Freak Museum we conducted in a back-yard woodshed two summers ago. The Fun was a stereopticon with slide views of Washington and New York lent us by a relative who had been to those places (she was furious when she discovered why we'd borrowed it); the Freak was a three-legged biddy chicken hatched by one of our own hens. Everybody hereabouts wanted to see that biddy: we charged grownups a nickel, kids two cents. And took in a good twenty dollars before the museum shut down due to the decease of the main attraction.

But one way and another we do each year accumulate Christmas savings, a Fruitcake Fund. These moneys we keep hidden in an ancient bead purse under a loose board under the floor under a chamber pot under my friend's bed. The purse is seldom removed from this safe location except to make a deposit, or, as happens every Saturday, a withdrawal; for on Saturdays I am allowed ten cents to go to the picture show. My friend has never been to a picture show, nor does she intend to: "I'd rather hear you tell the story, Buddy. That way I can imagine it more. Besides, a person my age shouldn't squander their eyes. When the Lord comes, let me see him clear." In addition to never having seen a movie, she has never: eaten in a restaurant, traveled more than five miles from home, received or sent a telegram, read anything except funny papers and the Bible, worn cosmetics, cursed, wished someone harm, told a lie on purpose, let a hungry dog go hungry. Here are a few things she has done, does do: killed with a hoe the biggest rattlesnake ever seen in this county (sixteen rattles), dip snuff (secretly), tame hummingbirds (just try it) till they balance on her finger, tell ghost stories (we both believe in ghosts) so tingling they chill you in July, talk to herself, take walks in the rain, grow the prettiest japonicas in town, know the recipe for every sort of old-time Indian cure, including a magical wart-remover.

Now, with supper finished, we retire to the room in a faraway part of the house where my friend sleeps in a scrap-quilt-covered iron bed painted rose pink, her favorite color. Silently, wallowing in the pleasures of conspiracy, we take the bead purse from its secret place and spill its contents on the scrap quilt. Dollar bills, tightly rolled and green as May buds. Somber fifty-cent pieces, heavy enough to weight a dead man's eyes. Lovely dimes, the liveliest coin, the one that really jingles. Nickels and quarters, worn smooth as creek pebbles. But mostly a hateful heap of bitter-odored pennies. Last summer others in the house contracted to pay us a penny for every twenty-five flies we killed. Oh, the carnage of August: the flies that flew to heaven! Yet it was not work in which we took pride. And, as we sit counting pennies, it is as though we were back tabulating dead flies. Neither of us has a head for figures; we count slowly, lose track, start again. According to her calculations, we have $12.73. According to mine, exactly $13. "I do hope you're wrong, Buddy. We can't mess around with thirteen. The cakes will fall. Or put somebody in the cemetery. Why, I wouldn't dream of getting out of bed on the thirteenth." This is true: she always spends thirteenths in bed. So, to be on the safe side, we subtract a penny and toss it out the window.

Of the ingredients that go into our fruitcakes, whiskey is the most expensive, as well as the hardest to obtain: State laws forbid its sale. But everybody knows you can buy a bottle from Mr. Haha Jones. And the next day, having completed our more prosaic shopping, we set out for Mr. Haha's business address, a "sinful" (to quote public opinion) fish-fry and dancing café down by the river. We've been there before, and on the same errand; but in previous years our dealings have been with Haha's wife, an iodine-dark Indian woman with brazzy peroxided hair and a dead-tired disposition. Actually, we've never laid eyes on her husband, though we've heard that he's an Indian too. A giant with razor scars across his cheeks. They call him Haha because he's so gloomy, a man who never laughs. As we approach his café (a large log cabin festooned inside and out with chains of garish-gay naked lightbulbs and standing by the river's muddy edge under the shade of river trees where moss drifts through the branches like gray mist) our steps slow down. Even Queenie stops prancing and sticks close by. People have been murdered in

Haha's café. Cut to pieces. Hit on the head. There's a case coming up in court next month. Naturally these goings-on happen at night when the colored lights cast crazy patterns and the victrola wails. In the daytime Haha's is shabby and deserted. I knock at the door, Queenie barks, my friend calls: "Mrs. Haha, ma'am? Anyone to home?"

Footsteps. The door opens. Our hearts overturn. It's Mr. Haha Jones himself! And he *is* a giant; he *does* have scars; he *doesn't* smile. No, he glowers at us through Satan-tilted eyes and demands to know: "What you want with Haha?"

For a moment we are too paralyzed to tell. Presently my friend half-finds her voice, a whispery voice at best: "If you please, Mr. Haha, we'd like a quart of your finest whiskey."

His eyes tilt more. Would you believe it? Haha is smiling! Laughing, too. "Which one of you is a drinkin' man?"

"It's for making fruitcakes, Mr. Haha. Cooking."

This sobers him. He frowns. "That's no way to waste good whiskey." Nevertheless, he retreats into the shadowed café and seconds later appears carrying a bottle of daisy yellow unlabeled liquor. He demonstrates its sparkle in the sunlight and says: "Two dollars."

We pay him with nickels and dimes and pennies. Suddenly, jangling the coins in his hand like a fistful of dice, his face softens. "Tell you what," he proposes, pouring the money back into our bead purse, "just send me one of them fruitcakes instead."

"Well," my friend remarks on our way home, "there's a lovely man. We'll put an extra cup of raisins in *his* cake."

The black stove, stoked with coal and firewood, glows like a lighted pumpkin. Eggbeaters whirl, spoons spin round in bowls of butter and sugar, vanilla sweetens the air, ginger spices it; melting, nose-tingling odors saturate the kitchen, suffuse the house, drift out to the world on puffs of chimney smoke. In four days our work is done. Thirty-one cakes, dampened with whiskey, bask on window sills and shelves.

Who are they for?

Friends. Not necessarily neighbor friends: indeed, the larger share are intended for persons we've met maybe once, perhaps not at all. People who've struck our fancy. Like President Roosevelt. Like the Reverend and Mrs. J. C. Lucey, Baptist missionaries to Borneo who lectured here last winter. Or the little knife grinder who comes through town twice a year. Or Abner Packer, the driver of the six o'clock bus from Mobile, who exchanges waves with us every day as he passes in a dustcloud whoosh. Or the young Wistons, a California couple whose car one afternoon broke down outside the house and who spent a pleasant hour chatting with us on the porch (young Mr. Wiston snapped our picture, the only one we've ever had taken). Is it because my friend is shy with everyone *except* strangers that these strangers, and merest acquaintances, seem to us our truest friends? I think yes. Also, the scrapbooks we keep of thank-you's on White House stationery, time-to-time communications from California and Borneo, the knife grinder's penny post cards, make us feel connected to eventful worlds beyond the kitchen with its view of a sky that stops.

Now a nude December fig branch grates against the window. The kitchen is empty, the cakes are gone; yesterday we carted the last of them to the post office, where the cost of stamps turned our purse inside out. We're broke. That rather depresses me, but my friend insists on celebrating—with two inches of whiskey left in Haha's bottle. Queenie has a spoonful in a bowl of coffee (she likes her coffee chicory-flavored and strong). The rest we divide between a pair of jelly glasses. We're both quite awed at the prospect of drinking straight whiskey; the taste of it brings screwed-up expressions and sour shudders. But by and by we begin to sing, the two of us singing different songs simultaneously. I don't know the words to mine, just: *Come on along, come on along, to the dark-town strutters' ball*. But I can dance:

that's what I mean to be, a tap dancer in the movies. My dancing shadow rollicks on the walls; our voices rock the chinaware; we giggle: as if unseen hands were tickling us. Queenie rolls on her back, her paws plow the air, something like a grin stretches her black lips. Inside myself, I feel warm and sparky as those crumbling logs, carefree as the wind in the chimney. My friend waltzes round the stove, the hem of her poor calico skirt pinched between her fingers as though it were a party dress: *Show me the way to go home,* she sings, her tennis shoes squeaking on the floor. *Show me the way to go home.*

Enter: two relatives. Very angry. Potent with eyes that scold, tongues that scald. Listen to what they have to say, the words tumbling together into a wrathful tune: "A child of seven! whiskey on his breath! are you out of your mind? feeding a child of seven! must be loony! road to ruination! remember Cousin Kate? Uncle Charlie? Uncle Charlie's brother-in-law? shame! scandal! humiliation! kneel, pray, beg the Lord!"

Queenie sneaks under the stove. My friend gazes at her shoes, her chin quivers, she lifts her skirt and blows her nose and runs to her room. Long after the town has gone to sleep and the house is silent except for the chimings of clocks and the sputter of fading fires, she is weeping into a pillow already as wet as a widow's handkerchief.

"Don't cry," I say, sitting at the bottom of her bed and shivering despite my flannel nightgown that smells of last winter's cough syrup, "don't cry," I beg, teasing her toes, tickling her feet, "you're too old for that."

"It's because," she hiccups, "I *am* too old. Old and funny."

"Not funny. Fun. More fun than anybody. Listen. If you don't stop crying you'll be so tired tomorrow we can't go cut a tree."

She straightens up. Queenie jumps on the bed (where Queenie is not allowed) to lick her cheeks. "I know where we'll find pretty trees, Buddy. And holly, too. With berries big as your eyes. It's way off in the woods.

Farther than we've ever been. Papa used to bring us Christmas trees from there: carry them on his shoulder. That's fifty years ago. Well, now: I can't wait for morning."

Morning. Frozen rime lusters the grass; the sun, round as an orange and orange as hot-weather moons, balances on the horizon, burnishes the silvered winter woods. A wild turkey calls. A renegade hog grunts in the undergrowth. Soon, by the edge of knee-deep, rapid-running water, we have to abandon the buggy. Queenie wades the stream first, paddles across barking complaints at the swiftness of the current, the pneumonia-making coldness of it. We follow, holding our shoes and equipment (a hatchet, a burlap sack) above our heads. A mile more: of chastising thorns, burs and briers that catch at our clothes; of rusty pine needles brilliant with gaudy fungus and molted feathers. Here, there, a flash, a flutter, an ecstasy of shrillings remind us that not all the birds have flown south. Always, the path unwinds through lemony sun pools and pitch vine tunnels. Another creek to cross: a disturbed armada of speckled trout froths the water round us, and frogs the size of plates practice belly flops; beaver workmen are building a dam. On the farther shore, Queenie shakes herself and trembles. My friend shivers, too: not with cold but enthusiasm. One of her hat's ragged roses sheds a petal as she lifts her head and inhales the pine-heavy air. "We're almost there; can you smell it, Buddy?" she says, as though we were approaching an ocean.

And, indeed, it is a kind of ocean. Scented acres of holiday trees, prickly-leafed holly. Red berries shiny as Chinese bells: black crows swoop upon them screaming. Having stuffed our burlap sacks with enough greenery and crimson to garland a dozen windows, we set about choosing a tree. "It should be," muses my friend, "twice as tall as a boy. So a boy can't steal the star." The one we pick is twice as tall as me. A brave handsome brute that survives thirty hatchet strokes before it keels with a creaking rending cry. Lugging it like a kill, we com-

mence the long trek out. Every few yards we abandon
the struggle, sit down and pant. But we have the strength
of triumphant huntsmen; that and the tree's virile, icy
perfume revive us, goad us on. Many compliments accompany our sunset return along the red clay road to
town; but my friend is sly and noncommittal when passers-by praise the treasure perched on our buggy: what
a fine tree and where did it come from? "Yonderways,"
she murmurs vaguely. Once a car stops and the rich mill
owner's lazy wife leans out and whines: "Giveya two-
bits cash for that ol tree." Ordinarily my friend is afraid
of saying no; but on this occasion she promptly shakes
her head: "We wouldn't take a dollar." The mill owner's
wife persists. "A dollar, my foot! Fifty cents. That's my
last offer. Goodness, woman, you can get another one."
In answer, my friend gently reflects: "I doubt it. There's
never two of anything."

Home: Queenie slumps by the fire and sleeps till
tomorrow, snoring loud as a human.

A trunk in the attic contains: a shoebox of ermine
tails (off the opera cape of a curious lady who once
rented a room in the house), coils of frazzled tinsel gone
gold with age, one silver star, a brief rope of dilapidated,
undoubtedly dangerous candy-like light bulbs. Excellent decorations, as far as they go, which isn't far enough:
my friend wants our tree to blaze "like a Baptist window,"
droop with weighty snows of ornament. But we can't
afford the made-in-Japan splendors at the five-and-
dime. So we do what we've always done: sit for days at
the kitchen table with scissors and crayons and stacks of
colored paper. I make sketches and my friend cuts them
out: lots of cats, fish too (because they're easy to draw),
some apples, some watermelons, a few winged angels
devised from saved-up sheets of Hershey-bar tin foil.
We use safety pins to attach these creations to the tree;
as a final touch, we sprinkle the branches with shredded
cotton (picked in August for this purpose). My friend,
surveying the effect, clasps her hands together. "Now

honest, Buddy. Doesn't it look good enough to eat?"
Queenie tries to eat an angel.

After weaving and ribboning holly wreaths for all
the front windows, our next project is the fashioning of
family gifts. Tie-dye scarves for the ladies, for the men a
home-brewed lemon and licorice and aspirin syrup to
be taken "at the first Symptoms of a Cold and after
Hunting." But when it comes time for making each
other's gift, my friend and I separate to work secretly.
I would like to buy her a pearl-handled knife, a radio,
a whole pound of chocolate-covered cherries (we tasted
some once, and she always swears: "I could live on them,
Buddy, Lord yes I could—and that's not taking His name
in vain"). Instead, I am building her a kite. She would
like to give me a bicycle (she's said so on several million
occasions: "If only I could, Buddy. It's bad enough in
life to do without something *you* want; but confound it,
what gets my goat is not being able to give somebody
something you want *them* to have. Only one of these days
I will, Buddy. Locate you a bike. Don't ask how. Steal it,
maybe"). Instead, I'm fairly certain that she is building
me a kite—the same as last year, and the year before:
the year before that we exchanged slingshots. All of
which is fine by me. For we are champion kite-fliers who
study the wind like sailors; my friend, more accomplished
than I, can get a kite aloft when there isn't enough
breeze to carry clouds.

Christmas Eve afternoon we scrape together a
nickel and go to the butcher's to buy Queenie's traditional gift, a good gnawable beef bone. The bone,
wrapped in funny paper, is placed high in the tree near
the silver star. Queenie knows it's there. She squats at the
foot of the tree staring up in a trance of greed: when
bedtime arrives she refuses to budge. Her excitement is
equaled by my own. I kick the covers and turn my pillow as though it were a scorching summer's night. Somewhere a rooster crows: falsely, for the sun is still on the
other side of the world.

"Buddy, are you awake?" It is my friend, calling from her room, which is next to mine; and an instant later she is sitting on my bed holding a candle. "Well, I can't sleep a hoot," she declares. "My mind's jumping like a jack rabbit. Buddy, do you think Mrs. Roosevelt will serve our cake at dinner?" We huddle in the bed, and she squeezes my hand I-love-you. "Seems like your hand used to be so much smaller. I guess I hate to see you grow up. When you're grown up, will we still be friends?" I say always. "But I feel so bad, Buddy. I wanted so bad to give you a bike. I tried to sell my cameo Papa gave me. Buddy"—she hesitates, as though embarrassed —"I made you another kite." Then I confess that I made her one, too; and we laugh. The candle burns too short to hold. Out it goes, exposing the starlight, the stars spinning at the window like a visible caroling that slowly, slowly daybreak silences. Possibly we doze; but the beginnings of dawn splash us like cold water: we're up, wide-eyed and wandering while we wait for others to waken. Quite deliberately my friend drops a kettle on the kitchen floor. I tap-dance in front of closed doors. One by one the household emerges, looking as though they'd like to kill us both; but it's Christmas, so they can't. First, a gorgeous breakfast: just everything you can imagine —from flapjacks and fried squirrel to hominy grits and honey-in-the-comb. Which puts everyone in a good humor except my friend and I. Frankly, we're so impatient to get at the presents we can't eat a mouthful.

Well, I'm disappointed. Who wouldn't be? With socks, a Sunday school shirt, some handkerchiefs, a hand-me-down sweater and a year's subscription to a religious magazine for children. *The Little Shepherd*. It makes me boil. It really does.

My friend has a better haul. A sack of Satsumas, that's her best present. She is proudest, however, of a white wool shawl knitted by her married sister. But she *says* her favorite gift is the kite I built her. And it *is* very beautiful; though not as beautiful as the one she made me, which is blue and scattered with gold and green Good Conduct stars; moreover, my name is painted on it, "Buddy."

"Buddy, the wind is blowing."

The wind is blowing, and nothing will do till we've run to a pasture below the house where Queenie has scooted to bury her bone (and where, a winter hence, Queenie will be buried, too). There, plunging through the healthy waist-high grass, we unreel our kites, feel them twitching at the string like sky fish as they swim into the wind. Satisfied, sun-warmed, we sprawl in the grass and peel Satsumas and watch our kites cavort. Soon I forget the socks and hand-me-down sweater. I'm as happy as if we'd already won the fifty-thousand-dollar Grand Prize in that coffee-naming contest.

"My, how foolish I am!" my friend cries, suddenly alert, like a woman remembering too late she has biscuits in the oven. "You know what I've always thought?" she asks in a tone of discovery, and not smiling at me but a point beyond. "I've always thought a body would have to be sick and dying before they saw the Lord. And I imagined that when He came it would be like looking at the Baptist window: pretty as colored glass with the sun pouring through, such a shine you don't know it's getting dark. And it's been a comfort: to think of that shine taking away all the spooky feeling. But I'll wager it never happens. I'll wager at the very end a body realizes the Lord has already shown Himself. That things as they are"—her hand circles in a gesture that gathers clouds and kites and grass and Queenie pawing earth over her bone—"just what they've always seen, was seeing Him. As for me, I could leave the world with today in my eyes."

This is our last Christmas together.

Life separates us. Those who Know Best decide that I belong in a military school. And so follows a miserable succession of bugle-blowing prisons, grim reveille-ridden summer camps. I have a new home too. But it doesn't count. Home is where my friend is, and there I never go.

And there she remains, puttering around the kitchen. Alone with Queenie. Then alone. ("Buddy dear," she writes in her wild hard-to-read script, "yesterday Jim Macy's horse kicked Queenie bad. Be thankful she didn't feel much. I wrapped her in a Fine Linen sheet and rode her in the buggy down to Simpson's pasture where she can be with all her Bones . . ."). For a few Novembers she continues to bake her fruitcakes single-handed; not as many, but some: and, of course, she always sends me "the best of the batch." Also, in every letter she encloses a dime wadded in toilet paper: "See a picture show and write me the story." But gradually in her letters she tends to confuse me with her other friend, the Buddy who died in the 1880's; more and more thirteenths are not the only days she stays in bed: a morning arrives in November, a leafless birdless coming of winter morning, when she cannot rouse herself to exclaim: "Oh my, it's fruitcake weather!"

And when that happens, I know it. A message saying so merely confirms a piece of news some secret vein had already received, severing from me an irreplaceable part of myself, letting it loose like a kite on a broken string. That is why, walking across a school campus on this particular December morning, I keep searching the sky. As if I expected to see, rather like hearts, a lost pair of kites hurrying toward heaven.

Breakfast at Tiffany's

I AM ALWAYS drawn back to places where I have lived, the houses and their neighborhoods. For instance, there is a brownstone in the East Seventies where, during the early years of the war, I had my first New York apartment. It was one room crowded with attic furniture, a sofa and fat chairs upholstered in that itchy, particular red velvet that one associates with hot days on a train. The walls were stucco, and a color rather like tobacco-spit. Everywhere, in the bathroom too, there were prints of Roman ruins freckled brown with age. The single window looked out on a fire escape. Even so, my spirits heightened whenever I felt in my pocket the key to this apartment; with all its gloom, it still was a place of my own, the first, and my books were there, and jars of pencils to sharpen, everything I needed, so I felt, to become the writer I wanted to be.

It never occurred to me in those days to write about Holly Golightly, and probably it would not now except for a conversation I had with Joe Bell that set the whole memory of her in motion again.

Holly Golightly had been a tenant in the old brownstone; she'd occupied the apartment below mine. As for Joe Bell, he ran a bar around the corner on Lexington Avenue; he still does. Both Holly and I used to go there six, seven times a day, not for a drink, not always, but to make telephone calls: during the war a private telephone was hard to come by. Moreover, Joe Bell was good about taking messages, which in Holly's case was no small favor, for she had a tremendous many.

Of course this was a long time ago, and until last week I hadn't seen Joe Bell in several years. Off and on we'd kept in touch, and occasionally I'd stopped by his bar when passing through the neighborhood; but actually we'd never been strong friends except in as much as we were both friends of Holly Golightly. Joe Bell hasn't an easy nature, he admits it himself, he says it's because he's a bachelor and has a sour stomach. Anyone who knows him will tell you he's a hard man to talk to. Impossible if you don't share his fixations, of which Holly is one. Some others are: ice hockey, Weimaraner dogs, *Our Gal Sunday* (a soap serial he has listened to for fifteen years), and Gilbert and Sullivan—he claims to be related to one or the other, I can't remember which.

And so when, late last Tuesday afternoon, the telephone rang and I heard "Joe Bell here," I knew it must be about Holly. He didn't say so, just: "Can you rattle right over here? It's important," and there was a croak of excitement in his froggy voice.

I took a taxi in a downpour of October rain, and on my way I even thought she might be there, that I would see Holly again.

But there was no one on the premises except the proprietor. Joe Bell's is a quiet place compared to most Lexington Avenue bars. It boasts neither neon nor television. Two old mirrors reflect the weather from the streets; and behind the bar, in a niche surrounded by photographs of ice-hockey stars, there is always a large bowl of fresh flowers that Joe Bell himself arranges with matronly care. That is what he was doing when I came in.

"Naturally," he said, rooting a gladiola deep into the bowl, "naturally I wouldn't have got you over here if it wasn't I wanted your opinion. It's peculiar. A very peculiar thing has happened."

"You heard from Holly?"

He fingered a leaf, as though uncertain of how to answer. A small man with a fine head of coarse white hair, he has a bony, sloping face better suited to someone far taller; his complexion seems permanently sunburned: now it grew even redder. "I can't say exactly heard from her. I mean, I don't know. That's why I want your opinion. Let me build you a drink. Something new. They call it a White Angel," he said, mixing one-half vodka, one-half gin, no vermouth. While I drank the result, Joe Bell stood sucking on a Tums and turning over in his mind what he had to tell me. Then: "You recall a certain Mr. I. Y. Yunioshi? A gentleman from Japan."

"From California," I said, recalling Mr. Yunioshi perfectly. He's a photographer on one of the picture magazines, and when I knew him he lived in the studio apartment on the top floor of the brownstone.

"Don't go mixing me up. All I'm asking, you know who I mean? Okay. So last night who comes waltzing in here but this selfsame Mr. I. Y. Yunioshi. I haven't seen him, I guess it's over two years. And where do you think he's been those two years?"

"Africa."

Joe Bell stopped crunching on his Tums, his eyes narrowed. "So how did you know?"

"Read it in Winchell." Which I had, as a matter of fact.

He rang open his cash register, and produced a manila envelope. "Well, see did you read this in Winchell."

In the envelope were three photographs, more or less the same, though taken from different angles: a tall delicate Negro man wearing a calico skirt and with a shy, yet vain smile, displaying in his hands an odd wood sculpture, an elongated carving of a head, a girl's, her hair sleek and short as a young man's, her smooth wood eyes too large and tilted in the tapering face, her mouth wide, overdrawn, not unlike clown-lips. On a glance it resembled most primitive carving; and then it didn't, for here was the spit-image of Holly Golightly, at least as much of a likeness as a dark still thing could be.

"Now what do you make of that?" said Joe Bell, satisfied with my puzzlement.

"It looks like her."

"Listen, boy," and he slapped his hand on the bar, "it *is* her. Sure as I'm a man fit to wear britches. The little Jap knew it was her the minute he saw her."

"He saw her? In Africa?"

"Well. Just the statue there. But it comes to the same thing. Read the facts for yourself," he said, turning over one of the photographs. On the reverse was written: Wood Carving, S Tribe, Tococul, East Anglia, Christmas Day, 1956.

He said, "Here's what the Jap says," and the story was this: On Christmas day Mr. Yunioshi had passed with his camera through Tococul, a village in the tangles of nowhere and of no interest, merely a congregation of mud huts with monkeys in the yards and buzzards on the roofs. He'd decided to move on when he saw suddenly a Negro squatting in a doorway carving monkeys on a walking stick. Mr. Yunioshi was impressed and asked to see more of his work. Whereupon he was shown the carving of the girl's head: and felt, so he told Joe Bell, as if he were falling in a dream. But when he offered to buy it the Negro cupped his private parts in his hand (apparently a tender gesture, comparable to tapping one's heart) and said no. A pound of salt and ten dollars, a wristwatch and two pounds of salt and twenty dollars, nothing swayed him. Mr. Yunioshi was in all events determined to learn how the carving came to be made. It cost him his salt and his watch, and the incident was conveyed in African and pig-English and finger-talk. But it would seem that in the spring of that year a party of three white persons had appeared out of the brush riding horseback. A young woman and two men. The men, both red-eyed with fever, were forced for several weeks to stay shut and shivering in an isolated hut, while the young woman, having presently taken a fancy to the woodcarver, shared the woodcarver's mat.

"I don't credit that part," Joe Bell said squeamishly. "I know she had her ways, but I don't think she'd be up to anything as much as that."

"And then?"

"Then nothing," he shrugged. "By and by she went like she come, rode away on a horse."

"Alone, or with the two men?"

Joe Bell blinked. "With the two men, I guess. Now the Jap, he asked about her up and down the country. But nobody else had ever seen her." Then it was as if he could feel my own sense of letdown transmitting itself to him, and he wanted no part of it. "One thing you got to admit, it's the only *definite* news in I don't know how many"—he counted on his fingers: there weren't enough —"years. All I hope, I hope she's rich. She must be rich. You got to be rich to go mucking around in Africa."

"She's probably never set foot in Africa," I said, believing it; yet I could see her there, it was somewhere she would have gone. And the carved head: I looked at the photographs again.

"You know so much, where is she?"

"Dead. Or in a crazy house. Or married. I think she's married and quieted down and maybe right in this very city."

He considered a moment. "No," he said, and shook his head. "I'll tell you why. If she was in this city I'd have seen her. You take a man that likes to walk, a man like me, a man's been walking in the streets going on ten or twelve years, and all those years he's got his eye out for one person, and nobody's ever her, don't stand to reason she's not there? I see pieces of her all the time, a flat little bottom, any skinny girl that walks fast and straight—" He paused, as though too aware of how intently I was looking at him. "You think I'm round the bend?"

"It's just that I didn't know you'd been in love with her. Not like that."

I was sorry I'd said it; it disconcerted him. He scooped up the photographs and put them back in their envelope. I looked at my watch. I hadn't any place to go, but I thought it was better to leave.

"Hold on," he said, gripping my wrist. "Sure I loved her. But it wasn't that I wanted to touch her." And he added, without smiling: "Not that I don't think about that side of things. Even at my age, and I'll be sixty-seven January ten. It's a peculiar fact—but, the older I grow, that side of things seems to be on my mind more and more. I don't remember thinking about it so much even when I was a youngster and it's every other minute. Maybe the older you grow and the less easy it is to put thought into action, maybe that's why it gets all locked up in your head and becomes a burden. Whenever I read in the paper about an old man disgracing himself, I know it's because of this burden. But"—he poured himself a jigger of whiskey and swallowed it neat—"I'll never disgrace myself. And I swear, it never crossed my mind about Holly. You can love somebody without it being like that. You keep them a stranger, a stranger who's a friend."

Two men came into the bar, and it seemed the moment to leave. Joe Bell followed me to the door. He caught my wrist again. "Do you believe it?"

"That you didn't want to touch her?"

"I mean about Africa."

At that moment I couldn't seem to remember the story, only the image of her riding away on a horse. "Anyway, she's gone."

"Yeah," he said, opening the door. "Just gone."

Outside, the rain had stopped, there was only a mist of it in the air, so I turned the corner and walked along the street where the brownstone stands. It is a street with trees that in the summer make cool patterns on the pavement; but now the leaves were yellowed and mostly down, and the rain had made them slippery, they skidded underfoot. The brownstone is midway in the block, next to a church where a blue tower-clock tolls the hours. It has been sleeked up since my day; a smart black door has replaced the old frosted glass, and gray elegant shutters frame the windows. No one I remember still lives there except Madame Sapphia Spanella, a husky coloratura who every afternoon went roller-skating in Central Park. I know she's still there because I went up the steps and looked at the mailboxes. It was one of these mailboxes that had first made me aware of Holly Golightly.

I'd been living in the house about a week when I noticed that the mailbox belonging to Apt. 2 had a name-slot fitted with a curious card. Printed, rather Cartier-formal, it read: *Miss Holiday Golightly;* and, under-neath, in the corner, *Traveling*. It nagged me like a tune: *Miss Holiday Golightly, Traveling.*

One night, it was long past twelve, I woke up at the sound of Mr. Yunioshi calling down the stairs. Since he lived on the top floor, his voice fell through the whole house, exasperated and stern. "Miss Golightly! I must protest!"

The voice that came back, welling up from the bot-tom of the stairs, was silly-young and self-amused. "Oh, darling, I *am* sorry. I lost the goddamn key."

"You cannot go on ringing my bell. You must please, please have yourself a key made."

"But I lose them all."

"I work, I have to sleep," Mr. Yunioshi shouted. "But always you are ringing my bell . . ."

"Oh, *don't* be angry, you *dear* little man: I *won't* do it again. And if you promise not to be angry"—her voice was coming nearer, she was climbing the stairs—"I might let you take those pictures we mentioned."

By now I'd left my bed and opened the door an inch. I could hear Mr. Yunioshi's silence: hear, because it was accompanied by an audible change of breath.

"When?" he said.

The girl laughed. "Sometime," she answered, slurring the word.

"Any time," he said, and closed his door.

I went out into the hall and leaned over the banister, just enough to see without being seen. She was still on the stairs, now she reached the landing, and the ragbag colors of her boy's hair, tawny streaks, strands of albino-blond and yellow, caught the hall light. It was a warm evening, nearly summer, and she wore a slim cool black dress, black sandals, a pearl choker. For all her chic thinness, she had an almost breakfast-cereal air of health, a soap and lemon cleanness, a rough pink darkening in the cheeks. Her mouth was large, her nose upturned. A pair of dark glasses blotted out her eyes. It was a face beyond childhood, yet this side of belonging to a woman. I thought her anywhere between sixteen and thirty; as it turned out, she was shy two months of her nineteenth birthday.

She was not alone. There was a man following behind her. The way his plump hand clutched at her hip seemed somehow improper; not morally, aesthetically. He was short and vast, sun-lamped and pomaded, a man in a buttressed pin-stripe suit with a red carnation withering in the lapel. When they reached her door she rummaged her purse in search of a key, and took no notice of the fact that his thick lips were nuzzling the nape of her neck. At last, though, finding the key and opening her door, she turned to him cordially: "Bless you, darling—you were sweet to see me home."

"Hey, baby!" he said, for the door was closing in his face.

"Yes, Harry?"

"Harry was the other guy. I'm Sid. Sid Arbuck. You like me."

"I worship you, Mr. Arbuck. But good night, Mr. Arbuck."

Mr. Arbuck stared with disbelief as the door shut firmly. "Hey, baby, let me in, baby. You like me, baby. I'm a liked guy. Didn't I pick up the check, five people, *your* friends, I never seen them before? Don't that give me the right you should like me? You like me, baby."

He tapped on the door gently, then louder; finally he took several steps back, his body hunched and lowering, as though he meant to charge it, crash it down. Instead, he plunged down the stairs, slamming a fist against the wall. Just as he reached the bottom, the door of the girl's apartment opened and she poked out her head.

"Oh, Mr. *Ar*buck . . ."

He turned back, a smile of relief oiling his face: she'd only been teasing.

"The next time a girl wants a little powder-room change," she called, not teasing at all, "take my advice, darling: *don't* give her twenty-cents!"

She kept her promise to Mr. Yunioshi; or I assume she did not ring his bell again, for in the next days she started ringing mine, sometimes at two in the morning, three and four: she had no qualms at what hour she got me out of bed to push the buzzer that released the downstairs door. As I had few friends, and none who would come around so late, I always knew that it was her. But on the first occasions of its happening, I went to my door, half-expecting bad news, a telegram; and Miss Golightly would call up: "Sorry, darling—I forgot my key."

Of course we'd never met. Though actually, on the stairs, in the street, we often came face-to-face; but she seemed not quite to see me. She was never without dark glasses, she was always well groomed, there was a consequential good taste in the plainness of her clothes, the blues and grays and lack of luster that made her, herself, shine so. One might have thought her a photographer's model, perhaps a young actress, except that it was obvious, judging from her hours, she hadn't time to be either.

Now and then I ran across her outside our neighborhood. Once a visiting relative took me to "21," and there, at a superior table, surrounded by four men, none of them Mr. Arbuck, yet all of them interchangeable with him, was Miss Golightly, idly, publicly combing her hair; and her expression, an unrealized yawn, put, by example, a dampener on the excitement I felt over dining at so swanky a place. Another night, deep in the summer, the heat of my room sent me out into the streets. I walked down Third Avenue to Fifty-first Street, where there was an antique store with an object in its window I admired: a palace of a bird cage, a mosque of minarets and bamboo rooms yearning to be filled with talkative parrots. But the price was three hundred and fifty dollars. On the way home I noticed a cab-driver crowd gathered in front of P. J. Clark's saloon, apparently attracted there by a happy group of whiskey-eyed Australian army officers baritoning, "Waltzing Matilda." As they sang they took turns spin-dancing a girl over the cobbles under the El; and the girl, Miss Golightly, to be sure, floated round in their arms light as a scarf.

But if Miss Golightly remained unconscious of my existence, except as a doorbell convenience, I became, through the summer, rather an authority on hers. I discovered, from observing the trash basket outside her door, that her regular reading consisted of tabloids and travel folders and astrological charts; that she smoked an esoteric cigarette called Picayunes; survived on cottage cheese and melba toast; that her vari-colored hair was somewhat self-induced. The same source made it evident that she received V-letters by the bale. They were always torn into strips like book marks. I used occasionally to pluck myself a bookmark in passing. *Remember* and *miss you* and *rain* and *please write* and *damn* and *goddamn* were the words that recurred most often on these slips; those, and *lonesome* and *love*.

Also, she had a cat and she played the guitar. On days when the sun was strong, she would wash her hair, and together with the cat, a red tiger-striped tom, sit out on the fire escape thumbing a guitar while her hair dried. Whenever I heard the music, I would go stand quietly by my window. She played very well, and sometimes sang too. Sang in the hoarse, breaking tones of a boy's adolescent voice. She knew all the show hits, Cole Porter and Kurt Weill; especially she liked the songs from *Oklahoma!*, which were new that summer and everywhere. But there were moments when she played songs that made you wonder where she learned them, where indeed she came from. Harsh-tender wandering tunes with words that smacked of pineywoods or prairie. One went: *Don't wanna sleep, Don't wanna die, Just wanna go a-travelin' through the pastures of the sky;* and this one seemed to gratify her the most, for often she continued it long after her hair had dried, after the sun had gone and there were lighted windows in the dusk.

But our acquaintance did not make headway until September, an evening with the first ripple-chills of autumn running through it. I'd been to a movie, come home and gone to bed with a bourbon nightcap and the newest Simenon: so much my idea of comfort that I couldn't understand a sense of unease that multiplied until I could hear my heart beating. It was a feeling I'd read about, written about, but never before experienced. The feeling of being watched. Of someone in the room. Then: an abrupt rapping at the window, a glimpse of ghostly gray: I spilled the bourbon. It was some little while before I could bring myself to open the window, and ask Miss Golightly what she wanted.

"I've got the most terrifying man downstairs," she said, stepping off the fire escape into the room. "I mean he's sweet when he isn't drunk, but let him start lapping up the vino, and oh God quel beast! If there's one thing I loathe, it's men who bite." She loosened a gray flannel robe off her shoulder to show me evidence of what happens if a man bites. The robe was all she was wearing. "I'm sorry if I frightened you. But when the beast got so tiresome I just went out the window. I think he thinks I'm in the bathroom, not that I give a damn what he thinks, the hell with him, he'll get tired, he'll go to sleep, my God he should, eight martinis before dinner and enough wine to wash an elephant. Listen, you can throw me out if you want to. I've got a gall barging in on you like this. But that fire escape was damned icy. And you looked so cozy. Like my brother Fred. We used to sleep four in a bed, and he was the only one that ever let me hug him on a cold night. By the way, do you mind if I call you Fred?" She'd come completely into the room now, and she paused there, staring at me. I'd never seen her before not wearing dark glasses, and it was obvious now that they were prescription lenses, for without them her eyes had an assessing squint, like a jeweler's. They were large eyes, a little blue, a little green, dotted with bits of brown: vari-colored, like her hair; and, like her hair, they gave out a lively warm light. "I suppose you think I'm very brazen. Or *très fou*. Or something."

"Not at all."

She seemed disappointed. "Yes, you do. Everybody does. I don't mind. It's useful."

She sat down on one of the rickety red-velvet chairs, curved her legs underneath her, and glanced round the room, her eyes puckering more pronouncedly. "How can you bear it? It's a chamber of horrors."

"Oh, you get used to anything," I said, annoyed with myself, for actually I was proud of the place.

"I don't. I'll never get used to anything. Anybody that does, they might as well be dead." Her dispraising eyes surveyed the room again. "What do you *do* here all day?"

I motioned toward a table tall with books and paper. "Write things."

"I thought writers were quite old. Of course Saroyan isn't old. I met him at a party, and really he isn't old at all. In fact," she mused, "if he'd give himself a closer shave . . . by the way, is Hemingway old?"

"In his forties, I should think."

"That's not bad. I can't get excited by a man until he's forty-two. I know this idiot girl who keeps telling me I ought to go to a head-shrinker; she says I have a father complex. Which is so much *merde*. I simply *trained* myself to like older men, and it was the smartest thing I ever did. How old is W. Somerset Maugham?"

"I'm not sure. Sixty-something."

"That's not bad. I've never been to bed with a writer. No, wait: do you know Benny Shacklett?" She frowned when I shook my head. "That's funny. He's written an awful lot of radio stuff. But quel rat. Tell me, are you a real writer?"

"It depends on what you mean by real."

"Well, darling, does anyone *buy* what you write?"

"Not yet."

"I'm going to help you," she said. "I can, too. Think of all the people I know who know people. I'm going to help you because you look like my brother Fred. Only smaller. I haven't seen him since I was fourteen, that's when I left home, and he was already six-feet-two. My other brothers were more your size, runts. It was the peanut butter that made Fred so tall. Everybody thought it was dotty, the way he gorged himself on peanut butter; he didn't care about anything in this world except horses and peanut butter. But he wasn't dotty, just sweet and vague and terribly slow; he'd been in the eighth grade three years when I ran away. Poor Fred. I wonder if the Army's generous with their peanut butter. Which reminds me, I'm starving."

I pointed to a bowl of apples, at the same time asked her how and why she'd left home so young. She looked at me blankly, and rubbed her nose, as though it tickled: a gesture, seeing often repeated, I came to recognize as a signal that one was trespassing. Like many people with a bold fondness for volunteering intimate information, anything that suggested a direct question, a pinning-down, put her on guard. She took a bite of apple, and said: "Tell me something you've written. The story part."

"That's one of the troubles. They're not the kind of stories you *can* tell."

"Too dirty?"

"Maybe I'll let you read one sometime."

"Whiskey and apples go together. Fix me a drink, darling. Then you can read me a story yourself."

Very few authors, especially the unpublished, can resist an invitation to read aloud. I made us both a drink and, settling in a chair opposite, began to read to her, my voice a little shaky with a combination of stage fright and enthusiasm: it was a new story, I'd finished it the day before, and that inevitable sense of shortcoming had not had time to develop. It was about two women who share a house, schoolteachers, one of whom, when the other becomes engaged, spreads with anonymous notes a scandal that prevents the marriage. As I read, each glimpse I stole of Holly made my heart contract. She fidgeted. She picked apart the butts in an ash tray, she mooned over her fingernails, as though longing for a file; worse, when I did seem to have her interest, there was actually a telltale frost over her eyes, as if she were wondering whether to buy a pair of shoes she'd seen in some window.

"Is that the *end?*" she asked, waking up. She floundered for something more to say. "Of course I like dykes themselves. They don't scare me a bit. But stories about dykes bore the bejesus out of me. I just can't put myself in their shoes. Well really, darling," she said, because I was clearly puzzled, "if it's not about a couple of old bull-dykes, what the hell *is* it about?"

But I was in no mood to compound the mistake of having read the story with the further embarrassment of explaining it. The same vanity that had led to such exposure, now forced me to mark her down as an insensitive, mindless show-off.

"Incidentally," she said, "do you happen to *know* any nice lesbians? I'm looking for a roommate. Well, don't laugh. I'm so disorganized, I simply can't afford a maid; and really, dykes are wonderful homemakers, they love to do all the work, you never have to bother about brooms and defrosting and sending out the laundry. I had a roommate in Hollywood, she played in Westerns,

they called her the Lone Ranger; but I'll say this for
her, she was better than a man around the house. Of
course people couldn't help but think I must be a bit of
a dyke myself. And of course I am. Everyone is: a bit.
So what? That never discouraged a man yet, in fact it
seems to goad them on. Look at the Lone Ranger, married twice. Usually dykes only get married once, just for
the name. It seems to carry such cachet later on to be
called Mrs. Something Another. That's not true!" She
was staring at an alarm clock on the table. "It can't be
four-thirty!"

The window was turning blue. A sunrise breeze
bandied the curtains.

"What is today?"

"Thursday."

"*Thursday*." She stood up. "My God," she said,
and sat down again with a moan. "It's too gruesome."

I was tired enough not to be curious. I lay down on
the bed and closed my eyes. Still it was irresistible:
"What's gruesome about Thursday?"

"Nothing. Except that I can never remember when
it's coming. You see, on Thursdays I have to catch the
eight forty-five. They're so particular about visiting
hours, so if you're there by ten that gives you an hour
before the poor men eat lunch. Think of it, lunch at
eleven. You *can* go at two, and I'd so much rather, but
he likes me to come in the morning, he says it sets him
up for the rest of the day. I've *got* to stay awake," she
said, pinching her cheeks until the roses came, "there
isn't time to sleep, I'd look consumptive, I'd sag like a
tenement, and that wouldn't be fair: a girl can't go to
Sing Sing with a green face."

"I suppose not." The anger I felt at her over my
story was ebbing; she absorbed me again.

"All the visitors *do* make an effort to look their best,
and it's very tender, it's sweet as hell, the way the women
wear their prettiest everything, I mean the old ones and
the really poor ones too, they make the dearest effort
to look nice and smell nice too, and I love them for it. I

love the kids too, especially the colored ones. I mean
the kids the wives bring. It should be sad, seeing the kids
there, but it isn't, they have ribbons in their hair and lots
of shine on their shoes, you'd think there was going to
be ice cream; and sometimes that's what it's like in the
visitors' room, a party. Anyway it's not like the movies:
you know, grim whisperings through a grille. There isn't
any grille, just a counter between you and them, and the
kids can stand on it to be hugged; all you have to do to
kiss somebody is lean across. What I like most, they're
so happy to see each other, they've saved up so much to
talk about, it isn't possible to be dull, they keep laughing
and holding hands. It's different afterwards," she said.
"I see them on the train. They sit so quiet watching the
river go by." She stretched a strand of hair to the corner
of her mouth and nibbled it thoughtfully. "I'm keeping
you awake. Go to sleep."

"Please. I'm interested."

"I know you are. That's why I want you to go to
sleep. Because if I keep on, I'll tell you about Sally. I'm
not sure that would be quite cricket." She chewed her
hair silently. "They never *told* me not to tell anyone.
In so many words. And it *is* funny. Maybe you could put it
in a story with different names and whatnot. Listen,
Fred," she said, reaching for another apple, "you've got
to cross your heart and kiss your elbow—"

Perhaps contortionists can kiss their elbow; she had
to accept an approximation.

"Well," she said, with a mouthful of apple, "you
may have read about him in the papers. His name is
Sally Tomato, and I speak Yiddish better than he speaks
English; but he's a darling old man, terribly pious. He'd
look like a monk if it weren't for the gold teeth; he says
he prays for me every night. Of course he was never my
lover; as far as that goes, I never knew him until he was
already in jail. But I adore him now, after all I've been
going to see him every Thursday for seven months, and
I think I'd go even if he didn't pay me. This one's
mushy," she said, and aimed the rest of the apple out the

window. "By the way, I *did* know Sally by sight. He used to come to Joe Bell's bar, the one around the corner: never talked to anybody, just stand there, like the kind of man who lives in hotel rooms. But it's funny to remember back and realize how closely he must have been watching me, because right after they sent him up (Joe Bell showed me his picture in the paper. Blackhand. Mafia. All that mumbo jumbo: but they gave him five years) along came this telegram from a lawyer. It said to contact him immediately for information to my advantage."

"You thought somebody had left you a million?"

"Not at all. I figured Bergdorf was trying to collect. But I took the gamble and went to see this lawyer (if he *is* a lawyer, which I doubt, since he doesn't seem to have an office, just an answering service, and he always wants to meet you in Hamburg Heaven: that's because he's fat, he can eat ten hamburgers and two bowls of relish and a whole lemon meringue pie). He asked me how I'd like to cheer up a lonely old man, at the same time pick up a hundred a week. I told him look, darling, you've got the wrong Miss Golightly, I'm not a nurse that does tricks on the side. I wasn't impressed by the honorarium either; you can do as well as that on trips to the powder room: any gent with the slightest chic will give you fifty for the girl's john, and I always ask for cab fare too, that's another fifty. But then he told me his client was Sally Tomato. He said dear old Sally had long admired me *à la distance,* so wouldn't it be a good deed if I went to visit him once a week. Well, I couldn't say no: it was too romantic."

"I don't know. It doesn't sound right."

She smiled. "You think I'm lying?"

"For one thing, they can't simply let *anyone* visit a prisoner."

"Oh, they don't. In fact they make quite a boring fuss. I'm supposed to be his niece."

"And it's as simple as that? For an hour's conversation he gives you a hundred dollars?"

"He doesn't, the lawyer does. Mr. O'Shaughnessy mails it to me in cash as soon as I leave the weather report."

"I think you could get into a lot of trouble," I said, and switched off a lamp; there was no need of it now, morning was in the room and pigeons were gargling on the fire escape.

"How?" she said seriously.

"There must be something in the law books about false identity. After all, you're *not* his niece. And what about this weather report?"

She patted a yawn. "But it's nothing. Just messages I leave with the anwering service so Mr. O'Shaughnessy will know for sure that I've been up there. Sally tells me what to say, things like, oh, 'there's a hurricane in Cuba' and 'it's snowing in Palermo.' Don't worry, darling," she said, moving to the bed, "I've taken care of myself a long time." The morning light seemed refracted through her: as she pulled the bed covers up to my chin she gleamed like a transparent child; then she lay down beside me. "Do you mind? I only want to rest a moment. So let's don't say another word. Go to sleep."

I pretended to, I made my breathing heavy and regular. Bells in the tower of the next-door church rang the half-hour, the hour. It was six when she put her hand on my arm, a fragile touch careful not to waken. "Poor Fred," she whispered, and it seemed she was speaking to me, but she was not. "Where are you, Fred? Because it's cold. There's snow in the wind." Her cheek came to rest against my shoulder, a warm damp weight.

"Why are you crying?"

She sprang back, sat up. "Oh, for God's sake," she said, starting for the window and the fire escape, "I *hate* snoops."

The next day, Friday, I came home to find outside my door a grand-luxe Charles & Co. basket with her card: *Miss Holiday Golightly, Traveling:* and scribbled on the back in a freakishly awkward, kindergarten hand: *Bless you darling Fred. Please forgive the other night. You were an angel about the whole thing. Mille tendresse—Holly. P.S. I won't bother you again.* I replied, *Please do,* and left this note at her door with what I could afford, a bunch of street-vender violets. But apparently she'd meant what she said; I neither saw nor heard from her, and I gathered she'd gone so far as to obtain a downstairs key. At any rate she no longer rang my bell. I missed that; and as the days merged I began to feel toward her certain far-fetched resentments, as if I were being neglected by my closest friend. A disquieting loneliness came into my life, but it induced no hunger for friends of longer acquaintance: they seemed now like a salt-free, sugarless diet. By Wednesday thoughts of Holly, of Sing Sing and Sally Tomato, of worlds where men forked over fifty dollars for the powder room, were so constant that I couldn't work. That night I left a message in her mailbox: *Tomorrow is Thursday.* The next morning rewarded me with a second note in the playpen script: *Bless you for reminding me. Can you stop for a drink tonight 6-ish?*

I waited until ten past six, then made myself delay five minutes more.

A creature answered the door. He smelled of cigars and Knize cologne. His shoes sported elevated heels; without these added inches, one might have taken him for a Little Person. His bald freckled head was dwarf-big: attached to it were a pair of pointed, truly elfin ears. He had Pekingese eyes, unpitying and slightly bulged. Tufts of hair sprouted from his ears, from his nose; his jowls were gray with afternoon beard, and his handsake almost furry.

"Kid's in the shower," he said, motioning a cigar toward a sound of water hissing in another room. The room in which we stood (we were standing because there was nothing to sit on) seemed as though it were being just moved into; you expected to smell wet paint.

Suitcases and unpacked crates were the only furniture. The crates served as tables. One supported the mixings of a martini; another a lamp, a Libertyphone, Holly's red cat and a bowl of yellow roses. Bookcases, covering one wall, boasted a half-shelf of literature. I warmed to the room at once, I liked its fly-by-night look.

The man cleared his throat. "You expected?"

He found my nod uncertain. His cold eyes operated on me, made neat, exploratory incisions. "A lot of characters come here, they're not expected. You know the kid long?"

"Not very."

"So you don't know the kid long?"

"I live upstairs."

The answer seemed to explain enough to relax him. "You got the same layout?"

"Much smaller."

He tapped ash on the floor. "This is a dump. This is unbelievable. But the kid don't know how to live even when she's got the dough." His speech had a jerky metallic rhythm, like a teletype. "So," he said, "what do you think: is she or ain't she?"

"Ain't she what?"

"A phony."

"I wouldn't have thought so."

"You're wrong. She is a phony. But on the other hand you're right. She isn't a phony because she's a *real* phony. She believes all this crap she believes. You can't talk her out of it. I've tried with tears running down my cheeks. Benny Polan, respected everywhere, Benny Polan tried. Benny had it on his mind to marry her, she don't go for it, Benny spent maybe thousands sending her to head-shrinkers. Even the famous one, the one can only speak German, boy, did he throw in the towel. You can't talk her out of these"—he made a fist, as though to crush an intangible—"ideas. Try it sometimes. Get her to tell you some of the stuff she believes. Mind you," he said, "I like the kid. Everybody does, but there's lots that don't. I do. I sincerely like the kid. I'm sensitive, that's why. You've got to be sensitive to appreciate her: a streak of the poet. But I'll tell you the truth. You can beat your brains out for her, and she'll hand you horse-shit on a platter. To give an example—who is she like you see her today? She's strictly a girl you'll read where she ends up at the bottom of a bottle of Seconals. I've seen it happen more times than you've got toes: and those kids, they weren't even nuts. She's nuts."

"But young. And with a great deal of youth ahead of her."

"If you mean future, you're wrong again. Now a couple of years back, out on the Coast, there was a time it could've been different. She had something working for her, she had them interested, she could've really rolled. But when you walk out on a thing like that, you don't walk back. Ask Luise Rainer. And Rainer was a star. Sure, Holly was no star; she never got out of the still department. But that was before *The Story of Dr. Wassell*. Then she could've really rolled. I know, see, cause I'm the guy was giving her the push." He pointed his cigar at himself. "O. J. Berman."

He expected recognition, and I didn't mind oblig-ing him, it was all right by me, except I'd never heard of O. J. Berman. It developed that he was a Hollywood actor's agent.

"I'm the first one saw her. Out at Santa Anita. She's hanging around the track every day. I'm interested: professionally. I find out she's some jock's regular, she's living with the shrimp. I get the jock told Drop It if he don't want conversation with the vice boys: see, the kid's fifteen. But stylish: she's okay, she comes across. Even when she's wearing glasses *this* thick; even when she opens her mouth and you don't know if she's a hill-billy or an Okie or what. I still don't. My guess, nobody'll ever know where she came from. She's such a god-damn liar, maybe she don't know herself any more. But it took us a year to smooth out that accent. How we did it finally, we gave her French lessons: after she could imi-tate French, it wasn't so long she could imitate English.

We modeled her along the Margaret Sullavan type, but she could pitch some curves of her own, people were interested, big ones, and to top it all, Benny Polan, a respected guy, Benny wants to marry her. An agent could ask for more? Then wham! *The Story of Dr. Wassell.* You see that picture? Cecil B. DeMille. Gary Cooper. Jesus. I kill myself, it's all set: they're going to test her for the part of Dr. Wassell's nurse. One of his nurses, anyway. Then wham! The phone rings." He picked a telephone out of the air and held it to his ear. "She says, this is Holly, I say honey, you sound far away, she says I'm in New York, I say what the hell are you doing in New York when it's Sunday and you got the test tomorrow? She says I'm in New York cause I've never been to New York. I say get your ass on a plane and get back here, she says I don't want it. I say what's your angle, doll? She says you got to want it to be good and I don't want it, I say well, what the hell do you want, and she says when I find out you'll be the first to know. See what I mean: horseshit on a platter."

The red cat jumped off its crate and rubbed against his leg. He lifted the cat on the toe of his shoe and gave him a toss, which was hateful of him except he seemed not aware of the cat but merely his own irritableness.

"This is what she wants?" he said, flinging out his arms. "A lot of characters they aren't expected? Living off tips. Running around with bums. So maybe she could marry Rusty Trawler? You should pin a medal on her for that?"

He waited, glaring.

"Sorry, I don't know him."

"You don't know Rusty Trawler, you can't know much about the kid. Bad deal," he said, his tongue clucking in his huge head. "I was hoping you maybe had influence. Could level with the kid before it's too late."

"But according to you, it already is."

He blew a smoke ring, let it fade before he smiled; the smile altered his face, made something gentle happen. "I could get it rolling again. Like I told you," he said, and now it sounded true, "I sincerely like the kid."

"What scandals are you spreading, O.J.?" Holly splashed into the room, a towel more or less wrapped round her and her wet feet dripping footmarks on the floor.

"Just the usual. That you're nuts."

"Fred knows that already."

"But you don't."

"Light me a cigarette, darling," she said, snatching off a bathing cap and shaking her hair. "I don't mean you, O.J. You're such a slob. You always nigger-lip."

She scooped up the cat and swung him onto her shoulder. He perched there with the balance of a bird, his paws tangled in her hair as if it were knitting yarn; and yet, despite these amiable antics, it was a grim cat with a pirate's cutthroat face; one eye was gluey-blind, the other sparkled with dark deeds.

"O.J. is a slob," she told me, taking the cigarette I'd lighted. "But he does know a terrific lot of phone numbers. What's David O. Selznick's number, O.J.?"

"Lay off."

"It's not a joke, darling. I want you to call him up and tell him what a genius Fred is. He's written barrels of the most marvelous stories. Well, don't blush, Fred: you didn't say you were a genius, I did. Come on, O.J. What are you going to do to make Fred rich?"

"Suppose you let me settle that with Fred."

"Remember," she said, leaving us, "I'm his agent. Another thing: if I holler, come zipper me up. And if anybody knocks, let them in."

A multitude did. Within the next quarter-hour a stag party had taken over the apartment, several of them in uniform. I counted two Naval officers and an Air Force colonel; but they were outnumbered by graying arrivals beyond draft status. Except for a lack of youth, the guests had no common theme, they seemed strangers among strangers; indeed, each face, on entering, had struggled to conceal dismay at seeing others there. It was as if the hostess had distributed her invitations while zigzagging through various bars; which was probably the case. After the initial frowns, however, they mixed without grumbling, especially O. J. Berman, who avidly exploited the new company to avoid discussing my Hollywood future. I was left abandoned by the bookshelves; of the books there, more than half were about horses, the rest baseball. Pretending an interest in *Horse-flesh and How to Tell It* gave me sufficiently private opportunity for sizing Holly's friends.

Presently one of these became prominent. He was a middle-aged child that had never shed its baby fat, though some gifted tailor had almost succeeded in camouflaging his plump and spankable bottom. There wasn't a suspicion of bone in his body; his face, a zero filled in with pretty miniature features, had an unused, a virginal quality: it was as if he'd been born, then expanded, his skin remaining unlined as a blown-up balloon, and his mouth, though ready for squalls and tantrums, a spoiled sweet puckering. But it was not appearance that singled him out; preserved infants aren't all that rare. It was, rather, his conduct; for he was behaving as though the party were his: like an energetic octopus, he was shaking martinis, making introductions, manipulating the phonograph. In fairness, most of his activities were dictated by the hostess herself: *Rusty, would you mind; Rusty, would you please.* If he was in love with her, then clearly he had his jealousy in check. A jealous man might have lost control, watching her as she skimmed around the room, carrying her cat in one hand but leaving the other free to straighten a tie or remove lapel lint; the Air Force colonel wore a medal that came in for quite a polish.

The man's name was Rutherfurd ("Rusty") Trawler. In 1908 he'd lost both his parents, his father the victim of an anarchist and his mother of shock, which double misfortune had made Rusty an orphan, a millionaire, and a celebrity, all at the age of five. He'd been a standby of the Sunday supplements ever since, a consequence that had gathered hurricane momentum when, still a schoolboy, he had caused his godfather-custodian to be arrested on charges of sodomy. After that, marriage and divorce sustained his place in the tabloid-sun. His first wife had taken herself, and her alimony, to a rival of Father Divine's. The second wife seems unaccounted for, but the third had sued him in New York State with a full satchel of the kind of testimony that entails. He himself divorced the last Mrs. Trawler, his principal complaint stating that she'd started a mutiny aboard his yacht, said mutiny resulting in his being deposited on the Dry Tortugas. Though he'd been a bachelor since, apparently before the war he'd proposed to Unity Mitford, at least he was supposed to have sent her a cable offering to marry her if Hitler didn't. This was said to be the reason Winchell always referred to him as a Nazi; that, and the fact that he attended rallies in Yorkville.

I was not told these things. I read them in *The Baseball Guide,* another selection off Holly's shelf which she seemed to use for a scrapbook. Tucked between the pages were Sunday features, together with scissored snippings from gossip columns. *Rusty Trawler and Holly Golightly two-on-the-aisle at "One Touch of Venus" preem.* Holly came up from behind, and caught me reading: *Miss Holiday Golightly, of the Boston Golightlys, making every day a holiday for the 24-karat Rusty Trawler.*

"Admiring my publicity, or are you just a baseball fan?" she said, adjusting her dark glasses as she glanced over my shoulder.

I said, "What was this week's weather report?"

She winked at me, but it was humorless: a wink of warning, "I'm all for horses, but I loathe baseball," she said, and the sub-message in her voice was saying she wished me to forget she'd ever mentioned Sally Tomato. "I hate the sound of it on a radio, but I have to listen, it's part of my research. There're so few things men can talk about. If a man doesn't like baseball, then he must like horses, and if he doesn't like either of them, well, I'm in trouble anyway: he don't like girls. And how are you making out with O.J.?"

"We've separated by mutual agreement."

"He's an opportunity, believe me."

"I do believe you. But what have I to offer that would strike him as an opportunity?"

She persisted. "Go over there and make him think he isn't funny-looking. He really can help you, Fred."

"I understand you weren't too appreciative." She seemed puzzled until I said: *"The Story of Doctor Wassell."*

"He's still harping?" she said, and cast across the room an affectionate look at Berman. "But he's got a point, I *should* feel guilty. Not because they would have given me the part or because I would have been good: they wouldn't and I wouldn't. If I do feel guilty, I guess it's because I let him go on dreaming when I wasn't dreaming a bit. I was just vamping for time to make a few self-improvements: I knew damn well I'd never be a movie star. It's too hard; and if you're intelligent, it's too embarrassing. My complexes aren't inferior enough: being a movie star and having a big fat ego are supposed to go hand-in-hand; actually, it's essential not to have any ego at all. I don't mean I'd mind being rich and famous. That's very much on my schedule, and someday I'll try to get around to it; but if it happens, I'd like to have my ego tagging along. I want to still be me when I wake up one fine morning and have breakfast at Tiffany's. You need a glass," she said, noticing my empty hands. "Rusty! Will you bring my friend a drink?"

She was still hugging the cat. "Poor slob," she said, tickling his head, "poor slob without a name. It's a little inconvenient, his not having a name. But I haven't any right to give him one: he'll have to wait until he *belongs* to somebody. We just sort of took up by the river one day, we don't belong to each other: he's an independent, and so am I. I don't want to own anything until I know I've found the place where me and things belong together. I'm not quite sure where that is just yet. But I

know what it's like." She smiled, and let the cat drop to
the floor. "It's like Tiffany's," she said. "Not that I give
a hoot about jewelry. Diamonds, yes. But it's tacky to
wear diamonds before you're forty; and even that's risky.
They only look right on the really old girls. Maria
Ouspenskaya. Wrinkles and bones, white hair and diamonds: I can't wait. But that's not why I'm mad about
Tiffany's. Listen. You know those days when you've got
the mean reds?"

"Same as the blues?"

"No," she said slowly. "No, the blues are because
you're getting fat or maybe it's been raining too long.
You're sad, that's all. But the mean reds are horrible.
You're afraid and you sweat like hell, but you don't
know what you're afraid of. Except something bad is going to happen, only you don't know what it is. You've
had that feeling?"

"Quite often. Some people call it *angst*."

"All right. *Angst*. But what do you do about it?"

"Well, a drink helps."

"I've tried that. I've tried aspirin, too. Rusty thinks
I should smoke marijuana, and I did for a while, but it
only makes me giggle. What I've found does the most
good is just to get into a taxi and go to Tiffany's. It calms
me down right away, the quietness and the proud look
of it; nothing very bad could happen to you there, not
with those kind men in their nice suits, and that lovely
smell of silver and alligator wallets. If I could find a real-
life place that made me feel like Tiffany's, then I'd buy
some furniture and give the cat a name. I've thought
maybe after the war, Fred and I—" She pushed up her
dark glasses, and her eyes, the differing colors of them,
the grays and wisps of blue and green, had taken on a
far-seeing sharpness. "I went to Mexico once. It's wonderful country for raising horses. I saw one place near
the sea. Fred's good with horses."

Rusty Trawler came carrying a martini; he handed
it over without looking at me. "I'm hungry," he announced, and his voice, retarded as the rest of him, pro-

duced an unnerving brat-whine that seemed to blame Holly. "It's seven-thirty, and I'm hungry. You know what the doctor said."

"Yes, Rusty. I know what the doctor said."

"Well, then break it up. Let's go."

"I want you to behave, Rusty." She spoke softly, but there was a governess threat of punishment in her tone that caused an odd flush of pleasure, of gratitude, to pink his face.

"You don't love me," he complained, as though they were alone.

"Nobody loves naughtiness."

Obviously she'd said what he wanted to hear; it appeared to both excite and relax him. Still he continued, as though it were a ritual: "Do you love me?"

She patted him. "Tend to your chores, Rusty. And when I'm ready, we'll go eat wherever you want."

"Chinatown?"

"But that doesn't mean sweet and sour spareribs. You know what the doctor said."

As he returned to his duties with a satisfied waddle, I couldn't resist reminding her that she hadn't answered his question. *"Do* you love him?"

"I told you: you can make yourself love anybody. Besides, he had a stinking childhood."

"If it was so stinking, why does he cling to it?"

"Use your head. Can't you see it's just that Rusty feels safer in diapers than he would in a skirt? Which is really the choice, only he's awfully touchy about it. He tried to stab me with a butter knife because I told him to grow up and face the issue, settle down and play house with a nice fatherly truck driver. Meantime, I've got him on my hands; which is okay, he's harmless, he thinks girls are dolls literally."

"Thank God."

"Well, if it were true of most men, I'd hardly be thanking God."

"I meant thank God you're not going to marry Mr. Trawler."

She lifted an eyebrow. "By the way, I'm not pretending I don't know he's rich. Even land in Mexico costs something. Now," she said, motioning me forward, "let's get hold of O.J."

I held back while my mind worked to win a postponement. Then I remembered: "Why *Traveling?*"

"On my card?" she said, disconcerted. "You think it's funny?"

"Not funny. Just provocative."

She shrugged. "After all, how do I know where I'll be living tomorrow? So I told them to put *Traveling.* Anyway, it was a waste of money, ordering those cards. Except I felt I owed it to them to buy some little *something.* They're from Tiffany's." She reached for my martini, I hadn't touched it; she drained it in two swallows, and took my hand. "Quit stalling. You're going to make friends with O.J."

An occurrence at the door intervened. It was a young woman, and she entered like a wind-rush, a squall of scarves and jangling gold. "H-H-Holly," she said, wagging a finger as she advanced, "you miserable h-h-hoarder. Hogging all these simply r-r-riveting m-m-men!"

She was well over six feet, taller than most men there. They straightened their spines, sucked in their stomachs; there was a general contest to match her swaying height.

Holly said, "What are you doing here?" and her lips were taut as drawn string.

"Why, n-n-nothing, sugar. I've been upstairs working with Yunioshi. Christmas stuff for the *Ba-ba-zaar.* But you sound vexed, sugar?" She scattered a roundabout smile. "You b-b-boys not vexed at me for butting in on your p-p-party?"

Rusty Trawler tittered. He squeezed her arm, as though to admire her muscle, and asked her if she could use a drink.

"I surely could," she said. "Make mine bourbon."

Holly told her, "There *isn't* any." Whereupon the Air Force colonel suggested he run out for a bottle.

"Oh, I declare, don't let's have a f-f-fuss. I'm happy with ammonia. Holly, honey," she said, slightly shoving her, "don't you bother about me. I can introduce myself." She stooped toward O. J. Berman, who, like many short men in the presence of tall women, had an aspiring mist in his eye. "I'm Mag W-w-wildwood, from Wild-w-w-wood, Arkansas. That's hill country."

It seemed a dance, Berman performing some fancy footwork to prevent his rivals cutting in. He lost her to a quadrille of partners who gobbled up her stammered jokes like popcorn tossed to pigeons. It was a comprehensible success. She was a triumph over ugliness, so often more beguiling than real beauty, if only because it contains paradox. In this case, as opposed to the scrupulous method of plain good taste and scientific grooming, the trick had been worked by exaggerating defects; she'd made them ornamental by admitting them boldly. Heels that emphasized her height, so steep her ankles trembled; a flat tight bodice that indicated she could go to a beach in bathing trunks; hair that was pulled straight back, accentuating the spareness, the starvation of her fashion-model face. Even the stutter, certainly genuine but still a bit laid on, had been turned to advantage. It was the master stroke, that stutter; for it contrived to make her banalities sound somehow original, and secondly, despite her tallness, her assurance, it served to inspire in male listeners a protective feeling. To illustrate: Berman had to be pounded on the back because she said, "Who can tell me w-w-where is the j-j-john?"; then, completing the cycle, he offered an arm to guide her himself.

"That," said Holly, "won't be necessary. She's been here before. She knows where it is." She was emptying ash trays, and after Mag Wildwood had left the room, she emptied another, then said, sighed rather: "It's really very sad." She paused long enough to calculate the number of inquiring expressions; it was sufficient. "And so mysterious. You'd think it would show more. But heaven knows, she *looks* healthy. So, well, *clean*. That's the extraordinary part. Wouldn't you," she asked with concern, but of no one in particular, "wouldn't you say she *looked* clean?"

Someone coughed, several swallowed. A Naval officer, who had been holding Mag Wildwood's drink, put it down.

"But then," said Holly, "I hear so many of these Southern girls have the same trouble." She shuddered delicately, and went to the kitchen for more ice.

Mag Wildwood couldn't understand it, the abrupt absence of warmth on her return; the conversations she began behaved like green logs, they fumed but would not fire. More unforgivably, people were leaving without taking her telephone number. The Air Force colonel decamped while her back was turned, and this was the straw too much: he'd asked her to dinner. Suddenly she was blind. And since gin to artifice bears the same relation as tears to mascara, her attractions at once dissembled. She took it out on everyone. She called her hostess a Hollywood degenerate. She invited a man in his fifties to fight. She told Berman, Hitler was right. She exhilarated Rusty Trawler by stiff-arming him into a corner. "You know what's going to happen to you?" she said, with no hint of a stutter. "I'm going to march you over to the zoo and feed you to the yak." He looked altogether willing, but she disappointed him by sliding to the floor, where she sat humming.

"You're a bore. Get up from there," Holly said, stretching on a pair of gloves. The remnants of the party were waiting at the door, and when the bore didn't budge Holly cast me an apologetic glance. "Be an angel, would you, Fred? Put her in a taxi. She lives at the Winslow."

"Don't. Live Barbizon. Regent 4-5700. Ask for Mag Wildwood."

"You *are* an angel, Fred."

They were gone. The prospect of steering an Amazon into a taxi obliterated whatever resentment I felt. But she solved the problem herself. Rising on her own steam, she stared down at me with a lurching loftiness. She said, "Let's go Stork. Catch lucky balloon," and fell full-length like an axed oak. My first thought was to run for a doctor. But examination proved her pulse fine and her breathing regular. She was simply asleep. After finding a pillow for her head, I left her to enjoy it.

The following afternoon I collided with Holly on the stairs. *"You"* she said, hurrying past with a package from the druggist. "There she is, on the verge of pneumonia. A hang-over out to here. And the mean reds on top of it." I gathered from this that Mag Wildwood was still in the apartment, but she gave me no chance to explore her surprising sympathy. Over the weekend, mystery deepened. First, there was the Latin who came to my door: mistakenly, for he was inquiring after Miss Wildwood. It took a while to correct his error, our accents seemed mutually incoherent, but by the time we had I was charmed. He'd been put together with care, his brown head and bullfighter's figure had an exactness, a perfection, like an apple, an orange, something nature has made just right. Added to this, as decoration, were an English suit and a brisk cologne and, what is still more unlatin, a bashful manner. The second event of the day involved him again. It was toward evening, and I saw him on my way out to dinner. He was arriving in a taxi; the driver helped him totter into the house with a load of suitcases. That gave me something to chew on: by Sunday my jaws were quite tired.

Then the picture became both darker and clearer.

Sunday was an Indian summer day, the sun was strong, my window was open, and I heard voices on the fire escape. Holly and Mag were sprawled there on a blanket, the cat between them. Their hair, newly washed, hung lankly. They were busy, Holly varnishing her toenails, Mag knitting on a sweater. Mag was speaking.

"If you ask me, I think you're l-l-lucky. At least there's one thing you can say for Rusty. He's an American."

"Bully for him."

"*Sugar*. There's a war on."

"And when it's over, you've seen the last of me, boy."

"I don't feel that way. I'm p-p-proud of my country. The men in my family were great soldiers. There's a statue of Papadaddy Wildwood smack in the center of Wildwood."

"Fred's a soldier," said Holly. "But I doubt if he'll ever be a statue. Could be. They say the more stupid you are the braver. He's pretty stupid."

"Fred's that boy upstairs? I didn't realize he was a soldier. But he *does* look stupid."

"Yearning. Not stupid. He wants awfully to be on the inside staring out: anybody with their nose pressed against a glass is liable to look stupid. Any how, he's a different Fred. Fred's my brother."

"You call your own f-f-flesh and b-b-blood stupid?"

"If he is he is."

"Well, it's poor taste to say so. A boy that's fighting for you and me and all of us."

"What is this: a bond rally?"

"I just want you to know where I stand. I appreciate a joke, but underneath I'm a s-s-serious person. Proud to be an American. That's why I'm sorry about José." She put down her knitting needles. "You *do* think he's terribly good-looking, don't you?" Holly said Hmn, and swiped the cat's whiskers with her lacquer brush. "If only I could get used to the idea of m-m-marrying a Brazilian. And *being* a B-b-brazilian myself. It's such a canyon to cross. Six thousand miles, and not knowing the language—"

"Go to Berlitz."

"Why on earth would they be teaching P-p-portuguese? It isn't as though anyone spoke it. No, my only chance is to try and make José forget politics and be-

come an American. It's such a useless thing for a man to
want to be: the p-p-president of *Brazil.*" She sighed and
picked up her knitting. "I must be madly in love. You
saw us together. Do you think I'm madly in love?"

"Well. Does he bite?"

Mag dropped a stitch. "Bite?"

"You. In bed."

"Why, no. *Should* he?" Then she added, cen-
soriously: "But he does laugh."

"Good. That's the right spirit. I like a man who
sees the humor; most of them, they're all pant and puff."

Mag withdrew her complaint; she accepted the comment as flattery reflecting on herself. "Yes. I suppose."

"Okay. He doesn't bite. He laughs. What else?"

Mag counted up her dropped stitch and began
again, knit, purl, purl.

"I said—"

"I heard you. And it isn't that I don't want to tell
you. But it's so difficult to remember. I don't d-d-dwell
on these things. The way you seem to. They go out of
my head like a dream. I'm sure that's the n-n-normal
attitude."

"It may be normal, darling; but I'd rather be natural." Holly paused in the process of reddening the rest
of the cat's whiskers. "Listen. If you can't remember, try
leaving the lights on."

"Please understand me, Holly. I'm a very-very-
very *conventional* person."

"Oh, balls. What's wrong with a decent look at a
guy you like? Men are beautiful, a lot of them are, José
is, and if you don't even want to *look* at him, well, I'd
say he's getting a pretty cold plate of macaroni."

"L-l-lower your voice."

"You can't possibly be in love with him. Now. Does
that answer your question?"

"No. Because I'm not a cold plate of m-m-maca-
roni. I'm a warm-hearted person. It's the basis of my
character."

"Okay. You've got a warm heart. But if I were a

man on my way to bed, I'd rather take along a hot-water bottle. It's more tangible."

"You won't hear any squawks out of José," she said complacently, her needles flashing in the sunlight. "What's more, I *am* in love with him. Do you realize I've knitted ten pairs of Argyles in less than three months? And this is the second sweater." She stretched the sweater and tossed it aside. "What's the point, though? Sweaters in Brazil. I ought to be making s-s-sun helmets."

Holly lay back and yawned. "It must be winter sometime."

"It *rains,* that I know. Heat. Rain. J-j-jungles."

"Heat. Jungles. Actually, I'd like that."

"Better you than me."

"Yes," said Holly, with a sleepiness that was not sleepy. "Better me than you."

On Monday, when I went down for the morning mail, the card on Holly's box had been altered, a name added: Miss Golightly and Miss Wildwood were now traveling together. This might have held my interest longer except for a letter in my own mailbox. It was from a small university review to whom I'd sent a story. They liked it; and, though I must understand they could not afford to pay, they intended to publish. Publish: that meant *print.* Dizzy with excitement is no mere phrase. I had to tell someone: and, taking the stairs two at a time, I pounded on Holly's door.

I didn't trust my voice to tell the news; as soon as she came to the door, her eyes squinty with sleep, I thrust the letter at her. It seemed as though she'd had time to read sixty pages before she handed it back. "I wouldn't let them do it, not if they don't pay you," she said, yawning. Perhaps my face explained she'd mis-construed, that I'd not wanted advice but congratulations: her mouth shifted from a yawn into a smile. "Oh, I see. It's wonderful. Well, come in," she said. "We'll make a pot of coffee and celebrate. No. I'll get dressed and take you to lunch."

Her bedroom was consistent with her parlor: it perpetuated the same camping-out atmosphere; crates and suitcases, everything packed and ready to go, like the belongings of a criminal who feels the law not far behind. In the parlor there was no conventional furniture, but the bedroom had the bed itself, a double one at that, and quite flashy: blond wood, tufted satin.

She left the door of the bathroom open, and conversed from there; between the flushing and the brushing, most of what she said was unintelligible, but the gist of it was: she *supposed* I knew Mag Wildwood had moved in, and wasn't that *convenient?* because if you're going to *have* a roommate, and she *isn't* a dyke, then the next best thing is a *perfect* fool, which Mag *was,* because then you can dump the lease on them *and* send them out for the laundry.

One could see that Holly had a laundry problem; the room was strewn, like a girl's gymnasium.

"—and you know, she's quite a successful model: isn't that *fan*tastic? But a good thing," she said, hobbling out of the bathroom as she adjusted a garter. "It ought to keep her out of my hair most of the day. And there shouldn't be too much trouble on the man front. She's engaged. Nice guy, too. Though there's a tiny difference in height: I'd say a foot, her favor. Where the hell—" She was on her knees poking under the bed. After she'd found what she was looking for, a pair of lizard shoes, she had to search for a blouse, a belt, and it was a subject to ponder, how, from such wreckage, she evolved the eventual effect: pampered, calmly immaculate, as though she'd been attended by Cleopatra's maids. She said, "Listen," and cupped her hand under my chin, "I'm glad about the story. Really I am."

That Monday in October, 1943. A beautiful day with the buoyancy of a bird. To start, we had Manhattans at Joe Bell's; and, when he heard of my good luck, champagne cocktails on the house. Later, we wandered toward Fifth Avenue, where there was a parade. The flags in the wind, the thump of military bands and military feet, seemed to have nothing to do with war, but to be, rather, a fanfare arranged in my personal honor.

We ate lunch at the cafeteria in the park. Afterwards, avoiding the zoo (Holly said she couldn't bear to see anything in a cage), we giggled, ran, sang along the paths toward the old wooden boathouse, now gone. Leaves floated on the lake; on the shore, a park-man was fanning a bonfire of them, and the smoke, rising like Indian signals, was the only smudge on the quivering air. Aprils have never meant much to me, autumns seem that season of beginning, spring; which is how I felt sitting with Holly on the railings of the boathouse porch. I thought of the future, and spoke of the past. Because Holly wanted to know about my childhood. She talked of her own, too; but it was elusive, nameless, placeless, an impressionistic recital, though the impression received was contrary to what one expected, for she gave an almost voluptuous account of swimming and summer, Christmas trees, pretty cousins and parties: in short, happy in a way that she was not, and never, certainly, the background of a child who had run away.

Or, I asked, wasn't it true that she'd been out on her own since she was fourteen? She rubbed her nose. "That's true. The other isn't. But really, darling, you made such a tragedy out of *your* childhood I didn't feel I should compete."

She hopped off the railing. "Anyway, it reminds me: I ought to send Fred some peanut butter." The rest of the afternoon we were east and west worming out of reluctant grocers cans of peanut butter, a wartime scarcity; dark came before we'd rounded up a half-dozen jars, the last at a delicatessen on Third Avenue. It was near the antique shop with the palace of a bird cage in its window, so I took her there to see it, and she enjoyed the point, its fantasy: "But still, it's a cage."

Passing a Woolworth's, she gripped my arm: "Let's

steal something," she said, pulling me into the store, where at once there seemed a pressure of eyes, as though we were already under suspicion. "Come on. Don't be chicken." She scouted a counter piled with paper pumpkins and Halloween masks. The saleslady was occupied with a group of nuns who were trying on masks. Holly picked up a mask and slipped it over her face; she chose another and put it on mine; then she took my hand and we walked away. It was as simple as that. Outside, we ran a few blocks, I think to make it more dramatic; but also because, as I'd discovered, successful theft exhilarates. I wondered if she'd often stolen. "I used to," she said. "I mean I had to. If I wanted anything. But I still do it every now and then, sort of to keep my hand in."

We wore the masks all the way home.

I have a memory of spending many hither and yonning days with Holly; and it's true, we did at odd moments see a great deal of each other; but on the whole, the memory is false. Because toward the end of the month I found a job: what is there to add? The less the better, except to say it was necessary and lasted from nine to five. Which made our hours, Holly's and mine, extremely different.

Unless it was Thursday, her Sing Sing day, or unless she'd gone horseback riding in the park, as she did occasionally, Holly was hardly up when I came home. sometimes, stopping there, I shared her wake-up coffee while she dressed for the evening. She was forever on her way out, not always with Rusty Trawler, but usually, and usually, too, they were joined by Mag Wildwood and the handsome Brazilian, whose name was José Ybarra-Jaegar: his mother was German. As a quartet, they struck an unmusical note, primarily the fault of Ybarra-Jaegar, who seemed as out of place in their company as a violin in a jazz band. He was intelligent, he was presentable, he appeared to have a serious link with his work, which was obscurely governmental, vaguely important, and took him to Washington several days a week. How, then, could he survive night after night in La Rue, El Morocco, listening to the Wildwood ch-ch-chatter and staring into Rusty's raw baby-buttocks face? Perhaps, like most of us in a foreign country, he was incapable of placing people, selecting a frame for their picture, as he would at home; therefore all Americans had to be judged in a pretty equal light, and on this basis his companions appeared to be tolerable examples of local color and national character. That would explain much; Holly's determination explains the rest.

Late one afternoon, while waiting for a Fifth Avenue bus, I noticed a taxi stop across the street to let out a girl who ran up the steps of the Forty-second Street public library. She was through the doors before I recognized her, which was pardonable, for Holly and libraries were not an easy association to make. I let curiosity guide me between the lions, debating on the way whether I should admit following her or pretend coincidence. In the end I did neither, but concealed myself some tables away from her in the general reading room, where she sat behind her dark glasses and a fortress of literature she'd gathered at the desk. She sped from one book to the next, intermittently lingering on a page, always with a frown, as if it were printed upside down. She had a pencil poised above paper—nothing seemed to catch her fancy, still now and then, as though for the hell of it, she made laborious scribblings. Watching her, I remembered a girl I'd known in school, a grind, Mildred Grossman. Mildred: with her moist hair and greasy spectacles, her stained fingers that dissected frogs and carried coffee to picket lines, her flat eyes that only turned toward the stars to estimate their chemical tonnage. Earth and air could not be more opposite than Mildred and Holly, yet in my head they acquired a Siamese twinship, and the thread of thought that had sewn them together ran like this: the average personality reshapes frequently, every few years even our bodies undergo a complete overhaul —desirable or not, it is a natural thing that we should change. All right, here were two people who never would.

That is what Mildred Grossman had in common with Holly Golightly. They would never change because they'd been given their character too soon; which, like sudden riches, leads to a lack of proportion: the one had splurged herself into a top-heavy realist, the other a lop-sided romantic. I imagined them in a restaurant of the future, Mildred still studying the menu for its nutritional values, Holly still gluttonous for everything on it. It would never be different. They would walk through life and out of it with the same determined step that took small notice of those cliffs at the left. Such profound observations made me forget where I was; I came to, startled to find myself in the gloom of the library, and surprised all over again to see Holly there. It was after seven, she was freshening her lipstick and perking up her appearance from what she deemed correct for a library to what, by adding a bit of scarf, some earrings, she considered suitable for the Colony. When she'd left, I wandered over to the table where her books remained; they were what I had wanted to see. *South by Thunderbird Byways of Brazil. The Political Mind of Latin America.* And so forth.

On Christmas Eve she and Mag gave a party. Holly asked me to come early and help trim the tree. I'm still not sure how they maneuvered that tree into the apartment. The top branches were crushed against the ceiling, the lower ones spread wall-to-wall; altogether it was not unlike the yuletide giant we see in Rockefeller Plaza. Moreover, it would have taken a Rockefeller to decorate it, for it soaked up baubles and tinsel like melting snow. Holly suggested she run out to Woolworth's and steal some balloons; she did: and they turned the tree into a fairly good show. We made a toast to our work, and Holly said: "Look in the bedroom. There's a present for you."

I had one for her, too: a small package in my pocket that felt even smaller when I saw, square on the bed and wrapped with a red ribbon, the beautiful bird cage.

"But, Holly! It's dreadful!"

"I couldn't agree more; but I thought you wanted it."

"The money! Three hundred and fifty dollars!"

She shrugged. "A few extra trips to the powder room. Promise me, though. Promise you'll never put a living thing in it."

I started to kiss her, but she held out her hand. "Gimme," she said, tapping the bulge in my pocket.

"I'm afraid it isn't much," and it wasn't: a St. Christopher's medal. But at least it came from Tiffany's.

Holly was not a girl who could keep anything, and surely by now she has lost that medal, left it in a suitcase or some hotel drawer. But the bird case is still mine. I've lugged it to New Orleans, Nantucket, all over Europe, Morocco, the West Indies. Yet I seldom remember that it was Holly who gave it to me, because at one point I chose to forget: we had a big falling-out, and among the objects rotating in the eye of our hurricane were the bird cage and O. J. Berman and my story, a copy of which I'd given Holly when it appeared in the university review.

Sometime in February, Holly had gone on a winter trip with Rusty, Mag and José Ybarra-Jaeger. Our altercation happened soon after she returned. She was brown as iodine, her hair was sun-bleached to a ghost-color, she'd had a wonderful time: "Well, first of all we were in Key West, and Rusty got mad at some sailors, or vice versa, *any*way he'll have to wear a spine brace the rest of his life. Dearest Mag ended up in the hospital, too. First-degree sunburn. Disgusting: all blisters and citronella. We couldn't stand the smell of her. So José and I left them in the hospital and went to Havana. He says wait till I see Rio; but as far as I'm concerned Havana can take my money right now. We had an irresistible guide, most of him Negro and the rest of him Chinese, and while I don't go much for one or the other, the combination was fairly riveting: so I let him play kneesie under the table, because frankly I didn't find him at all banal; but then one night he took us to a blue movie, and what do you suppose? There *he* was *on* the screen. Of course when we got back to Key West, Mag was positive I'd spent the whole time sleeping with José. So was Rusty: but he doesn't care about that, he simply wants to hear the details. Actually, things were pretty tense until I had a heart-to-heart with Mag."

We were in the front room, where, though it was now nearly March, the enormous Christmas tree, turned brown and scentless, its balloons shriveled as an old cow's dugs, still occupied most of the space. A recognizable piece of furniture had been added to the room: an army cot; and Holly, trying to preserve her tropic look, was sprawled on it under a sun lamp.

"And you convinced her?"

"That I hadn't slept with José? God, yes. I simply told—but you know: made it sound like an agonized confession—simply told her I was a dyke."

"She couldn't have believed that."

"The hell she didn't. Why do you think she went out and bought this army cot? Leave it to me: I'm always top banana in the shock department. Be a darling, darling, rub some oil on my back." While I was performing this service, she said: "O. J. Berman's in town, and listen, I gave him your story in the magazine. He was quite impressed. He thinks maybe you're worth helping. But he says you're on the wrong track. Negroes and children: who cares?"

"Not Mr. Berman, I gather."

"Well, I agree with him. I read that story twice. Brats and niggers. Trembling leaves. *Description.* It doesn't *mean* anything."

My hand, smoothing oil on her skin, seemed to have a temper of its own: it yearned to raise itself and come down on her buttocks. "Give me an example," I said quietly. "Of something that means something. In your opinion."

"*Wuthering Heights,*" she said, without hesitation.

The urge in my hand was growing beyond control. "But that's unreasonable. You're talking about a work of genius."

"It was, wasn't it? *My wild sweet Cathy.* God, I cried buckets. I saw it ten times."

I said, "Oh" with recognizable relief, "oh" with a shameful, rising inflection, "the *movie.*"

Her muscles hardened, the touch of her was like stone warmed by the sun. "Everybody has to feel superior to somebody," she said. "But it's customary to present a little proof before you take the privilege."

"I don't compare myself to you. Or Berman. Therefore I can't feel superior. We want different things."

"Don't you want to make money?"

"I haven't planned that far."

"That's how your stories sound. As though you'd written them without knowing the end. Well, I'll tell you: you'd better make money. You have an expensive imagination. Not many people are going to buy you bird cages."

"Sorry."

"You will be if you hit me. You wanted to a minute ago: I could feel it in your hand; and you want to now."

I did, terribly; my hand, my heart was shaking as I recapped the bottle of oil. "Oh no, I wouldn't regret that. I'm only sorry you wasted your money on me: Rusty Trawler is too hard a way of earning it."

She sat up on the army cot, her face, her naked breasts coldly blue in the sun-lamp light. "It should take you about four seconds to walk from here to the door. I'll give you two."

I went straight upstairs, got the bird cage, took it down and left it in front of her door. That settled that. Or so I imagined until the next morning when, as I was leaving for work, I saw the cage perched on a sidewalk ashcan waiting for the garbage collector. Rather sheepishly, I rescued it and carried it back to my room, a capitulation that did not lessen my resolve to put Holly Golightly absolutely out of my life. She was, I decided, "a crude exhibitionist," "a time waster," "an utter fake": someone never to be spoken to again.

And I didn't. Not for a long while. We passed each other on the stairs with lowered eyes. If she walked into Joe Bell's, I walked out. At one point, Madame Sapphia Spanella, the coloratura and roller-skating enthusiast who lived on the first floor, circulated a petition among the brownstone's other tenants asking them to join her in having Miss Golightly evicted: she was, said Madame Spanella, "morally objectionable" and the "perpetrator of all-night gatherings that endanger the safety and sanity of her neighbors." Though I refused to sign, secretly I felt Madame Spanella had cause to complain. But her petition failed, and as April approached May, the open-windowed, warm spring nights were lurid with the party sounds, the loud-playing phonograph and martini laughter that emanated from Apt. 2.

It was no novelty to encounter suspicious specimens among Holly's callers, quite the contrary; but one day late that spring, while passing through the brownstone's vestibule, I noticed a *very* provocative man examining her mailbox. A person in his early fifties with a hard, weathered face, gray forlorn eyes. He wore an old sweat-stained gray hat, and his cheap summer suit, a pale blue, hung too loosely on his lanky frame; his shoes were brown and brand-new. He seemed to have no intention of ringing Holly's bell. Slowly, as though he were reading Braille, he kept rubbing a finger across the embossed lettering of her name.

That evening, on my way to supper, I saw the man again. He was standing across the street, leaning against a tree and staring up at Holly's windows. Sinister speculations rushed through my head. Was he a detective? Or some underworld agent connected with her Sing Sing friend, Sally Tomato? The situation revived my tenderer feelings for Holly; it was only fair to interrupt our feud long enough to warn her that she was being watched.

As I walked to the corner, heading east toward the Hamburg Heaven at Seventy-ninth and Madison, I could feel the man's attention focused on me. Presently, without turning my head, I knew that he was following me. Because I could hear him whistling. Not any ordinary tune, but the plaintive, prairie melody Holly sometimes played on her guitar: *Don't wanna sleep, don't wanna die, just wanna go a-travelin' through the pastures of the sky*. The whistling continued across Park Avenue and up Madison. Once, while waiting for a traffic light to change, I watched him out of the corner of my eye as he stooped to pet a sleazy Pomeranian. "That's a fine animal you got there," he told the owner in a hoarse, countrified drawl.

Hamburg Heaven was empty. Nevertheless, he took a seat right beside me at the long counter. He smelled of tobacco and sweat. He ordered a cup of coffee, but when it came he didn't touch it. Instead, he chewed on a toothpick and studied me in the wall mirror facing us.

"Excuse me," I said, speaking to him via the mirror, "but what do you want?"

The question didn't embarrass him; he seemed relieved to have had it asked. "Son," he said, "I need a friend."

He brought out a wallet. It was as worn as his leathery hands, almost falling to pieces; and so was the brittle, cracked, blurred snapshot he handed me. There were seven people in the picture, all grouped together on the sagging porch of a stark wooden house, and all children, except for the man himself, who had his arm around the waist of a plump blond little girl with a hand shading her eyes against the sun.

"That's me," he said, pointing at himself. "That's her . . ." he tapped the plump girl. "And this one over here," he added, indicating a tow-headed beanpole, "that's her brother, Fred."

I looked at "her" again: and yes, now I could see it, an embryonic resemblance to Holly in the squinting, fat-cheeked child. At the same moment, I realized who the man must be.

"You're Holly's *father*."

He blinked, he frowned. "Her name's not Holly. She was a Lulamae Barnes. Was," he said, shifting the toothpick in his mouth, "till she married me. I'm her husband. Doc Golightly. I'm a horse doctor, animal man. Do some farming, too. Near Tulip, Texas. Son, why are you laughin'?"

It wasn't real laughter: it was nerves. I took a swallow of water and choked; he pounded me on the back. "This here's no humorous matter, son. I'm a tired man. I've been five years lookin' for my woman. Soon as I got that letter from Fred, saying where she was, I bought myself a ticket on the Greyhound. Lulamae belongs home with her husband and her churren."

"Children?"

"Them's her churren," he said, almost shouted. He meant the four other young faces in the picture, two barefooted girls and a pair of overalled boys. Well, of course: the man was deranged. "But Holly can't be the mother of those children. They're older than she is. Bigger."

"Now, son," he said in a reasoning voice, "I didn't claim they was her natural-born children. Their own precious mother, precious woman, Jesus rest her soul, she passed away July 4th, Independence Day, 1936. The year of the drought. When I married Lulamae, that was in December, 1938, she was going on fourteen. Maybe an ordinary person, being only fourteen, wouldn't know their right mind. But you take Lulamae, she was an exceptional woman. She knew good-and-well what she was doing when she promised to be my wife and the mother of my churren. She plain broke our hearts when she ran off like she done." He sipped his cold coffee, and glanced at me with a searching earnestness. "Now, son, do you doubt me? Do you believe what I'm saying is so?"

I did. It was too implausible not to be fact; moreover, it dovetailed with O. J. Berman's description of the Holly he'd first encountered in California: "You don't know whether she's a hillbilly or an Okie or what." Berman couldn't be blamed for not guessing that she was a child-wife from Tulip, Texas.

"Plain broke our hearts when she ran off like she done," the horse doctor repeated. "She had no cause. All the housework was done by her daughters. Lulamae could just take it easy: fuss in front of mirrors and wash her hair. Our own cows, our own garden, chickens, pigs: son, that woman got positively fat. While her brother growed into a giant. Which is a sight different from how they come to us. 'Twas Nellie, my oldest girl, 'twas Nellie brought 'em into the house. She come to me one morning, and said: 'Papa, I got two wild yunguns locked in the kitchen. I caught 'em outside stealing milk and turkey eggs.' That was Lulamae and Fred. Well, you never saw a more pitiful something. Ribs sticking out everywhere, legs so puny they can't hardly stand, teeth wobbling so bad they can't chew mush. Story was: their mother died of the TB, and their papa done the same— and all the churren, a whole raft of 'em, they been sent off to live with different mean people. Now Lulamae and her brother, them two been living with some mean, no-count people a hundred miles east of Tulip. She had good cause to run off from that house. She didn't have none to leave mine. 'Twas her home." He leaned his elbows on the counter and, pressing his closed eyes with his fingertips, sighed. "She plumped out to be a real pretty woman. Lively, too. Talky as a jaybird. With something smart to say on every subject: better than the radio. First thing you know, I'm out picking flowers. I tamed her a crow and taught it to say her name. I showed her how to play the guitar. Just to look at her made the tears spring to my eyes. The night I proposed, I cried like a baby. She said: 'What you want to cry for, Doc? 'Course we'll be married. I've never been married before.' Well, I had to laugh, hug and squeeze her:

never been married before!" He chuckled, chewed on his toothpick a moment. "Don't tell me that woman wasn't happy!" he said, challengingly. "We all doted on her. She didn't have to lift a finger, 'cept to eat a piece of pie. 'Cept to comb her hair and send away for all the magazines. We must've had a hunnerd dollars' worth of magazines come into that house. Ask me, that's what done it. Looking at show-off pictures. Reading dreams. That's what started her walking down the road. Every day she'd walk a little further: a mile, and come home. Two miles, and come home. One day she just kept on." He put his hands over his eyes again; his breathing made a ragged noise. "The crow I give her went wild and flew away. All summer you could hear him. In the yard. In the garden. In the woods. All summer that damned bird was calling: Lulamae, Lulamae."

He stayed hunched over and silent, as though listening to the long-ago summer sound. I carried our checks to the cashier. While I was paying, he joined me. We left together and walked over to Park Avenue. It was a cool, blowy evening; swanky awnings flapped in the breeze. The quietness between us continued until I said: "But what about her brother? He didn't leave?"

"No, sir," he said, clearing his throat. "Fred was with us right till they took him in the Army. A fine boy. Fine with horses. He didn't know what got into Lulamae, how come she left her brother and husband and churren. After he was in the Army, though, Fred started hearing from her. The other day he wrote me her address. So I come to get her. I know she's sorry for what she done. I know she wants to go home." He seemed to be asking me to agree with him. I told him that I thought he'd find Holly, or Lulamae, somewhat changed. "Listen, son," he said, as we reached the steps of the brownstone, "I advised you I need a friend. Because I don't want to surprise her. Scare her none. That's why I've held off. Be my friend: let her know I'm here."

The notion of introducing Mrs. Golightly to her husband had its satisfying aspects; and, glancing up at her lighted windows, I hoped her friends were there, for the prospect of watching the Texan shake hands with Mag and Rusty and José was more satisfying still. But Doc Golightly's proud earnest eyes and sweat-stained hat made me ashamed of such anticipations. He followed me into the house and prepared to wait at the bottom of the stairs. "Do I look nice?" he whispered, brushing his sleeves, tightening the knot of his tie.

Holly was alone. She answered the door at once; in fact, she was on her way out—white satin dancing pumps and quantities of perfume announced gala intentions. "Well, idiot," she said, and playfully slapped me with her purse. "I'm in too much of a hurry to make up now. We'll smoke the pipe tomorrow, okay?"

"Sure, Lulamae. If you're still around tomorrow."

She took off her dark glasses and squinted at me. It was as though her eyes were shattered prisms, the dots of blue and gray and green like broken bits of sparkle. *"He* told you that," she said in a small, shivering voice. "Oh, please. *Where* is he?" She ran past me into the hall. "Fred!" she called down the stairs. "Fred! Where are you, darling?"

I could hear Doc Golightly's footsteps climbing the stairs. His head appeared above the banisters, and Holly backed away from him, not as though she were frightened, but as though she were retreating into a shell of disappointment. Then he was standing in front of her, hangdog and shy. "Gosh, Lulamae," he began, and hesitated, for Holly was gazing at him vacantly, as though she couldn't place him. "Gee, honey," he said, "don't they feed you up here? You're so skinny. Like when I first saw you. All wild around the eye."

Holly touched his face; her fingers tested the reality of his chin, his beard stubble. "Hello, Doc," she said gently, and kissed him on the cheek. "Hello, Doc," she repeated happily, as he lifted her off her feet in a rib-crushing grip. Whoops of relieved laughter shook him. "Gosh, Lulamae. Kingdom come."

Neither of them noticed me when I squeezed past

them and went up to my room. Nor did they seem aware
of Madame Sapphia Spanella, who opened her door and
yelled: "Shut up! It's a disgrace. Do your whoring elsewhere."

"*Divorce* him? Of course I never divorced him. I
was only fourteen, for God's sake. It couldn't have been
legal." Holly tapped an empty martini glass. "Two more,
my darling Mr. Bell."

Joe Bell, in whose bar we were sitting, accepted the
order reluctantly. "You're rockin' the boat kinda early,"
he complained, crunching on a Tums. It was not yet
noon, according to the black mahogany clock behind the
bar, and he'd already served us three rounds.

"But it's Sunday, Mr. Bell. Clocks are slow on Sundays. Besides, I haven't been to bed yet," she told him,
and confided to me: "Not to sleep." She blushed, and
glanced away guiltily. For the first time since I'd known
her, she seemed to feel a need to justify herself: "Well,
I had to. Doc really loves me, you know. And I love him.
He may have looked old and tacky to *you*. But you don't
know the sweetness of him, the confidence he can give
to birds and brats and fragile things like that. Anyone
who ever gave you confidence, you owe them a lot. I've
always remembered Doc in my prayers. Please stop
smirking!" she demanded, stabbing out a cigarette. "I
do say my prayers."

"I'm not smirking. I'm smiling. You're the most
amazing person."

"I suppose I am," she said, and her face, wan, rather
bruised-looking in the morning light, brightened; she
smoothed her tousled hair, and the colors of it glim-
mered like a shampoo advertisement. "I must look fierce.
But who wouldn't? We spent the rest of the night roaming around in a bus station. Right up till the last minute
Doc thought I was going to go with him. Even though I
kept telling him: But, Doc, I'm not fourteen any more,
and I'm not Lulamae. But the terrible part is (and I realized it while we were standing there) I am. I'm still

stealing turkey eggs and running through a brier patch. Only now I call it having the mean reds."

Joe Bell disdainfully settled the fresh martinis in front of us.

"Never love a wild thing, Mr. Bell," Holly advised him. "That was Doc's mistake. He was always lugging home wild things. A hawk with a hurt wing. One time it was a full-grown bobcat with a broken leg. But you can't give your heart to a wild thing: the more you do, the stronger they get. Until they're strong enough to run into the woods. Or fly into a tree. Then a taller tree. Then the sky. That's how you'll end up, Mr. Bell. If you let yourself love a wild thing. You'll end up looking at the sky."

"She's drunk," Joe Bell informed me.

"Moderately," Holly confessed. "But Doc knew what I meant. I explained it to him very carefully, and it was something he could understand. We shook hands and held on to each other and he wished me luck." She glanced at the clock. "He must be in the Blue Mountains by now."

"What's she talkin' about?" Joe Bell asked me.

Holly lifted her martini. "Let's wish the Doc luck, too," she said, touching her glass against mine. "Good luck: and believe me, dearest Doc—it's better to look at the sky than live there. Such an empty place; so vague. Just a country where the thunder goes and things disappear."

TRAWLER MARRIES FOURTH. I was on a subway somewhere in Brooklyn when I saw that headline. The paper that bannered it belonged to another passenger. The only part of the text that I could see read: *Rutherfurd "Rusty" Trawler, the millionaire playboy often accused of pro-Nazi sympathies, eloped to Greenwich yesterday with a beautiful*— Not that I wanted to read any more. Holly had married him: well, well. I wished I were under the wheels of the train. But I'd been wishing that before I spotted the headline. For a headful of reasons. I hadn't seen Holly, not really, since our drunken Sunday at Joe Bell's bar. The intervening weeks had given me my own case of the mean reds. First off, I'd been fired from my job: deservedly, and for an amusing misdemeanor too complicated to recount here. Also, my draft board was displaying an uncomfortable interest; and, having so recently escaped the regimentation of a small town, the idea of entering another form of disciplined life made me desperate. Between the uncertainty of my draft status and a lack of specific experience, I couldn't seem to find another job. That was what I was doing on a subway in Brooklyn: returning from a discouraging interview with an editor of the now defunct newspaper, *PM*. All this, combined with the city heat of the summer, had reduced me to a state of nervous inertia. So I more than half meant it when I wished I were under the wheels of the train. The headline made the desire quite positive. If Holly could marry that "absurd foetus," then the army of wrongness rampant in the world might as well march over me. Or, and the question is apparent, was my outrage a little the result of being in love with Holly myself? A little. For I *was* in love with her. Just as I'd once been in love with my mother's elderly colored cook and a postman who let me follow him on his rounds and a whole family named McKendrick. That category of love generates jealousy, too.

When I reached my station I bought a paper; and, reading the tail-end of that sentence, discovered that Rusty's bride was: *a beautiful cover girl from the Arkansas hills, Miss Margaret Thatcher Fitzhue Wildwood.* Mag! My legs went so limp with relief I took a taxi the rest of the way home.

Madame Sapphia Spanella met me in the hall, wild-eyed and wringing her hands. "Run," she said. "Bring the police. She is killing somebody! Somebody is killing her!"

It sounded like it. As though tigers were loose in Holly's apartment. A riot of crashing glass, of rippings and fallings and overturned furniture. But there were no quarreling voices inside the uproar, which made it seem unnatural. "Run," shrieked Madame Spanella, pushing me. "Tell the police murder!"

I ran; but only upstairs to Holly's door. Pounding on it had one result: the racket subsided. Stopped altogether. But pleadings to let me in went unanswered, and my efforts to break down the door merely culminated in a bruised shoulder. Then below I heard Madame Spanella commanding some newcomer to go for the police. "Shut up," she was told, "and get out of my way."

It was José Ybarra-Jaegar. Looking not at all the smart Brazilian diplomat; but sweaty and frightened. He ordered me out of his way, too. And, using his own key, opened the door. "In here, Dr. Goldman," he said, beckoning to a man accompanying him.

Since no one prevented me, I followed them into the apartment, which was tremendously wrecked. At last the Christmas tree had been dismantled, very literally: its brown dry branches sprawled in a welter of torn-up books, broken lamps and phonograph records. Even the icebox had been emptied, its contents tossed around the room: raw eggs were sliding down the walls, and in the midst of the debris Holly's no-name cat was calmly licking a puddle of milk.

In the bedroom, the smell of smashed perfume bottles made me gag. I stepped on Holly's dark glasses; they were lying on the floor, the lenses already shattered, the frames cracked in half.

Perhaps that is why Holly, a rigid figure on the bed, stared at José so blindly, seemed not to see the doctor, who, testing her pulse, crooned: "You're a tired young lady. Very tired. You want to go to sleep, don't you? Sleep."

Holly rubbed her forehead, leaving a smear of blood from a cut finger. "Sleep," she said, and whimpered like an exhausted, fretful child. "He's the only one would ever let me. Let me hug him on cold nights. I saw a place in Mexico. With horses. By the sea."

"With horses by the sea," lullabied the doctor, selecting from his black case a hypodermic.

José averted his face, queasy at the sight of a needle. "Her sickness is only grief?" he asked, his difficult English lending the question an unintended irony. "She is grieving only?"

"Didn't hurt a bit, now did it?" inquired the doctor, smugly dabbing Holly's arm with a scrap of cotton.

She came to sufficiently to focus the doctor. "*Everything* hurts. Where are my glasses?" But she didn't need them. Her eyes were closing of their own accord.

"She is only grieving?" insisted José.

"Please, sir," the doctor was quite short with him, "if you will leave me alone with the patient."

José withdrew to the front room, where he released his temper on the snooping, tiptoeing presence of Madame Spanella. "Don't touch me! I'll call the police," she threatened as he whipped her to the door with Portuguese oaths.

He considered throwing me out, too; or so I surmised from his expression. Instead, he invited me to have a drink. The only unbroken bottle we could find contained dry vermouth. "I have a worry," he confided. "I have a worry that this should cause scandal. Her crashing everything. Conducting like a crazy. I must have no public scandal. It is too delicate: my name, my work."

He seemed cheered to learn that I saw no reason for a "scandal"; demolishing one's own possessions was, presumably, a private affair.

"It is only a question of grieving," he firmly declared. "When the sadness came, first she throws the drink she is drinking. The bottle. Those books. A lamp. Then I am scared. I hurry to bring a doctor."

"But why?" I wanted to know. "Why should she have a fit over Rusty? If I were her, I'd celebrate."

"Rusty?"

I was still carrying my newspaper, and showed him the headline.

"Oh, that." He grinned rather scornfully. "They do us a grand favor, Rusty and Mag. We laugh over it: how they think they break our hearts when all the time we *want* them to run away. I assure you, we were laughing when the sadness came." His eyes searched the litter on the floor; he picked up a ball of yellow paper. "This," he said.

It was a telegram from Tulip, Texas: *Received notice young Fred killed in action overseas stop your husband and children join in the sorrow of our mutual loss stop letter follows love Doc.*

Holly never mentioned her brother again: except once. Moreover, she stopped calling me Fred. June, July, all through the warm months she hibernated like a winter animal who did not know spring had come and gone. Her hair darkened, she put on weight. She became rather careless about her clothes: used to rush round to the delicatessen wearing a rain-slicker and nothing underneath. José moved into the apartment, his name replacing Mag Wildwood's on the mailbox. Still, Holly was a good deal alone, for José stayed in Washington three days a week. During his absences she entertained no one and seldom left the apartment—except on Thursdays, when she made her weekly trip to Ossining.

Which is not to imply that she had lost interest in life; far from it, she seemed more content, altogether happier than I'd ever seen her. A keen sudden un-Holly-like enthusiasm for homemaking resulted in several un-Holly-like purchases: at a Parke-Bernet auction she acquired a stag-at-bay hunting tapestry and, from the William Randolph Hearst estate, a gloomy pair of Gothic "easy" chairs; she bought the complete Modern Library, shelves of classical records, innumerable Metropolitan Museum reproductions (including a statue of a Chinese cat that her own cat hated and hissed at and ultimately broke), a Waring mixer and a pressure cooker and a library of cook books. She spent whole hausfrau afternoons slopping about in the sweatbox of her midget kitchen: "José says I'm better than the Colony. Really, who would have dreamed I had such a great natural talent? A month ago I couldn't scramble eggs." And still couldn't, for that matter. Simple dishes, steak, a proper salad, were beyond her. Instead, she fed José, and occasionally myself, *outré* soups (brandied black terrapin poured into avocado shells) Nero-ish novelties (roasted pheasant stuffed with pomegranates and persimmons) and other dubious innovations (chicken and saffron rice served with a chocolate sauce: "An East Indian classic, *my* dear"). Wartime sugar and cream rationing restricted her imagination when it came to sweets—nevertheless, she once managed something called Tobacco Tapioca: best not describe it.

Nor describe her attempts to master Portuguese, an ordeal as tedious to me as it was to her, for whenever I visited her an album of Linguaphone records never ceased rotating on the phonograph. Now, too, she rarely spoke a sentence that did not begin, "After we're married—" or "When we move to Rio—" Yet José had never suggested marriage. She admitted it. "But, after all, he *knows* I'm preggers. Well, I am, darling. Six weeks gone. I don't see why *that* should surprise you. It didn't me. Not *un peu* bit. I'm delighted. I want to have at least nine. I'm sure some of them will be rather dark —José has a touch of *le nègre,* I suppose you guessed that? Which is fine by me: what could be prettier than a quite coony baby with bright green beautiful eyes? I wish, please don't laugh—but I wish I'd been a virgin for him, for José. Not that I've warmed the multitudes some people say: I don't blame the bastards for *saying* it, I've always thrown out such a jazzy line. Really, though, I toted up the other night, and I've only had eleven lovers —not counting anything that happened before I was thirteen because, after all, that just *doesn't* count. Eleven. Does that make me a whore? Look at Mag Wildwood. Or Honey Tucker. Or Rose Ellen Ward. They've had the old clap-yo'-hands so many times it amounts to applause. Of course I haven't anything *against* whores. Except this:

some of them may have an honest tongue but they all have dishonest hearts. I mean, you can't bang the guy and cash his checks and at least not *try* to believe you love him. I never have. Even Benny Shacklett and all those rodents. I sort of hypnotized myself into thinking their sheer rattiness had a certain allure. Actually, except for Doc, if you want to count Doc, José is my first non-rat romance. Oh, he's not my idea of the absolute finito. He tells little lies and he worries what people *think* and he takes about fifty baths a day: men ought to smell *some*what. He's too prim, too cautious to be my guy ideal; he always turns his back to get undressed and he makes too much noise when he eats and I don't like to see him run because there's something funny-looking about him when he runs. If I were free to choose from everybody alive, just snap my fingers and say come here you, I wouldn't pick José. Nehru, he's nearer the mark. Wendell Willkie. I'd settle for Garbo any day. Why not? A person ought to be able to marry men or women or— listen, if you came to me and said you wanted to hitch up with Man o' War, I'd respect your feeling. No, I'm serious. Love should be allowed. I'm all for it. Now that I've got a pretty good idea what it is. Because I *do* love José—I'd stop smoking if he asked me to. He's *friendly,* he can laugh me out of the mean reds, only I don't have them much any more, except sometimes, and even then they're not so hideola that I gulp Seconal or have to haul myself to Tiffany's: I take his suit to the cleaner, or stuff some mushrooms, and I feel fine, just great. Another thing, I've thrown away my horoscopes. I must have spent a dollar on every goddamn star in the goddamn planetarium. It's a bore, but the answer is good things only happen to you if you're good. Good? Honest is more what I mean. Not law-type honest—I'd rob a grave, I'd steal two-bits off a dead man's eyes if I thought it would contribute to the day's enjoyment—but unto-thyself-type honest. Be anything but a coward, a pretender, an emotional crook, a whore: I'd rather have cancer than a dishonest heart. Which isn't being pious.

Just practical. Cancer *may* cool you, but the other's sure to. Oh, screw it, cookie—hand me my guitar and I'll sing you a *fada* in *the* most perfect Portuguese."

Those final weeks, spanning end of summer and the beginning of another autumn, are blurred in memory, perhaps because our understanding of each other had reached that sweet depth where two people communicate more often in silence than in words: an affectionate quietness replaces the tensions, the unrelaxed chatter and chasing about that produce a friendship's more showy, more, in the surface sense, dramatic moments. Frequently, when *he* was out of town (I'd developed hostile attitudes toward *him,* and seldom used his name) we spent entire evenings together during which we exchanged less than a hundred words; once, we walked all the way to Chinatown, ate a chow-mein supper, bought some paper lanterns and stole a box of joss sticks, then moseyed across the Brooklyn Bridge, and on the bridge, as we watched seaward-moving ships pass between the cliffs of burning skyline, she said: "Years from now, years and years, one of those ships will bring me back, me and my nine Brazilian brats. Because yes, they *must* see this, these lights, the river—I love New York, even though it isn't mine, the way something has to be, a tree or a street or a house, something, anyway, that belongs to me because I belong to it." And I said: "Do shut up," for I felt infuriatingly left out—a tugboat in drydock while she, glittery voyager of secure destination, steamed down the harbor with whistles whistling and confetti in the air.

So the days, the last days, blow about in memory, hazy, autumnal, all alike as leaves: until a day unlike any other I've lived.

It happened to fall on the thirtieth of September, my birthday, a fact which had no effect on events, except that, expecting some form of monetary remembrance from my family, I was eager for the postman's morning visit. Indeed, I went downstairs and waited for him. If I had not been loitering in the vestibule, then Holly would not have asked me to go horseback riding; and would not, consequently, have had the opportunity to save my life.

"Come on," she said, when she found me awaiting the postman. "Let's walk a couple of horses around the park." She was wearing a windbreaker and a pair of blue jeans and tennis shoes; she slapped her stomach, drawing attention to its flatness: "Don't think I'm out to lose the heir. But there's a horse, my darling old Mabel Minerva—I can't go without saying good-bye to Mabel Minerva."

"Good-bye?"

"A week from Saturday. José bought the tickets." In rather a trance, I let her lead me down to the street. "We change planes in Miami. Then over the sea. Over the Andes. Taxi!"

Over the Andes. As we rode in a cab across Central Park it seemed to me as though I, too, were flying, desolately floating over snow-peaked and perilous territory.

"But you can't. After all, what about. Well, what about. Well, you can't *really* run off and leave everybody."

"I don't think anyone will miss me. I have no friends."

"I will. Miss you. So will Joe Bell. And oh—millions. Like Sally. Poor Mr. Tomato."

"I loved old Sally," she said, and sighed. "You know I haven't been to see him in a month? When I told him I was going away, he was an angel. *Actually"* —she frowned—"he seemed *delighted* that I was leaving the country. He said it was all for the best. Because sooner or later there might be trouble. If they found out I wasn't his real niece. That fat lawyer, O'Shaughnessy, O'Shaughnessy sent me five hundred dollars. In cash. A wedding present from Sally."

I wanted to be unkind. "You can expect a present from me, too. When, and if, the wedding happens."

She laughed. "He'll marry me, all right. In church.

And with his family there. That's why we're waiting till we get to Rio."

"Does he know you're married already?"

"What's the matter with you? Are you trying to ruin the day? It's a beautiful day: leave it alone!"

"But it's perfectly possible—"

"It *isn't* possible. I've told you, that wasn't legal. It *couldn't* be." She rubbed her nose, and glanced at me sideways. "Mention that to a living soul, darling. I'll hang you by your toes and dress you for a hog."

The stables—I believe they have been replaced by television studios—were on West Sixty-sixth Street. Holly selected for me an old sway-back black and white mare: "Don't worry, she's safer than a cradle." Which, in my case, was a necessary guarantee, for ten-cent pony rides at childhood carnivals were the limit of my equestrian experience. Holly helped hoist me into the saddle, then mounted her own horse, a silvery animal that took the lead as we jogged across the traffic of Central Park West and entered a riding path dappled with leaves denuding breezes danced about.

"See?" she shouted. "It's great!"

And suddenly it was. Suddenly, watching the tangled colors of Holly's hair flash in the red-yellow leaf light, I loved her enough to forget myself, my self-pitying despairs, and be content that something she thought happy was going to happen. Very gently the horses began to trot, waves of wind splashed us, spanked our faces, we plunged in and out of sun and shadow pools, and joy, a glad-to-be-alive exhilaration, jolted through me like a jigger of nitrogen. That was one minute; the next introduced farce in grim disguise.

For all at once, like savage members of a jungle ambush, a band of Negro boys leapt out of the shrubbery along the path. Hooting, cursing, they launched rocks and thrashed at the horse's rumps with switches.

Mine, the black and white mare, rose on her hind legs, whinnied, teetered like a tightrope artist, then blue-streaked down the path, bouncing my feet out of the stirrups and leaving me scarcely attached. Her hooves made the gravel stones spit sparks. The sky careened. Trees, a lake with little-boy sailboats, statues went by licketysplit. Nursemaids rushed to rescue their charges from our awesome approach; men, bums and others, yelled: "Pull in the reins!" and "Whoa, boy, whoa!" and "Jump!" It was only later that I remembered these voices; at the time I was simply conscious of Holly, the cowboy-sound of her racing behind me, never quite catching up, and over and over calling encouragements. Onward: across the park and out into Fifth Avenue: stampeding against the noonday traffic, taxis, buses that screechingly swerved. Past the Duke mansion, the Frick Museum, past the Pierre and the Plaza. But Holly gained ground; moreover, a mounted policeman had joined the chase: flanking my runaway mare, one on either side, their horses performed a pincer movement that brought her to a steamy halt. It was then, at last, that I fell off her back. Fell off and picked myself up and stood there, not altogether certain where I was. A crowd gathered. The policeman huffed and wrote in a book: presently he was most sympathetic, grinned and said he would arrange for our horses to be returned to their stable.

Holly put us in a taxi. "Darling. How do you feel?"

"Fine."

"But you haven't *any* pulse," she said, feeling my wrist.

"Then I must be dead."

"No, idiot. This is serious. Look at me."

The trouble was, I couldn't see her; rather, I saw several Holly's, a trio of sweaty faces so white with concern that I was both touched and embarrassed. "Honestly. I don't feel anything. Except ashamed."

"Please. Are you sure? Tell me the truth. You might have been killed."

"But I wasn't. And thank you. For saving my life. You're wonderful. Unique. I love you."

"Damn fool." She kissed me on the cheek. Then there were four of her, and I fainted dead away.

. . .

That evening, photographs of Holly were front-
paged by the late edition of the *Journal-American* and
by the early editions of both the *Daily News* and the
Daily Mirror. The publicity had nothing to do with
runaway horses. It concerned quite another matter, as
the headlines revealed: PLAYGIRL ARRESTED IN
NARCOTICS SCANDAL (*Journal-American*), AR-
REST DOPE-SMUGGLING ACTRESS (*Daily News*),
DRUG RING EXPOSED, GLAMOUR GIRL HELD
(*Daily Mirror*).

Of the lot, the *News* printed the most striking picture: Holly, entering police headquarters, wedged between two muscular detectives, one male, one female.
In this squalid context even her clothes (she was still
wearing her riding costume, windbreaker and blue
jeans) suggested a gang-moll hooligan: an impression
dark glasses, disarrayed coiffure and a Picayune cigarette dangling from sullen lips did not diminish. The
caption read: *Twenty-year-old Holly Golightly, beautiful movie starlet and café society celebrity D.A. alleges
to be key figure in international drug-smuggling racket
linked to racketeer Salvatore "Sally" Tomato. Dets. Pat-
rick Connor and Sheilah Fezzonetti (L. and R.) are shown
escorting her into 67th St. Precinct. See story on Pg.
3.* The story, featuring a photograph of a man identified
as Oliver "Father" O'Shaughnessy (shielding his face
with a fedora), ran three full columns. Here, somewhat condensed, are the pertinent paragraphs: *Members
of café society were stunned today by the arrest of gorgeous Holly Golightly, twenty-year-old Hollywood starlet and highly publicized girl-about-New York. At the
same time, 2 P.M., police nabbed Oliver O'Shaughnessy,
52, of the Hotel Seabord, W. 49th St., as he exited from
a Hamburg Heaven on Madison Ave. Both are alleged
by District Attorney Frank L. Donovan to be important
figures in an international drug ring dominated by the
notorious Mafia-führer Salvatore "Sally" Tomato, currently in Sing Sing serving a five-year rap for political*

bribery. . . . O'Shaughnessy, a defrocked priest variously known in crimeland circles as "Father" and "The Padre," has a history of arrests dating back to 1934, when he served two years for operating a phony Rhode Island mental institution, The Monastery. Miss Golightly, who has no previous criminal record, was arrested in her luxurious apartment at a swank East Side address. . . . Although the D.A.'s office has issued no formal statement, responsible sources insist the blond and beautiful actress, not long ago the constant companion of multimillionaire Rutherfurd Trawler, has been acting as "liaison" between the imprisoned Tomato and his chief-lieutenant, O'Shaughnessy. . . . Posing as a relative of Tomato's, Miss Golightly is said to have paid weekly visits to Sing Sing, and on these occasions Tomato supplied her with verbally coded messages which she then transmitted to O'Shaughnessy. Via this link, Tomato, believed to have been born in Cefalu, Sicily, in 1874, was able to keep first-hand control of a worldwide narcotics syndicate with outposts in Mexico, Cuba, Sicily, Tangier, Tehran and Dakar. But the D.A.'s office refused to offer any detail on these allegations or even verify them. . . . Tipped off, a large number of reporters were on hand at the E. 67th St. Precinct station when the accused pair arrived for booking. O'Shaughnessy, a burly red-haired man, refused comment and kicked one cameraman in the groin. But Miss Golightly, a fragile eyeful, even though attired like a tomboy in slacks and leather jacket, appeared relatively unconcerned. "Don't ask me what the hell this is about," she told reporters. "Parce-que Je ne sais pas, mes chères. (Because I do not know, my dears). Yes—I have visited Sally Tomato. I used to go to see him every week. What's wrong with that? He believes in God, and so do I." . . . Then, under the subheading ADMITS OWN DRUG ADDICTION: *Miss Golightly smiled when a reporter asked whether or not she herself is a narcotics user. "I've had a little go at marijuana. It's not half so destructive as brandy. Cheaper, too. Unfortunately, I prefer brandy. No, Mr. Tomato never mentioned drugs to me. It makes me furious, the way these wretched people keep persecuting him. He's a sensitive, a religious person. A darling old man."*

There is one especially gross error in this report: she was not arrested in her "luxurious apartment." It took place in my own bathroom. I was soaking away my horse-ride pains in a tub of scalding water laced with Epsom salts; Holly, an attentive nurse, was sitting on the edge of the tub waiting to rub me with Sloan's liniment and tuck me into bed. There was a knock at the front door. As the door was unlocked, Holly called Come in. In came Madame Sapphia Spanella, trailed by a pair of civilian-clothed detectives, one of them a lady with thick yellow braids roped round her head.

"Here she is: the wanted woman!" boomed Madame Spanella, invading the bathroom and leveling a finger, first at Holly's, then my nakedness. "Look. What a whore she is." The male detective seemed embarrassed: by Madame Spanella and by the situation; but a harsh enjoyment tensed the face of his companion—she plumped a hand on Holly's shoulder and, in a surprising baby-child voice, said: "Come along, sister. You're going places." Whereupon Holly coolly told her: "Get them cotton-pickin' hands off of me, you dreary, driveling old bull-dyke." Which rather enraged the lady: she slapped Holly damned hard. So hard, her head twisted on her neck, and the bottle of liniment, flung from her hand, smithereened on the tile floor—where I, scampering out of the tub to enrich the fray, stepped on it and all but severed both big toes. Nude and bleeding a path of bloody footprints, I followed the action as far as the hall. "Don't forget," Holly managed to instruct me as the detectives propelled her down the stairs, "please feed the cat."

Of course I believed Madame Spanella to blame: she'd several times called the authorities to complain about Holly. It didn't occur to me the affair could have dire dimensions until that evening when Joe Bell showed up flourishing the newspapers. He was too agitated to speak sensibly; he caroused the room hitting his fists together while I read the accounts.

Then he said: "You think it's so? She was mixed up in this lousy business?"

"Well, yes."

He popped a Tums in his mouth and, glaring at me, chewed it as though he were crunching my bones. "Boy, that's rotten. And you meant to be her friend. What a bastard!"

"Just a minute. I didn't say she was involved *knowingly*. She wasn't. But there, she did do it. Carry messages and whatnot—"

He said: "Take it pretty calm, don't you? Jesus, she could get ten years. More." He yanked the papers away from me. "You know her friends. These rich fellows. Come down to the bar, we'll start phoning. Our girl's going to need fancier shysters than I can afford."

I was too sore and shaky to dress myself; Joe Bell had to help. Back at his bar he propped me in the telephone booth with a triple martini and a brandy tumbler full of coins. But I couldn't think who to contact. José was in Washington, and I had no notion where to reach him there. Rusty Trawler? Not that bastard! Only: what other friends of hers did I know? Perhaps she'd been right when she'd said she had none, not really.

I put through a call to Crestview 5-6958 in Beverly Hills, the number long-distance information gave me for O. J. Berman. The person who answered said Mr. Berman was having a massage and couldn't be disturbed: sorry, try later. Joe Bell was incensed—told me I should have said it was a life and death matter; and he insisted on my trying Rusty. First, I spoke to Mr. Trawler's butler—Mr. and Mrs. Trawler, he announced, were at dinner and might he take a message? Joe Bell shouted into the receiver: "This is urgent, mister. Life and death." The outcome was that I found myself talking—listening, rather—to the former Mag Wildwood: "Are you starkers?" she demanded. "My husband and I will positively *sue* anyone who attempts to connect our names with that ro-ro-ro*vol*ting and de-de-de*gen*erate girl. I always *knew* she was a hop-hop-head with no more morals than a hound-bitch in heat. Prison is where she belongs. And my husband agrees one thousand percent. We will positively *sue* anyone who—" Hanging up, I remembered old Doc down in Tulip, Texas; but no, Holly wouldn't like it if I called him, she'd kill me good.

I rang California again; the circuits were busy, stayed busy, and by the time O. J. Berman was on the line I'd emptied so many martinis he had to tell me why I was phoning him: "About the kid, is it? I know already. I spoke already to Iggy Fitelstein. Iggy's the best shingle in New York. I said Iggy you take care of it, send me the bill, only keep my name anonymous, see. Well, I owe the kid something. Not that I owe her *any*thing, you want to come down to it. She's crazy. A phony. But a *real* phony, you know? Anyway, they only got her in ten thousand bail. Don't worry, Iggy'll spring her tonight—it wouldn't surprise me she's home already."

But she wasn't; nor had she returned the next morning when I went down to feed her cat. Having no key to the apartment, I used the fire escape and gained entrance through a window. The cat was in the bedroom, and he was not alone: a man was there, crouching over a suitcase. The two of us, each thinking the other a burglar, exchanged uncomfortable stares as I stepped through the window. He had a pretty face, lacquered hair, he resembled José; moreover, the suitcase he'd been packing contained the wardrobe José kept at Holly's, the shoes and suits she fussed over, was always carting to menders and cleaners. And I said, certain it was so: "Did Mr. Ybarra-Jaegar send you?"

"I am the cousin," he said with a wary grin and just-penetrable accent.

"Where is José?"

He repeated the question, as though translating it

into another language. "Ah, *where* she is! She is waiting," he said and, seeming to dismiss me, resumed his
valet activities.

So: the diplomat was planning a powder. Well, I
wasn't amazed; or in the slightest sorry. Still, what a
heartbreaking stunt: "He ought to be horsewhipped."

The cousin giggled, I'm sure he understood me. He
shut the suitcase and produced a letter. "My cousin, she
ask me leave that for his chum. You will oblige?"

On the envelope was scribbled: *For Miss H. Golightly—Courtesy Bearer*.

I sat down on Holly's bed, and hugged Holly's cat
to me, and felt as badly for Holly, every iota, as she
could feel for herself.

"Yes, I will oblige."

And I did: without the least wanting to. But I hadn't
the courage to destroy the letter; or the will power to
keep it in my pocket when Holly very tentatively inquired if, if by any chance, I'd had news of José. It was
two mornings later; I was sitting by her bedside in a
room that reeked of iodine and bedpans, a hospital room.
She had been there since the night of her arrest. "Well,
darling," she'd greeted me, as I tiptoed toward her carrying a carton of Picayune cigarettes and a wheel of new-
autumn violets, "I lost the heir." She looked not quite
twelve years: her pale vanilla hair brushed back, her
eyes, for once minus their dark glasses, clear as rain
water—one couldn't believe how ill she'd been.

Yet it was true: "Christ, I nearly cooled. No fooling,
the fat woman almost had me. She was yakking up a
storm. I guess I couldn't have told you about the fat
woman. Since I didn't know about her myself until my
brother died. Right away I was wondering where he'd
gone, what it meant, Fred's dying; and then I saw her,
she was there in the room with me, and she had Fred
cradled in her arms, a fat mean red bitch rocking in a
rocking chair with Fred on her lap and laughing like a
brass band. The mockery of it! But it's all that's ahead

for us, my friend: this comedienne waiting to give you the old razz. Now do you see why I went crazy and broke everything?"

Except for the lawyer O. J. Berman had hired, I was the only visitor she had been allowed. Her room was shared by other patients, a trio of triplet-like ladies who, examining me with an interest not unkind but total, speculated in whispered Italian. Holly explained that: "They think you're my downfall, darling. The fellow what done me wrong"; and, to a suggestion that she set them straight, replied: "I can't. They don't speak English. Anyway, I wouldn't dream of spoiling their fun." It was then that she asked about José.

The instant she saw the letter she squinted her eyes and bent her lips in a tough tiny smile that advanced her age immeasurably. "Darling," she instructed me, "would you reach in the drawer there and give me my purse. A girl doesn't read this sort of thing without her lipstick."

Guided by a compact mirror, she powdered, painted every vestige of twelve-year-old out of her face. She shaped her lips with one tube, colored her cheeks from another. She penciled the rims of her eyes, blued the lids, sprinkled her neck with 4711; attached pearls to her ears and donned her dark glasses; thus armored, and after a displeased appraisal of her manicure's shabby condition, she ripped open the letter and let her eyes race through it while her stony small smile grew smaller and harder. Eventually she asked for a Picayune. Took a puff: "Tastes bum. But divine," she said and, tossing me the letter: "Maybe this will come in handy—if you ever write a rat-romance. Don't be hoggy: read it aloud. I'd like to hear it myself."

It began: "My dearest little girl—"

Holly at once interrupted. She wanted to know what I thought of the handwriting. I thought nothing: a tight, highly legible, uneccentric script. "It's him to a T. Buttoned up and constipated," she declared. "Go on."

"My dearest little girl, I have loved you knowing you were not as others. But conceive of my despair upon discovering in such a brutal and public style how very different you are from the manner of woman a man of my faith and career could hope to make his wife. Verily I grief for the disgrace of your present circumstance, and do not find it in my heart to add my condemn to the condemn that surrounds you. So I hope you will find it in your heart not to condemn me. I have my family to protect, and my name, and I am a coward where those institutions enter. Forget me, beautiful child. I am no longer here. I am gone home. But may God always be with you and your child. May God be not the same as—José."

"Well?"

"In a way it seems quite honest. And even touching."

"*Touching?* That square-ball jazz!"

"But after all, he *says* he's a coward; and from his point of view, you must see—"

Holly, however, did not want to admit that she saw; yet her face, despite its cosmetic disguise, confessed it. "All right, he's not a rat without reason. A super-sized, King Kong-type rat like Rusty. Benny Shacklett. But oh gee, golly goddamn," she said, jamming a fist into her mouth like a bawling baby, "I *did* love him. The rat."

The Italian trio imagined a lover's *crise* and, placing the blame for Holly's groanings where they felt it belonged, tut-tutted their tongues at me. I was flattered: proud that anyone should think Holly cared for me. She quieted when I offered her another cigarette. She swallowed and said: "Bless you, Buster. And bless you for being such a bad jockey. If I hadn't had to play Calamity Jane I'd still be looking forward to the grub in an unwed mama's home. Strenuous exercise, that's what did the trick. But I've scared *la merde* out of the whole badge-department by saying it was because Miss Dykeroo slapped me. Yessir, I can sue them on several counts, including false arrest."

Until then, we'd skirted mention of her more sinister tribulations, and this jesting reference to them seemed appalling, pathetic, so definitely did it reveal how incapable she was of recognizing the bleak realities before her. "Now, Holly," I said, thinking: be strong, mature, an uncle. "Now, Holly. We can't treat it as a joke. We have to make plans."

"You're too young to be stuffy. Too small. By the way, what business is it of yours?"

"None. Except you're my friend, and I'm worried. I mean to know what you intend doing."

She rubbed her nose, and concentrated on the ceiling. "Today's Wednesday, isn't it? So I suppose I'll sleep until Saturday, really get a good *schluffen*. Saturday morning I'll skip out to the bank. Then I'll stop by the apartment and pick up a nightgown or two and my Mainbocher. Following which, I'll report to Idlewild. Where, as you damn well know, I have a perfectly fine reservation on a perfectly fine plane. And since you're such a friend I'll let you wave me off. *Please* stop shaking your head."

"Holly. Holly. You can't do that."

"Et pourquoi pas? I'm not hot-footing after José, if that's what you suppose. According to my census, he's strictly a citizen of Limboville. It's only: why should I waste a perfectly fine ticket? Already paid for? Besides, I've never been to Brazil."

"Just what kind of pills have they been feeding you here? Can't you realize, you're under a criminal indictment. If they catch you jumping bail, they'll throw away the key. Even if you get away with it, you'll never be able to come home."

"Well, so, tough titty. Anyway, home is where you feel at home. I'm still looking."

"No, Holly, it's stupid. You're innocent. You've got to stick it out."

She said, "Rah, team, rah," and blew smoke in my face. She was impressed, however; her eyes were dilated by unhappy visions, as were mine: iron rooms, steel corridors of gradually closing doors. "Oh, screw it," she said, and stabbed out her cigarette. "I have a fair chance they *won't* catch me. Provided *you* keep your *bouche fermez*.

Look. Don't despise me, darling." She put her hand over mine and pressed it with sudden immense sincerity. "I haven't much choice. I talked it over with the lawyer: oh, I didn't tell *him* anything *re* Rio—he'd tip the badgers himself, rather than lose his fee, to say nothing of the nickels O.J. put up for bail. Bless O.J.'s heart; but once on the coast I helped him win more than ten thou in a single poker hand: we're square. No, here's the real shake: all the badgers want from me is a couple of free grabs and my services as a state's witness against Sally —nobody has any intention of prosecuting me, they haven't a ghost of a case. Well, I may be rotten to the core, Maude, *but:* testify against a friend I will not. Not if they can prove he doped Sister Kenny. My yardstick is how somebody treats me, and old Sally, all right he wasn't absolutely white with me, say he took a slight advantage, just the same Sally's an okay shooter, and I'd let the fat woman snatch me sooner than help the lawboys pin him down." Tilting her compact mirror above her face, smoothing her lipstick with a crooked pinkie, she said: "And to be honest, that isn't all. Certain shades of limelight wreck a girl's complexion. Even if a jury gave me the Purple Heart, this neighborhood holds no future: they'd still have up every rope from LaRue to Perona's Bar and Grill—take my word, I'd be about as welcome as Mr. Frank E. Campbell. And if you lived off my particular talents, Cookie, you'd understand the kind of bankruptcy I'm describing. Uh, uh, I don't just fancy a fade-out that finds me belly-bumping around Roseland with a pack of West Side hillbillies. While the excellent Madame Trawler sashayes her twat in and out of Tiffany's. I couldn't take it. Give me the fat woman any day."

A nurse, soft-shoeing into the room, advised that visiting hours were over. Holly started to complain, and was curtailed by having a thermometer popped in her mouth. But as I took leave, she unstoppered herself to say: "Do me a favor, darling. Call up the *Times,* or whatever you call, and get a list of the fifty richest men in

Brazil. I'm *not* kidding. The fifty richest: regardless of race or color. Another favor—poke around my apartment till you find that medal you gave me. The St. Christopher. I'll need it for the trip."

The sky was red Friday night, it thundered, and Saturday, departing day, the city swayed in a squall-like downpour. Sharks might have swum through the air, though it seemed improbable a plane could penetrate it.

But Holly, ignoring my cheerful conviction that her flight would not go, continued her preparations—placing, I must say, the chief burden of them on me. For she had decided it would be unwise of her to come near the brownstone. Quite rightly, too: it was under surveillance, whether by police or reporters or other interested parties one couldn't tell—simply a man, sometimes men, who hung around the stoop. So she'd gone from the hospital to a bank and straight then to Joe Bell's bar. "She don't figure she was followed," Joe Bell told me when he came with a message that Holly wanted me to meet her there as soon as possible, a half-hour at most, bringing: "Her jewelry. Her guitar. Toothbrushes and stuff. And a bottle of hundred-year-old brandy: she says you'll find it hid down in the bottom of the dirty-clothes basket. Yeah, oh, and the cat. She wants the cat. But hell," he said, "I don't know we should help her at all. She ought to be protected against herself. Me, I feel like telling the cops. Maybe if I go back and build her some drinks, maybe I can get her drunk enough to call it off."

Stumbling, skidding up and down the fire escape between Holly's apartment and mine, wind-blown and winded and wet to the bone (clawed to the bone as well, for the cat had not looked favorably upon evacuation, especially in such inclement weather) I managed a fast, first-rate job of assembling her going-away belongings. I even found the St. Christopher's medal. Everything was piled on the floor of my room, a poignant pyramid of brassières and dancing slippers and pretty things I packed in Holly's only suitcase. There was a mass left over that I had to put in paper grocery bags. I couldn't think how to carry the cat; until I thought of stuffing him in a pillowcase.

Never mind why, but once I walked from New Orleans to Nancy's Landing, Mississippi, just under five hundred miles. It was a light-hearted lark compared to the journey to Joe Bell's bar. The guitar filled with rain, rain softened the paper sacks, the sacks split and perfume spilled on the pavement, pearls rolled in the gutter: while the wind pushed and the cat scratched, the cat screamed —but worse, I was frightened, a coward to equal José: those storming streets seemed aswarm with unseen presences waiting to trap, imprison me for aiding an outlaw.

The outlaw said: "You're late, Buster. Did you bring the brandy?"

And the cat, released, leaped and perched on her shoulder: his tail swung like a baton conducting rhapsodic music. Holly, too, seemed inhabited by melody, some bouncy *bon voyage* oompahpah. Uncorking the brandy, she said: "This was meant to be part of my hope chest. The idea was, every anniversary we'd have a swig. Thank Jesus I never bought the chest. Mr. Bell, sir, three glasses."

"You'll only need two," he told her. "I won't drink to your foolishness."

The more she cajoled him ("Ah, Mr. Bell. The lady doesn't vanish every day. Won't you toast her?"), the gruffer he was: "I'll have no part of it. If you're going to hell, you'll go on your own. With no further help from me." An inaccurate statement: because seconds after he'd made it a chauffeured limousine drew up outside the bar, and Holly, the first to notice it, put down her brandy, arched her eyebrows, as though she expected to see the District Attorney himself alight. So did I. And when I saw Joe Bell blush, I had to think: by God, he *did* call the police. But then, with burning ears, he announced: "It's nothing. One of them Carey Cadillacs. I hired it. To take you to the airport."

He turned his back on us to fiddle with one of his

flower arrangements. Holly said: "Kind, dear Mr. Bell. Look at me, sir."

He wouldn't. He wrenched the flowers from the vase and thrust them at her; they missed their mark, scattered on the floor. "Good-bye," he said; and, as though he were going to vomit, scurried to the men's room. We heard the door lock.

The Carey chauffeur was a worldly specimen who accepted our slapdash luggage most civilly and remained rock-faced when, as the limousine swished uptown through a lessening rain, Holly stripped off her clothes, the riding costume she'd never had a chance to substitute, and struggled into a slim black dress. We didn't talk: talk could have only led to argument; and also, Holly seemed too preoccupied for conversation. She hummed to herself, swigged brandy, she leaned constantly forward to peer out the windows, as if she were hunting an address—or, I decided, taking a last impression of a scene she wanted to remember. It was neither of these. But this: "Stop here," she ordered the driver, and we pulled to the curb of a street in Spanish Harlem. A savage, a garish, a moody neighborhood garlanded with poster-portraits of movie stars and Madonnas. Sidewalk litterings of fruit-rind and rotted newspaper were hurled about by the wind, for the wind still boomed, though the rain had hushed and there were bursts of blue in the sky.

Holly stepped out of the car; she took the cat with her. Cradling him, she scratched his head and asked. "What do you think? This ought to be the right kind of place for a tough guy like you. Garbage carts. Rats galore. Plenty of cat-bums to gang around with. So scram," she said, dropping him; and when he did not move away, instead raised his thug-face and questioned her with yellowish pirate-eyes, she stamped her foot: "I said beat it!" He rubbed against her leg. "I said fuck off!" she shouted, then jumped back in the car, slammed the door, and: "Go," she told the driver. "Go. Go."

I was stunned. "Well, you *are*. You *are* a bitch."

We'd traveled a block before she replied. "I told

you. We just met by the river one day: that's all. Independents, both of us. We never made each other any promises. We never—" she said, and her voice collapsed, a tic, an invalid whiteness seized her face. The car had paused for a traffic light. Then she had the door open, she was running down the street; and I ran after her.

But the cat was not at the corner where he'd been left. There was no one, nothing on the street except a urinating drunk and two Negro nuns herding a file of sweet-singing children. Other children emerged from doorways and ladies leaned over their window sills to watch as Holly darted up and down the block, ran back and forth chanting: "You. Cat. Where are you? Here, cat." She kept it up until a bumpy-skinned boy came forward dangling an old tom by the scruff of its neck: "You wants a nice kitty, miss? Gimme a dollar."

The limousine had followed us. Now Holly let me steer her toward it. At the door, she hesitated; she looked past me, past the boy still offering his cat ("Half a dollar. Two-bits, maybe? Two-bits, it ain't much"), and she shuddered, she had to grip my arm to stand up: "Oh, Jesus God. We did belong to each other. He was mine."

Then I made her a promise, I said I'd come back and find her cat: "I'll take care of him, too. I promise."

She smiled: that cheerless new pinch of a smile. "But what about me?" she said, whispered, and shivered again. "I'm very scared, Buster. Yes, at last. Because it could go on forever. Not knowing what's yours until you've thrown it away. The mean reds, they're nothing. The fat woman, she's nothing. This, though: my mouth's so dry, if my life depended on it I couldn't spit." She stepped in the car, sank in the seat. "Sorry, driver. Let's go."

TOMATO'S TOMATO MISSING. And: DRUG-CASE ACTRESS BELIEVED GANGLAND VICTIM. In due time, however, the press reported: FLEEING PLAYGIRL TRACED TO RIO. Apparently no attempt was made by American authorities to recover her,

and soon the matter diminished to an occasional gossip-
column mention; as a news story, it was revived only
once: on Christmas Day, when Sally Tomato died of a
heart attack at Sing Sing. Months went by, a winter of
them, and not a word from Holly. The owner of the
brownstone sold her abandoned possessions, the white-
satin bed, the tapestry, her precious Gothic chair; a new
tenant acquired the apartment, his name was Quaint-
ance Smith, and he entertained as many gentlemen callers of a noisy nature as Holly ever had—though in this
instance Madame Spanella did not object, indeed she
doted on the young man and supplied filet mignon whenever he had a black eye. But in the spring a postcard
came: it was scribbled in pencil, and signed with a lipstick kiss: *Brazil was beastly but Buenos Aires the best.
Not Tiffany's, but almost. Am joined at the hip with
duhvine $enor. Love? Think so. Anyhoo am looking for
somewhere to live ($enor has wife, 7 brats) and will let
you know address when I know it myself. Mille tendresse.*
But the address, if it ever existed, never was sent, which
made me sad, there was so much I wanted to write her:
that I'd *sold* two stories, had read where the Trawlers
were countersuing for divorce, was moving out of the
brownstone because it was haunted. But mostly, I
wanted to tell about her cat. I had kept my promise; I
had found him. It took weeks of after-work roaming
through those Spanish Harlem streets, and there were
many false alarms—flashes of tiger-striped fur that,
upon inspection, were not him. But one day, one cold
sunshiny Sunday winter afternoon, it was. Flanked by
potted plants and framed by clean lace curtains, he was
seated in the window of a warm-looking room: I wondered what his name was, for I was certain he had one
now, certain he'd arrived somewhere he belonged. African hut or whatever, I hope Holly has, too.

Among the Paths to Eden

ONE SATURDAY IN MARCH, an occasion of pleasant winds and sailing clouds, Mr. Ivor Belli bought from a Brooklyn florist a fine mass of jonquils and conveyed them, first by subway, then foot, to an immense cemetery in Queens, a site unvisited by him since he had seen his wife buried there the previous autumn. Sentiment could not be credited with returning him today, for Mrs. Belli, to whom he had been married twenty-seven years, during which time she had produced two now-grown and matrimonially-settled daughters, had been a woman of many natures, most of them trying: he had no desire to renew so unsoothing an acquaintance, even in spirit. No; but a hard winter had just passed, and he felt in need of exercise, air, a heart-lifting stroll through the handsome, spring-prophesying weather; of course, rather as an extra dividend, it was nice that he would be able to tell his daughters of a journey to their mother's grave, especially so since it might a little appease the elder girl, who seemed resentful of Mr. Belli's too comfortable acceptance of life as lived alone.

The cemetery was not a reposeful, pretty place; was, in fact, a damned frightening one: acres of fog-colored stone spilled across a sparsely grassed and shadeless plateau. An unhindered view of Manhattan's skyline provided the location with beauty of a stage-prop sort—

it loomed beyond the graves like a steep headstone honoring these quiet folk, its used-up and very former citizens: the juxtaposed spectacle made Mr. Belli, who was by profession a tax accountant and therefore equipped to enjoy irony however sadistic, smile, actually chuckle —yet, oh God in heaven, its inferences chilled him, too, deflated the buoyant stride carrying him along the cemetery's rigid, pebbled paths. He slowed until he stopped, thinking: "I ought to have taken Morty to the zoo"; Morty being his grandson, aged three. But it would be churlish not to continue, vengeful: and why waste a bouquet? The combination of thrift and virtue reactivated him; he was breathing hard from hurry when, at last, he stooped to jam the jonquils into a rock urn perched on a rough gray slab engraved with Gothic calligraphy declaring that

SARAH BELLI
1901-1959

had been the

DEVOTED WIFE OF IVOR
BELOVED MOTHER OF IVY AND REBECCA.

Lord, what a relief to know the woman's tongue was finally stilled. But the thought, pacifying as it was, and though supported by visions of his new and silent bachelor's apartment, did not relight the suddenly snuffed-out sense of immortality, of glad-to-be-aliveness, which the day had earlier kindled. He had set forth expecting such good from the air, the walk, the aroma of another spring about to be. Now he wished he had worn a scarf; the sunshine was false, without real warmth, and the wind, it seemed to him, had grown rather wild. As he gave the jonquils a decorative pruning, he regretted he could not delay their doom by supplying them with water; relinquishing the flowers, he turned to leave.

A woman stood in his way. Though there were few other visitors to the cemetery, he had not noticed her before, or heard her approach. She did not step aside. She glanced at the jonquils; presently her eyes, situated behind steel-rimmed glasses, swerved back to Mr. Belli.

"Uh. Relative?"

"My wife," he said, and sighed as though some such noise was obligatory.

She sighed, too; a curious sigh that implied gratification. "Gee, I'm sorry."

Mr. Belli's face lengthened. "Well."

"It's a shame."

"Yes."

"I hope it wasn't a long illness. Anything painful."

"No-o-o," he said, shifting from one foot to the other. "In her sleep." Sensing an unsatisfied silence, he added, "Heart condition."

"Gee. That's how I lost my father. Just recently. Kind of gives us something in common. Something," she said, in a tone alarmingly plaintive, "something to talk about."

"—know how you must feel."

"At least they didn't suffer. That's a comfort."

The fuse attached to Mr. Belli's patience shortened. Until now he had kept his gaze appropriately lowered, observing, after his initial glimpse of her, merely the woman's shoes, which were of the sturdy, so-called sensible type often worn by aged women and nurses. "A great comfort," he said, as he executed three tasks: raised his eyes, tipped his hat, took a step forward.

Again the woman held her ground; it was as though she had been employed to detain him. "Could you give me the time? My old clock," she announced, self-consciously tapping some dainty machinery strapped to her wrist, "I got it for graduating high school. That's why it doesn't run so good any more. I mean, it's pretty old. But it makes a nice appearance."

Mr. Belli was obliged to unbutton his topcoat and plow around for a gold watch embedded in a vest pocket. Meanwhile, he scrutinized the lady, really took her apart. She must have been blond as a child, her general coloring suggested so: the clean shine of her Scandinavian skin, her chunky cheeks, flushed with peasant health, and the blueness of her genial eyes—such honest eyes, attractive despite the thin silver spectacles surrounding them; but the hair itself, what could be discerned of it under a drab felt hat, was poorly permanented frizzle of no particular tint. She was a bit taller than Mr. Belli, who was five-foot-eight with the aid of shoe lifts, and she may have weighed more; at any rate he couldn't imagine that she mounted scales too cheerfully. Her hands: kitchen hands; and the nails: not only nibbled ragged, but painted with a pearly lacquer queerly phosphorescent. She wore a plain brown coat and carried a plain black purse. When the student of these components recomposed them he found they assembled themselves into a very decent-looking person whose looks he liked; the nail polish was discouraging; still he felt that here was someone you could trust. As he trusted Esther Jackson, Miss Jackson, his secretary. Indeed, that was who she reminded him of, Miss Jackson; not that the comparison was fair—to Miss Jackson, who possessed, as he had once in the course of a quarrel informed Mrs. Belli, "intellectual elegance and elegance otherwise." Nevertheless, the woman confronting him seemed imbued with that quality of good-will he appreciated in his secretary, Miss Jackson, Esther (as he'd lately, absent-mindedly, called her). Moreover, he guessed them to be about the same age: rather on the right side of forty.

"Noon. Exactly."

"Think of that! Why, you must be famished," she said, and unclasped her purse, peered into it as though it were a picnic hamper crammed with sufficient treats to furnish a smörgåsbord. She scooped out a fistful of peanuts. "I practically live on peanuts since Pop—since I haven't anyone to cook for. I must say, even if I do say so, I miss my own cooking; Pop always said I was better than any restaurant he ever went to. But it's no pleasure cooking just for yourself, even when you *can* make pastries light as a leaf. Go on. Have some. They're fresh-roasted."

Mr. Belli accepted; he'd always been childish about peanuts and, as he sat down on his wife's grave to eat them, only hoped his friend had more. A gesture of his hand suggested that she sit beside him; he was surprised to see that the invitation seemed to embarrass her; sudden additions of pink saturated her cheeks, as though he'd asked her to transform Mrs. Belli's bier into a love bed.

"It's okay for you. A relative. But me. Would she like a stranger sitting on her—resting place?"

"Please. Be a guest. Sarah won't mind," he told her, grateful the dead cannot hear, for it both awed and amused him to consider what Sarah, that vivacious scene-maker, that energetic searcher for lipstick traces and stray blond strands, would say if she could see him shelling peanuts on her tomb with a woman not entirely unattractive.

And then, as she assumed a prim perch on the rim of the grave, he noticed her leg. Her left leg; it stuck straight out like a stiff piece of mischief with which she planned to trip passers-by. Aware of his interest, she smiled, lifted the leg up and down. "An accident. You know. When I was a kid. I fell off a roller coaster at Coney. Honest. It was in the paper. Nobody knows why I'm alive. The only thing is I can't bend my knee. Otherwise it doesn't make any difference. Except to go dancing. Are you much of a dancer?"

Mr. Belli shook his head; his mouth was full of peanuts.

"So that's something else we have in common. Dancing. I *might* like it. But I don't. I like music, though."

Mr. Belli nodded his agreement.

"And flowers," she added, touching the bouquet of jonquils; then her fingers traveled on and, as though she were reading Braille, brushed across the marble lettering on his name. "Ivor," she said, mispronouncing it. Ivor Belli. My name is Mary O'Meaghan. But I wish *I* were Italian. My sister is; well, she married one. And oh, he's full of fun; happy-natured and outgoing, like all Italians. He says my spaghetti's the best he's ever had. Especially the kind I make with sea-food sauce. You ought to taste it."

Mr. Belli, having finished the peanuts, swept the hulls off his lap. "You've got a customer. But he's not Italian. Belli sounds like that. Only I'm Jewish."

She frowned, not with disapproval, but as if he had mysteriously daunted her.

"My family came from Russia; I was born there."

This last information restored her enthusiasm, accelerated it. "I don't care what they say in the papers. I'm sure Russians are the same as everybody else. Human. Did you see the Bolshoi Ballet on TV? Now didn't that make you proud to be a Russian?"

He thought: she means well; and was silent.

"Red cabbage soup—hot or cold—with sour cream. Hmnn. See," she said, producing a second helping of peanuts, "you *were* hungry. Poor fellow." She sighed. "How you must miss your wife's cooking."

It was true, he did; and the conversational pressure being applied to his appetite made him realize it. Sarah had set an excellent table: varied, on time, and well flavored. He recalled certain cinnamon-scented feast-days. Afternoons of gravy and wine, starchy linen, the "good" silver; followed by a nap. Moreover, Sarah had never asked him to dry a dish (he could hear her calmly humming in the kitchen), had never complained of house-work; and she had contrived to make the raising of two girls a smooth series of thought-out, affectionate events; Mr. Belli's contribution to their upbringing had been to be an admiring witness; if his daughters were a credit to him (Ivy living in Bronxville, and married to a dental surgeon; her sister the wife of A. J. Krakower, junior partner in the law firm of Finnegan, Loeb and Krakower), he had Sarah to thank; they were her accomplishment. There was much to be said for Sarah, and he was glad to discover himself thinking so, to find himself remembering not the long hell of hours she had spent honing her tongue on his habits, supposed poker-playing, woman-chasing vices, but gentler episodes: Sarah showing off her self-made hats, Sarah scattering crumbs on snowy window sills for winter pigeons: a tide of visions that towed to sea the junk of harsher recollections. He felt, was all at once happy to feel, mournful, sorry he had not been sorry sooner; but, though he did genuinely value Sarah suddenly, he could not pretend regret that their life together had terminated, for the current arrangement was, on the whole, preferable by far. However, he wished that, instead of jonquils, he had brought her an orchid, the gala sort she'd always salvaged from her daughters' dates and stored in the icebox until they shriveled.

"—aren't they?" he heard, and wondered who had spoken until, blinking, he recognized Mary O'Meaghan, whose voice had been playing along unlistened to: a shy and lulling voice, a sound strangely small and young to come from so robust a figure.

"I said they must be cute, aren't they?"

"Well," was Mr. Belli's safe reply.

"Be modest. But I'm sure they are. If they favor their father; ha ha, don't take me serious, I'm joking. But, seriously, kids just slay me. I'll trade any kid for any grownup that ever lived. My sister has five, four boys and a girl. Dot, that's my sister, she's always after me to baby-sit now that I've got the time and don't have to look after Pop every minute. She and Frank, he's my brother-in-law, the one I mentioned, they say Mary, nobody can handle kids like *you*. At the same time have fun. But it's so easy; there's nothing like hot cocoa and a mean pillow fight to make kids sleepy. Ivy," she said, reading aloud the tombstone's dour script. "Ivy and Rebecca. Sweet names. And I'm sure you do your best. But two little girls without a mother."

"No, no," said Mr. Belli, at last caught up. "Ivy's a mother herself. And Becky's expecting."

Her face restyled momentary chagrin into an expression of disbelief. "A grandfather? You?"

Mr. Belli had several vanities: for example, he thought he was *saner* than other people; also, he believed himself to be a walking compass; his digestion, and an ability to read upside down, were other ego-enlarging items. But his reflection in a mirror aroused little inner applause; not that he disliked his appearance; he just knew that it was very so-what. The harvesting of his hair had begun decades ago; now his head was an almost barren field. While his nose had character, his chin, though it made a double effort, had none. His shoulders were broad; but so was the rest of him. Of course he was neat: kept his shoes shined, his laundry laundered, twice a day scraped and talcumed his bluish jowls; but such measures failed to camouflage, actually they emphasized, his middle-class, middle-aged ordinariness. Nonetheless, he did not dismiss Mary O'Meaghan's flattery; after all, an undeserved compliment is often the most potent.

"Hell, I'm fifty-one," he said, subtracting four years. "Can't say I feel it." And he didn't; perhaps it was because the wind had subsided, the warmth of the sun grown more authentic. Whatever the reason, his expectations had re-ignited, he was again immortal, a man planning ahead.

"Fifty-one. That's nothing. The prime. Is if you take care of yourself. A man your age needs tending so. Watching after."

Surely in a cemetery one was safe from husband stalkers? The question, crossing his mind, paused midway while he examined her cozy and gullible face, tested her gaze for guile. Though reassured, he thought it best to remind her of their surroundings. "Your father. Is he"—Mr. Belli gestured awkwardly—"near by?"

"Pop? Oh, no. He was very firm; absolutely refused to be buried. So he's at home." A disquieting image gathered in Mr. Belli's head, one that her next words, "His ashes are," did not fully dispel. "Well," she shrugged, "that's how he wanted it. Or—I see—you wondered why *I'm* here? I don't live too far away. It's somewhere to walk, and the view . . ." They both turned to stare at the skyline where the steeples of certain buildings flew pennants of cloud, and sun-dazzled windows glittered like a million bits of mica. Mary O'Meaghan said, "What a perfect day for a parade!"

Mr. Belli thought, *You're a very nice girl;* then he said it, too, and wished he hadn't, for naturally she asked him why. "Because. Well, that was nice what you said. About parades."

"See? So many things in common! I never miss a parade," she told him triumphantly. "The bugles. I play the bugle myself; used to, when I was at Sacred Heart. You said before—" She lowered her voice, as though approaching a subject that required grave tones. "You indicated you were a music lover. Because I have thousands of old records. Hundreds. Pop was in the business and that was his job. Till he retired. Shellacking records in a record factory. Remember Helen Morgan? She slays me, she really knocks me out."

"*Jesus* Christ," he whispered. Ruby Keeler, Jean Harlow: those had been keen but curable infatuations; but Helen Morgan, albino-pale, a sequinned wraith shimmering beyond Ziegfeld footlights—truly, truly he had loved her.

"Do you believe it? That she drank herself to death? On account of a gangster?"

"It doesn't matter. She was lovely."

"Sometimes, like when I'm alone and sort of fed up, I pretend I'm her. Pretend I'm singing in a night club. It's fun; you know?"

"Yes, I know," said Mr. Belli, whose own favorite fantasy was to imagine the adventures he might have if he were invisible.

"May I ask: would you do me a favor?"

"If I can. Certainly."

She inhaled, held her breath as if she were swimming under a wave of shyness; surfacing, she said: "Would you listen to my imitation? And tell me your honest opinion?" Then she removed her glasses: the silver rims had bitten so deeply their shape was permanently printed on her face. Her eyes, nude and moist and helpless, seemed stunned by freedom; the skimpily lashed lids fluttered like long-captive birds abruptly let loose. "There: everything's soft and smoky. Now you've got to use your imagination. So pretend I'm sitting on a piano—gosh, for*give* me, Mr. Belli."

"Forget it. Okay. You're sitting on a piano."

"I'm sitting on a piano," she said, dreamily drooping her head backward until it assumed a romantic posture. She sucked in her cheeks, parted her lips; at the same moment Mr. Belli bit into his. For it was a tactless visit that glamour made on Mary O'Meaghan's filled-out and rosy face; a visit that should not have been paid at all; it was the wrong address. She waited, as though listening for music to cue her; then, *"Don't ever leave me, now that you're here! Here is where you belong. Everything seems so right when you're near, When you're away it's all wrong."* and Mr. Belli was shocked, for what he was hearing was exactly Helen Morgan's voice, and the voice, with its vulnerable sweetness, refinement, its tender quaver toppling high notes, seemed not to be borrowed, but Mary O'Meaghan's own, a natural expression of some secluded identity. Gradually she abandoned theatrical poses, sat upright singing with her eyes squeezed shut: *"—I'm so dependent, When I need comfort, I always run to you. Don't ever leave me! 'Cause if you do, I'll have no one to run to."* Until too late, neither she nor Mr. Belli noticed the coffin-laden entourage invading their privacy: a black caterpillar composed of sedate Negroes who stared at the white couple as though they had stumbled upon a pair of drunken grave robbers—except one mourner, a dry-eyed little girl who started laughing and couldn't stop; her hiccup-like hilarity resounded long after the procession had disappeared around a distant corner.

"If that kid was mine," said Mr. Belli.

"I feel so ashamed."

"Say, listen. What for? That was beautiful. I mean it; you can sing."

"Thanks," she said; and, as though setting up a barricade against impending tears, clamped on her spectacles.

"Believe me, I was touched. What I'd like is, I'd like an encore."

It was as if she were a child to whom he'd handed a balloon, a unique balloon that kept swelling until it swept her upward, danced her along with just her toes now and then touching ground. She descended to say: "Only not here. Maybe," she began, and once more seemed to be lifted, lilted through the air, "maybe sometime you'll let me cook you dinner. I'll plan it really Russian. And we can play records."

The thought, the apparitional suspicion that had previously passed on tiptoe, returned with a heavier tread, a creature fat and foursquare that Mr. Belli could not evict. "Thank you, Miss O'Meaghan. That's something to look forward to," he said. Rising, he reset his hat, adjusted his coat. "Sitting on cold stone too long, you can catch something."

"When?"

"Why, never. You should *never* sit on cold stone."

"When will you come to dinner?"

Mr. Belli's livelihood rather depended upon his being a skilled inventor of excuses. "Any time," he answered smoothly. "Except any time soon. I'm a tax man; you know what happens to us fellows in March. Yes sir," he said, again hoisting out his watch, "back to the grind for me." Still he couldn't—could he?—simply saunter off, leave her sitting on Sarah's grave? He owed her courtesy; for the peanuts, if nothing more, though there was more—perhaps it was due to her that he had remembered Sarah's orchids withering in the icebox. And anyway, she *was* nice, as likeable a woman, stranger, as he'd ever met. He thought to take advantage of the weather, but the weather offered none: clouds were fewer, the sun exceedingly visible. "Turned chilly," he observed, rubbing his hands together. "Could be going to rain."

"Mr. Belli. Now I'm going to ask you a very personal question," she said, enunciating each word decisively. "Because I wouldn't want you to think I go about inviting just anybody to dinner. My intentions are—" her eyes wandered, her voice wavered, as though the forthright manner had been a masquerade she could not sustain. "So I'm going to ask you a very personal question. Have you considered marrying again?"

He hummed, like a radio warming up before it speaks; when he did, it amounted to static: "Oh, at *my* age. Don't even want a dog. Just give me TV. Some beer. Poker once a week. Hell. Who the hell would want me?" he said; and, with a twinge, remembered Rebecca's mother-in-law, Mrs. A. J. Krakower, Sr., Dr. Pauline Krakower, a female dentist (retired) who had been an audacious participant in a certain family plot. Or what about Sarah's best friend, the persistent "Brownie" Pollock? Odd, but as long as Sarah lived he had enjoyed, upon occasion taken advantage of, "Brownie's" admiration; afterwards—finally he had *told* her not to telephone him any more (and she had shouted: "Everything Sarah ever said, she was right. You fat little *hairy* little bastard"). Then; and then there was Miss Jackson. Despite Sarah's suspicions, her in fact devout conviction, nothing untoward, very untoward, had transpired between him and the pleasant Esther, whose hobby was bowling. But he had always surmised, and in recent months known, that if one day he suggested drinks, dinner, a workout in some bowling alley . . . He said: "I *was* married. For twenty-seven years. That's enough for any lifetime"; but as he said it, he realized that, in just this moment, he had come to a decision, which was: he *would* ask Esther to dinner, he would take her bowling and buy her an orchid, a gala purple one with a lavender-ribbon bow. And where, he wondered, do couples honeymoon in April? At the latest May. Miami? Bermuda? Bermuda! "No, I've never considered it. Marrying again."

One would have assumed from her attentive posture that Mary O'Meaghan was raptly listening to Mr. Belli—except that her eyes played hookey, roamed as though she were hunting at a party for a different, more promising face. The color had drained from her own face; and with it had gone most of her healthy charm. She coughed.

He coughed. Raising his hat, he said: "It's been very pleasant meeting you, Miss O'Meaghan."

"Same here," she said, and stood up. "Mind if I walk with you to the gate?"

He did, yes; for he wanted to mosey along alone, devouring the tart nourishment of this spring-shiny, parade-weather, be alone with his many thoughts of Esther, his hopeful, zestful, live-forever mood. "A pleasure," he said, adjusting his stride to her slower pace and the slight lurch her stiff leg caused.

"But it *did* seem like a sensible idea," she said argumentatively. "And there was old Annie Austin: the living proof. Well, nobody had a *better* idea. I mean, everybody was at me: Get married. From the day Pop died, my sister and everybody was saying: Poor Mary, what's to become of her? A girl that can't type. Take shorthand. With her leg and all; can't even wait on table. What happens to a girl—a *grown* woman—that doesn't know anything, never done anything? Except cook and look after her father. All I heard was: Mary, you've got to get married."

"So. Why fight that? A fine person like you, you ought to be married. You'd make some fellow very happy."

"Sure I would. But *who?*" She flung out her arms, extended a hand toward Manhattan, the country, the continents beyond. "So I've looked; I'm not lazy by nature. But honestly, frankly, how does anybody ever find a husband? If they're not very, very pretty; a terrific dancer. If they're just—oh ordinary. Like me."

"No, no, not at all," Mr. Belli mumbled. "Not ordinary, no. Couldn't you make something of your talent? Your voice?"

She stopped, stood clasping and unclasping her purse. "Don't poke fun. Please. My life is at stake." And she insisted: "I *am* ordinary. So is old Annie Austin. And she says the place for me to find a husband—a decent, comfortable man—is in the obituary column."

For a man who believed himself a human compass, Mr. Belli had the anxious experience of feeling he had lost his way; with relief he saw the gates of the cemetery a hundred yards ahead. "She does? She says that? Old Annie Austin?"

"Yes. And she's a very practical woman. She feeds six people on $58.75 a week: food, clothes, everything. And the way she explained it, it certainly *sounded* logical. Because the obituaries are full of unmarried men. Widowers. You just go to the funeral and sort of introduce yourself: sympathize. Or the cemetery: come here on a nice day, or go to Woodlawn, there are always widowers walking around. Fellows thinking how much they miss home life and maybe wishing they were married again."

When Mr. Belli understood that she was in earnest, he was appalled; but he was also entertained: and he laughed, jammed his hands in his pockets and threw back his head. She joined him, spilled a laughter that restored her color, that, in skylarking style, made her rock against him. "Even I—" she said, clutching at his arm, "even *I* can see the humor." But it was not a lengthy vision; suddenly solemn, she said: "But that is how Annie met her husbands. Both of them: Mr. Cruikshank, and then Mr. Austin. So it *must* be a practical idea. Don't you think?"

"Oh, I do think."

She shrugged. "But it hasn't worked out too well.

Us, for instance. *We* seemed to have such a lot in common."

"One day," he said, quickening his steps. "With a livelier fellow."

"I don't know. I've met some grand people. But it always ends like this. Like us . . ." she said, and left unsaid something more, for a new pilgrim, just entering through the gates of the cemetery, had attached her interest: an alive little man spouting cheery whistlings and with plenty of snap to his walk. Mr. Belli noticed him, too, observed the black band sewn round the sleeve of the visitor's bright green tweed coat, and commented: "Good luck, Miss O'Meaghan. Thanks for the peanuts."

NONFICTION

New Orleans

In the courtyard there was an angel of black stone, and its angel head rose above giant elephant leaves; the stark glass angel eyes, bright as the bleached blue of sailor eyes, stared upward. One observed the angel from an intricate green balcony—mine, this balcony, for I lived beyond in three old white rooms, rooms with elaborate wedding-cake ceilings, wide sliding doors, tall French windows. On warm evenings, with these windows open, conversation was pleasant there, tuneful, for wind rustled the interior like fan-breeze made by ancient ladies. And on such warm evenings the town is quiet. Only voices: family talk weaving on an ivy-curtained porch; a barefoot woman humming as she rocks a sidewalk chair, lulling to sleep a baby she nurses quite publicly; the complaining foreign tongue of an irritated lady who, sitting on her balcony, plucks a fryer, the loosened feathers floating from her hands, slipping into air, sliding lazily downward.

One morning—it was December, I think, a cold Sunday with a sad gray sun—I went up through the Quarter to the old market where, at that time of year, there are exquisite winter fruits, sweet satsumas, twenty cents a dozen, and winter flowers, Christmas poinsettia and snow japonica. New Orleans streets have long, lonesome perspectives; in empty hours their atmosphere is like Chirico, and things innocent, ordinarily (a face behind the slanted light of shutters, nuns moving in the distance, a fat dark arm lolling lopsidedly out some window, a lonely black boy squatting in an alley, blowing soap bubbles and watching sadly as they rise to burst), acquire qualities of violence. Now, on that morning, I stopped still in the middle of a block, for I'd caught out of the corner of my eye a tunnel-passage, an overgrown courtyard. A crazy-looking white hound stood stiffly in the green fern light shining at the tunnel's end, and compulsively I went toward it. Inside there was a fountain; water spilled delicately from a monkey-statue's bronze mouth and made on pool pebbles desolate bell-like sounds. He was hanging from a willow, a bandit-faced man with kinky platinum hair; he hung so limply, like the willow itself. There was terror in that silent suffocated garden. Closed windows looked on blindly; snail tracks glittered silver on elephant ears; nothing moved except his shadow. It swung a little, back and forth, yet there was no wind. A rhinestone ring he wore winked in the sun, and on his arm was tattooed a name, "Francy." The hound lowered its head to drink in the fountain, and I ran. Francy—was it for her he'd killed himself? I do not know. N.O. is a secret place.

My rock angel's glass eyes were like sundials, for they told, by the amount of light focused on them, time: white at noon, they grew gradually dimmer, dark at dusk, black—nightfall eyes in a nightfall head.

The torn lips of golden-haired girls leer luridly on faded leaning house fronts: Drink Dr. Nutt, Dr. Pepper, NEHI, Grapeade, 7 Up, Koke, Coca-Cola. N.O., like every southern town, is a city of soft-drink signs; the streets of forlorn neighborhoods are paved with Coca-Cola caps and, after rain, they glint in the dust like lost dimes. Posters peel away, lie mangled until storm wind blows them along the street, like desert sage—and there are those who think them beautiful; there are those who paper their walls with Dr. Nutt and Dr. Pepper, with Coca-Cola beauties who, smiling above tenement beds, are night guardians and saints of the morning. Signs everywhere, chalked, printed, painted: Madame Ortega— Readings, Love-potions, Magic Literature, C Me; If You Haven't Anything To Do . . . Don't Do It Here; Are You Ready To Meet Your Maker?; B Ware, Bad Dog; Pity The Poor Little Orphans; I Am A Deaf & Dumb Widow With 2 Mouths To Feed; Attention; Blue Wing Singers At Our Church Tonight (signed) The Reverend.

There was once this notice on a door in the Irish Channel district, "Come In And See Where Jesus Stood."

"And so?" said a woman who answered when I rang the bell. "I'd like to see where Jesus stood," I told her, and for a moment she looked blank; her face, cut in razorlike lines, was marshmallow white; she had no eyebrows, no lashes, and she wore a calico kimono. "You too little, honey," she said, a jerky laugh bouncing her breasts, "you too damn little for to see where Jesus stood."

In my neighborhood there was a certain café no fun whatever, for it was the emptiest café around N.O., a regular funeral place. The proprietress, Mrs. Morris Otto Kunze, did not, however, seem to mind; she sat all day behind her bar, cooling herself with a palmetto fan, and seldom stirred except to swat flies. Now glued over an old cracked mirror backing the bar were seven little signs all alike: Don't Worry About Life . . . You'll Never Get Out Of It Alive.

July 3. An "at home" card last week from Miss Y., so I made a call this afternoon. She is delightful in her archaic way, amusing, too, though not by intent. The first time we met, I thought: Edna May Oliver; and there is a resemblance most certainly. Miss Y. speaks in premeditated tones but what she says is haphazard, and her sherry-colored eyes are forever searching the surroundings. Her posture is military, and she carries a man's Malacca cane, one of her legs being shorter than the other, a condition which gives her walk a penguin-like lilt. "It made me unhappy when I was your age; yes, I must say it did, for Papa had to squire me to all the balls, and there we sat on such pretty little gold chairs, and there we sat. None of the gentlemen ever asked Miss Y. to dance, indeed no, though a young man from Baltimore, a Mr. Jones, came here one winter, and gracious! —poor Mr. Jones—fell off a ladder, you know—broke his neck—died instantly."

My interest in Miss Y. is rather clinical, and I am not, I embarrassedly confess, quite the friend she believes, for one cannot feel close to Miss Y.: she is too much a fairy tale, someone real—and improbable. She is like the piano in her parlor—elegant, but a little out of tune. Her house, old even for N.O., is guarded by a black broken iron fence; it is a poor neighborhood she lives in, one sprayed with room-for-rent signs, gasoline stations, jukebox cafés. And yet, in the days when her family first lived here—that, of course, was long ago—there was in all N.O. no finer place. The house, smothered by slanting trees, has a graying exterior; but inside, the fantasy of Miss Y.'s heritage is everywhere visible: the tapping of her cane as she descends birdwing stairs trembles crystal; her face, a heart of wrinkled silk, reflects fumelike on ceiling-high mirrors; she lowers herself (notice, as this happens, how carefully she preserves the comfort of her bones) into father's father's father's chair, a wickedly severe receptacle with lion-head handrests. She is beautiful here in the cool dark of her house, and safe. These are the walls, the fence, the furniture of her childhood. "Some people are born to be old; I, for instance, was an atrocious child lacking any quality whatever. But I like being old. It makes me feel somehow more"—she paused, indicated with a gesture the dim parlor—"more suitable."

Miss Y. does not believe in the world beyond N.O.; at times her insularity results, as it did today, in rather chilling remarks. I had mentioned a recent trip to New York, whereupon she, arching an eyebrow, replied gently, "Oh? And how *are* things in the country?"

1. Why is it, I wonder, that all N.O. cab drivers sound as though they were imported from Brooklyn?

2. One hears so much about food here, and it is probably true that such restaurants as Arnaud's and Kolb's are the best in America. There is an attractive, lazy atmosphere about these restaurants: the slow-wheeling fans, the enormous tables and lack of crowding, the silence, the casual but expert waiters who all look as though they were sons of the management. A friend of mine, discussing N.O. and New York, once pointed out that comparable meals in the East, aside from being considerably more expensive, would arrive elaborate with some chef's mannerisms, with all kinds of froufrou and false accessories. Like most good things, the quality of N.O. cookery derived, he thought, from its essential simplicity.

3. I am more or less disgusted by that persistent phrase, "old charm." You will find it, I suppose, in the architecture here, and in the antique shops (where it rightly belongs), or in the minglings of dialect one hears around the French Market. But N.O. is no more charming than any other Southern city—less so, in fact, for it is the largest. The main portion of this city is made up of spiritual bottomland, streets and sections rather outside the tourist belt.

(From a letter to R.R.) There are new people in the apartment below, the third tenants in the last year; a transient place, this Quarter, hello and good-bye. A real bona-fide scoundrel lived there when I first came. He was unscrupulous, unclean, and crooked—a kind of dissipated satyr. Mr. Buddy, the one-man band. More than likely you have seen him—not here of course, but in some other city, for he keeps on the move, he and his old banjo, drum, harmonica. I used to come across him banging away on various street corners, a gang of loafers gathered round. Realizing he was my neighbor, these meetings always gave me rather a turn. Now to tell the truth, he was not a bad musician—an extraordinary one, in fact, when, late of an afternoon, and for his own pleasure, he sang to his guitar, sang ghostly ballads in a grieving whiskey voice: how terrible it was for those in love.

"Hey, boy, you! You up there . . ." I was *you,* for he never knew my name, and never showed much interest in finding it out. "Come on down and help me kill a couple."

His balcony, smaller than mine, was screened with sweet-smelling wistaria; as there was no furniture to speak of we would sit on the floor in the green shade, drinking a brand of gin close kin to rubbing alcohol, and he would finger his guitar, its steady plaintive whine emphasizing the deep roll of his voice. "Been all over, been in and out, all around; sixty-five, and any woman takes up with me ain't got no use for nobody else; yessir, had myself a lota wives and a lota kids, but christamighty if I know what come of any of 'em—and don't give a hoot in hell—'cept maybe about Rhonda Kay. There was a woman, man, sweet as swamp honey, and was she hot on me! On fire all the time, and her married to a Baptist preacher, too, and her got four kids—five, countin' mine. Always kinda wondered what it was— boy or girl—boy, I spec. I always give 'em boys. . . . Now that's all a long time ago, and it happened in Memphis, Tennessee. Yessir, been everywhere, been to the penitentiary, been in big fine houses like the Rockefeller's houses, been in and out, been all around."

And he could carry on this way until moonrise, his voice growing froggy, his words locking together to make a chant.

His face, stained and wrinkled, had a certain deceptive kindness, a childish twinkle, but his eyes slanted in an Oriental manner, and he kept his fingernails long, knife-sharp and polished as a Chinaman's. "Good for scratching, and handy in a fight, too."

He always wore a kind of costume: black trousers, engine-red socks, tennis shoes with the toes slit for comfort, a morning coat, a gray velvet waistcoat which, he said, had belonged to his ancestor Benjamin Franklin, and a beret studded with Vote For Roosevelt buttons.

And there is no getting around it—he *did* have a good many lady friends—a different one each week, to be sure, but there was hardly ever a time when some woman wasn't cooking his meals; and on those occasions when I came to visit he would invariably, and in a most courtly fashion, say, "Meet Mrs. Buddy."

Late one night I woke with the feeling I was not alone; sure enough, there was someone in the room, and I could see him in the moonlight on my mirror. It was he, Mr. Buddy, furtively opening, closing bureau drawers, and suddenly my box of pennies splattered on the floor, rolled riotously in all directions. There was no use pretending then, so I turned on a lamp, and Mr. Buddy looked at me squarely, scarcely fazed, and grinned. "Listen," he said, and he was the most sober I'd ever seen him. "Listen, I've got to get out of here in a hurry."

I did not know what to say, and he looked down at the floor, his face turning slightly red. "Come on, be a good guy, have you got any money?"

I could only point to the spilt pennies; without another word he got down on his knees, gathered them, and, walking very erectly, went out the door.

He was gone the next morning. Three women have come around asking for him, but I do not know his whereabouts. Maybe he is in Mobile. If you see him around there, R., won't you drop me a card, please?

I want a big fat mama, yes yes! Shotgun's fingers, long as bananas, thick as dill pickles, pound the keys, and his foot, pounding the floor, shakes the café. Shotgun! The biggest show in town! Can't sing worth a damn, but man can he rattle that piano—listen: *She's cool in the summer and warm in the fall, she's a four-season mama and that ain't all* . . . There he goes, his fat mouth yawning like a crocodile's, his wicked red tongue tasting the tune, loving it, making love to it; jelly, Shotgun, jelly-jelly-jelly. Look at him laugh, that black, crazy face all scarred with bullet-shot, all glistening with sweat. Is there any human vice he doesn't know about? A shame, though . . . Hardly any white folks ever see Shotgun, for this is a Negro café. Last year's dusty Christmas decorations color the peeling arsenic walls; orange-green-purple strips of fluted paper, dangling from naked light bulbs, flutter in the wind of a tired fan; the proprietor, a handsome quadroon with hooded milk-blue eyes, leans over the bar, squalling, "Look here, what you think this, some kinda charity? Get up that two-bits, nigger, and mighty quick."

And tonight is Saturday. The room floats in cigarette smoke and Saturday-night perfume. All the little greasy wood tables have double rings of chairs, and everyone knows everyone, and for a moment the world is this room, this dark, jazzy, terrible room; our heartbeat is Shotgun's stamping foot, every joyous element of our lives is focused in the shine of his malicious eyes. *I want a big fat mama, yes yes!* He rocks forward on his stool, and, as he lifts his face to look straight at us, a great riding holler goes up in the night: *I want a big fat mama with the meat shakin' on her, yes!*

Ischia

I FORGET WHY we came here: Ischia. It was being very much talked about, though few people seemed actually to have seen it—except, perhaps, as a jagged blue shadow glimpsed across the water from the heights of its celebrated neighbor, Capri. Some people advised against Ischia and, as I remember, they gave rather spooky reasons: you realize that there is an active volcano? And do you know about the plane? A plane, flying a regular flight between Cairo and Rome, crashed on top an Ischian mountain; there were three survivors, but no one ever saw them alive, for they were stoned to death by goatherds intent on looting the wreckage.

Consequently, we watched the chalky façade of Naples fade with mixed anticipation. It was a classic day, a little cold for southern Italy in March, but crisp and lofty as a kite, and the *Princepessa* spanked across the bay like a sassy dolphin. It is a small civilized boat with a tiny bar and a somewhat *outré* clientele: convicts on their way to the prison island of Procida or, at the opposite extreme, young men about to enter the monastery on Ischia. Of course, there are less dramatic passengers: islanders who have been shopping in Naples; here and there a foreigner—extraordinarily few, however: Capri is the tourist catchall.

Islands are like ships at permanent anchor. To set

foot on one is like starting up a gangplank: one is seized by the same feeling of charmed suspension: it seems nothing unkind or vulgar can happen to you; and as the *Princepessa* eased into the covelike harbor of Porto d'Ischia it seemed, seeing the pale, peeling ice-cream colors of the waterfront, as intimate and satisfying as one's own heartbeat. In the wrangle of disembarking, I dropped and broke my watch—an outrageous bit of symbolism, too pointed: at a glance it was plain that Ischia was no place for the rush of hours, islands never are.

I suppose you might say that Porto is the capital of Ischia; at any rate it is the largest town, and even rather fashionable. Most people who visit the island seldom stray from there, for there are several superior hotels, excellent beaches and, perched in the offing like a giant hawk, the renaissance castle of Vittoria Colonna. The three other fair-sized towns are more rugged. These are: Lacco Ameno, Cassamiciola and, at the farthest end of the island, Forio. It was in Forio that we planned to settle.

We drove there through a green twilight and under a sky of early stars. The road passed high above the sea where fishing boats, lighted with torches, crawled below like brilliant water-spiders. Furry little bats skimmed in the dusk; *buena séra, buena séra,* dim evening voices called along the way, and herds of goats, jogging up the hills, bleated like rusty flutes; the carriage spun through a village square—there was no electricity, and in the cafés the tricky light of candles and kerosene lamps smoked the faces of masculine company. Two children chased after us into the darkness beyond the village. They clung panting to the carriage as we began a steep careening climb, and our horse, nearing the crest, breathed back on the chilled air a stream of mist. The driver flecked his whip, the horse swayed, the children pointed: look. It was there, Forio, distant, moon-white, the sea simmering at its edges, a faint sound of vesper bells rising off it like a whirl of birds. *Multo bella?* said the driver, *Multo bella?* said the children.

* * *

When one rereads a journal it is usually the less ambitious jottings, the haphazard, accidental notations that, seen again, plow a furrow through your memory. For example: "Today Gioconda left in the room assorted slips of colored paper. Are they presents? Because I gave her the bottle of cologne? They will make delightful bookmarks." This reverberates. First, Gioconda. She is a beautiful girl, though her beauty depends upon her mood: when she is feeling glum, and this seems too often the case, she looks like a bowl of cold oatmeal: you are likely to forget the richness of her hair and the mildness of her Mediterranean eyes. Heaven knows, she is overworked: here at the *pensione,* where she is both chambermaid and waitress, she gets up before dawn and is kept on the run sometimes until midnight. To be truthful, she is lucky to have the job, for employment is the island's major problem: most girls here would like nothing better than to supplant her. Considering that there is no running water (with all that that implies), Gioconda makes us remarkably comfortable. It is the pleasantest *pensione* in Forio, an interesting bargain, too: we have two huge rooms with great expanses of tiled floor and tall shutter-doors which lead onto little iron balconies overlooking the sea; the food is good, and there is rather too much of it—five courses with wine at lunch and dinner: all included, this costs each of us about one hundred dollars a month. Gioconda speaks no English, and my Italian is—well, never mind. Nevertheless, we are confidants. With pantomime and extravagant use of a bilingual dictionary we manage to convey an astonishing lot—which is why the cakes are always a flop: on gloomy days when there is nothing else to do we sit in the patio-kitchen experimenting with recipes for American pastries ("Toll House, what is?"), but these are never a success because we are too busy thumbing through the dictionary to give our baking much attention. Gioconda: "Last year, in the room where you are, there was a man from Rome. Is Rome like he said, so wonderful? He said I should come and visit him in Rome, and that it would be all right because he was a veteran of three wars. First World War, Second, and Ethiopia. You can see how old he was. No, I have never seen Rome. I have friends who have been there, and who have sent me postcards. You know the woman who works at the posta? Of course you believe in the evil eye? She has one. It is known, yes. That is why my letter never comes from Argentina."

Not receiving this Argentina letter is the real cause of Gioconda's misery. A faithless lover? I have no idea; she refuses to discuss it. So many young Italians have migrated to South America looking for work; there are wives here who have waited five years for their husbands to send them passage. Each day, when I come bringing the mail, Gioconda rushes to meet me.

Collecting the mail is a self-appointed chore. It is the first time during the day that I see the other Americans living here: there are four at the moment and we meet at Maria's café in the piazza (from the journal: "We all know that Maria waters her drinks. But does she water them with water? God, I feel awful!"). With the sun warming you, and Maria's bamboo curtains tinkling in the breeze, there is no nicer place to wait for the postman. Maria is a sawed-off woman with a gypsy face and a shrugging, cynical nature; if there is anything you want around here, from a house to a package of American cigarettes, she can arrange it; some people claim she is the richest person in Forio. There are never any women in her café; I doubt that she would allow it. As noon heightens the village converges in the piazza: like blackbirds schoolchildren in capes and wooden sandals flock and sing in the alleys, and squadrons of unemployed men lounge under the trees laughing roughly—women passing them lower their eyes. When the mailman comes he gives me the letters for our *pensione;* then I must go down the hill to face Gioconda. Sometimes she looks at me as though it were my fault that the letter never comes, as though the evil eye were mine. One day she warned me not to come home empty-handed; and so I brought her a bottle of cologne.

But the slips of gaudy paper that I found in my room were not, as I had supposed, a present in return. It was intended that we should shower these upon a statue of the Virgin which, newly arrived on the island, was being toured through most of the villages. The day the Virgin was to visit here every balcony was draped with fine laces, finer linens—an old bedspread if the family had nothing better; woven flowers garlanded the cramped streets, old ladies brought out their longest shawls, men combed their mustaches, someone put the town idiot into a clean shirt, and the children, dressed all in white, had angel-wings of golden cardboard strapped to their shoulders. The procession was supposed to enter town and pass below our balcony at about four o'clock. Alerted by Gioconda, we were at our station on time, ready to throw the pretty papers and shout, as instructed, *"Viva La Vergenie Immocalata."* A drizzling dull rain began; at six it was getting dark but, like the street-tightening crowd that waited below, we remained steadfast. A priest, scowling with annoyance, and his black skirts flapping, roared off on a motorcycle—he'd been sent to hurry along the procession. It was night, then, and a flare-path of kerosene was spilled along the route the procession was to follow. Suddenly, incongruously, the stirring ratata of a military band sounded and, with a scary crackle, the flare-path leapt alive as if to salute the arriving Virgin: swaying on a flower-filled litter, Her face shrouded in a black veil, and followed by half the island, she was laden with gold and silver watches, and as she passed, a hush surrounding her immediate presence, there was only the enchanting, surrealistic noise of these offerings, the watches: tickticktick. Later, Gioconda was very put out to discover us still clutching the bits of bright paper which, in our excitement, we'd forgotten to throw.

"April 5. A long, perilous walk. We discovered a new beach." Ischia is stony, a stark island that suggests Greece or the coast of Africa. There are orange trees, lemon trees; and, terracing the mountains, silvery green grape arbors: the wine of Ischia is highly considered, and

it is here that they make Lachrimae Christi. When you
walk beyond the town you soon come upon the branching
paths that climb through the grape fields where bees are
like a blizzard and lizards burn greenly on the budding
leaves. The peasants are brown and thick as earthenware,
and they are horizon-eyed, like sailors. For the sea is always with them. The path by the sea runs along straight-
dropping volcanic cliffs; there are junctures when it is
best just to close your eyes: it would make a long fall,
and the rocks below are like sleeping dinosaurs. One day,
walking on the cliffs, we found a poppy, then another;
they were growing singly among the somber stones, like
Chinese bells strung on a stretching string. Presently the
trail of poppies led us down a path to a strange and hidden beach. It was enclosed by the cliffs, and the water
was so clear you could observe seaflowers and the dag-
ger movements of fish; not far from shore, flat, exposed
rocks were like swimming rafts, and we paddled from
one to another: hauling ourselves into the sun, we could
look back above the cliffs and see the green grape ter-
races and a cloudy mountain. Into one rock the sea had
carved a chair, and it was the greatest pleasure to sit
there and let the waves rush up and over you.

But it is not hard to find a private beach on Ischia.
I know of at least three that no one ever goes to. The
town beach in Forio is strewn with fishing nets and overturned boats. It was on this beach that I first encountered the Mussolini family. The late dictator's widow
and three of their children live here in what I presume
to be a quiet self-imposed exile. Something about them
is sad and sympathetic. The daughter is young, blonde,
lame, and apparently witty: the local boys who talk with
her on the beach seem always to be laughing. Like any
of the island's plain women, Signora Mussolini is often
to be seen dressed in shabby black and trudging up a hill
with the weight of a shopping bag lopsiding her figure.
She is quite expressionless, but once I saw her smile.
There was a man passing through town with a parrot

who plucked printed fortunes out of a glass jar, and
Signora Mussolini, pausing to consult him, read her future with a shadowy, Da Vincian curling of her lips.

"June 5. The afternoon is a white midnight." Now
that hot weather is here the afternoons are like white
midnights; shutters are drawn, sleep stalks the streets.
At five the shops will open again, a crowd will gather
in the harbor to welcome the *Princepessa,* and later
everyone will promenade in the piazza where someone
will be playing a banjo, a harmonica, a guitar. But now
it is siesta, and there is only the blue unbroken sky, the
crowing of a cock. There are two idiots in the town,
and they are friends. One is always carrying a bouquet
of flowers which, when he meets his friend, he divides
into equal parts. In the silent shadowless afternoons
they alone are seen in the streets. Hand in hand, and
holding their flowers, they stroll across the beach and
out along the stone wall that juts far into the water.
From my balcony I can see them there, sitting among
the fishnets and the slowly rocking boats, their shaved
heads glinting in the sun, their eyes pale as space. The
white midnight is meant for them; it is then that the
island is theirs.

We have followed spring. In the four months since
we came here the nights have warmed, the sea has
grown softer, the green, still wintry water of March has
turned in June to blue, and the grape vines, once gray
and barren on their twisting stalks, are fat with their
first green bunches. There is a hatching of butterflies,
and on the mountain there are many sweet things for
the bees; in the garden, after a rainfall, you can faintly,
yes, hear the breaking of new blooms. And we are waking earlier, a sign of summer, and stay lingering out
late in the evening, which is a sign, too. But it is hard
to bring yourself indoors these nights: the moon is drawing nearer, it winks on the water with a frightful brightness; and on the parapet of the fishermen's church,
which points to sea like the prow of a ship, the young

whispering people wander back and forth and through the piazza and into some secret dark. Gioconda says it has been the longest spring she can remember: the longest is the loveliest.

A Ride Through Spain

CERTAINLY THE TRAIN was old. The seats sagged like the jowls of a bulldog, windows were out and strips of adhesive held together those that were left; in the corridor a prowling cat appeared to be hunting mice, and it was not unreasonable to assume his search would be rewarded.

Slowly, as though the engine were harnessed to elderly coolies, we crept out of Granada. The southern sky was as white and burning as a desert; there was one cloud, and it drifted like a traveling oasis.

We were going to Algeciras, a Spanish seaport facing the coast of Africa. In our compartment there was a middle-aged Australian wearing a soiled linen suit; he had tobacco-colored teeth and his fingernails were unsanitary. Presently, he informed us that he was a ship's doctor. It seemed curious, there on the dry, dour plains of Spain, to meet someone connected with the sea. Seated next to him there were two women, a mother and daughter. The mother was an overstuffed, dusty woman with sluggish, disapproving eyes and a faint mustache. The focus for her disapproval fluctuated; first, she eyed me rather strongly because, as the sunlight fanned brighter, waves of heat blew through the broken windows and I had removed my jacket—which she considered, perhaps rightly, discourteous. Later on, she took a dislike to the young soldier who also occupied our compartment. The soldier, and the woman's not very discreet daughter, a buxom girl with the scrappy features of a prizefighter, seemed to have agreed to flirt. Whenever the wandering cat appeared at our door, the daughter pretended to be frightened, and the soldier would gallantly shoo the cat into the corridor: this by-play gave them frequent opportunity to touch each other.

The young soldier was one of many on the train. With their tasseled caps set at snappy angles, they hung about in the corridors smoking sweet black cigarettes and laughing confidentially. They seemed to be enjoying themselves, which apparently was wrong of them, for whenever an officer appeared the soldiers would stare fixedly out the windows, as though enraptured by the landslides of red rock, the olive fields and stern stone mountains. Their officers were dressed for a parade, many ribbons, much brass; and some wore gleaming, improbable swords strapped to their sides. They did not mix with the soldiers, but sat together in a first-class compartment, looking bored and rather like unemployed actors. It was a blessing, I suppose, that something finally happened to give them a chance at rattling their swords.

The compartment directly ahead was taken over by one family: a delicate, attenuated, exceptionally elegant man with a mourning ribbon sewn around his sleeve, and, traveling with him, six thin, summery girls, presumably his daughters. They were beautiful, the father and his children, all of them, and in the same way: hair that had a dark shine, lips the color of pimentos, eyes like sherry. The soldiers would glance into their compartment, then look away. It was as if they had seen straight into the sun.

Whenever the train stopped, the man's two youngest daughters would descend from the carriage and stroll under the shade of parasols. They enjoyed many lengthy promenades, for the train spent the greatest part of our journey standing still. No one appeared to be exasperated by this except myself. Several passengers seemed to have friends at every station with whom they could sit around a fountain and gossip long and lazily. One old woman was met by different little groups in a dozen-odd towns—between these encounters she wept with such abandon that the Australian doctor became alarmed: why no, she said, there was nothing he could do, it was just that seeing all her relatives made her so happy.

At each stop cyclones of barefooted women and somewhat naked children ran beside the train sloshing earthen jars of water and furrily squalling *Agua! Agua!* For two pesetas you could buy a whole basket of dark runny figs, and there were trays of curious white-coated candy doughnuts that looked as though they should be eaten by young girls wearing Communion dresses. Toward noon, having collected a bottle of wine, a loaf of bread, a sausage and a cheese, we were prepared for lunch. Our companions in the compartment were hungry, too. Packages were produced, wine uncorked, and for a while there was a pleasant, almost graceful festiveness. The soldier shared a pomegranate with the girl, the Australian told an amusing story, the witch-eyed mother pulled a paper-wrapped fish from between her bosoms and ate it with a glum relish.

Afterwards, everyone was sleepy; the doctor went so solidly to sleep that a fly meandered undisturbed over his open-mouthed face. Stillness etherized the whole train; in the next compartment the lovely girls leaned loosely, like six exhausted geraniums; even the cat had ceased to prowl, and lay dreaming in the corridor. We had climbed higher, the train moseyed across a plateau of rough yellow wheat, then between the granite walls of deep ravines where wind, moving down from the mountains, quivered in strange, thorny trees. Once, at a parting in the trees, there was something I'd wanted to see, a castle on a hill, and it sat there like a crown.

It was a landscape for bandits. Earlier in the summer, a young Englishman I know (rather, know of) had been motoring through this part of Spain when, on the lonely side of a mountain, his car was surrounded by swarthy scoundrels. They robbed him, then tied him to a tree and tickled his throat with the blade of a knife. I was thinking of this when, without preface, a spatter of bullet fire strafed the dozy silence.

It was a machine gun. Bullets rained in the trees like the rattle of castanets, and the train, with a wounded creak, slowed to a halt. For a moment there was no sound except the machine gun's cough. Then, "Bandits!" I said, in a loud dreadful voice.

"Bandidos!" screamed the daughter.

"Bandidos!" echoed her mother, and the terrible word swept through the train like something drummed on a tomtom. The result was slapstick in a grim key. We collapsed on the floor, one cringing heap of arms and legs. Only the mother seemed to keep her head; standing up, she began systematically to stash away her treasures. She stuck a ring into the buns of her hair and, without shame, hiked up her skirts and dropped a pearl-studded comb into her bloomers. Like the cryings of birds at twilight, airy twitterings of distress came from the charming girls in the next compartment. In the corridor the officers bumped about yapping orders and knocking into each other.

Suddenly, silence. Outside, there was the murmur of wind in leaves, of voices. Just as the weight of the doctor's body was becoming too much for me, the outer door of our compartment swung open, and a young man stood there. He did not look clever enough to be a bandit.

"Hay un médico en el tren?" he said, smiling.

The Australian, removing the pressure of his elbow from my stomach, climbed to his feet. "I'm a doctor," he admitted, dusting himself. "Has someone been wounded?"

"Si, Señor. An old man. He is hurt in the head," said the Spaniard, who was not a bandit: alas, merely another passenger. Settling back in our seats, we listened, expressionless with embarrassment, to what had happened. It seemed that for the last several hours an old man had been stealing a ride by clinging to the rear of the train. Just now he'd lost his hold, and a soldier, seeing him fall, had started firing a machine gun as a signal for the engineer to stop the train.

My only hope was that no one remembered who had first mentioned bandits. They did not seem to. After acquiring a clean shirt of mine which he intended to use as a bandage, the doctor went off to his patient, and the mother, turning her back with sour prudery, reclaimed her pearl comb. Her daughter and the soldier followed after us as we got out of the carriage and strolled under the trees where many passengers had gathered to discuss the incident.

Two soldiers appeared carrying the old man. My shirt was wrapped around his head. They propped him under a tree and all the women clustered about, vying with each other to lend him their rosary; someone brought a bottle of wine, which pleased him more. He seemed quite happy, and moaned a great deal. The children who had been on the train circled around him giggling.

We were in a small wood that smelled of oranges. There was a path, and it led to a shaded promontory: from here, one looked across a valley where sweeping stretches of scorched golden grass shivered as though the earth were trembling. Admiring the valley, and the shadowy changes of light on the hills beyond, the six sisters, escorted by their elegant father, sat with their parasols raised above them like guests at a *fête champêtre*. The soldiers moved around them in a vague, ambitious manner; they did not quite dare to approach, though one brash, sassy fellow went to the edge of the promontory and called: *"Yo te quiero mucho."* The words returned with the hollow sub-music of a perfect echo, and the sisters, blushing, looked more deeply into the valley.

A cloud, somber as the rocky hills, had massed in the sky, and the grass below stirred like the sea before a storm. Someone said he thought it would rain. But no one wanted to go: not the injured man, who was well on his way through a second bottle of wine, nor the children who, having discovered the echo, stood happily caroling into the valley. It was like a party, and we all drifted back to the train as though each of us wished to be the last to leave. The old man, with my shirt like a grand turban on his head, was put into a first-class carriage and several eager ladies were left to attend him.

In our compartment, the dark, dusty mother sat just as we had left her. She had not seen fit to join the party. She gave me a long, glittering look. *"Bandidos,"* she said, with a surly, unnecessary vigor.

The train moved away so slowly butterflies blew in and out the windows.

The Muses Are Heard

Part I

WHEN THE CANNONS
ARE SILENT

ON SATURDAY, the seventeenth of December, 1955, a foggy wet day in West Berlin, the cast of the American production, *Porgy and Bess,* and others associated with the company, a total of ninety-four persons, were asked to assemble at the company's rehearsal hall for a "briefing" to be conducted by Mr. Walter N. Walmsley, Jr., and Mr. Roye L. Lowry, respectively Counsel and Second Secretary of the American Embassy in Moscow. Mr. Walmsley and Mr. Lowry had traveled from Moscow expressly to advise and answer any questions members of the production might have concerning their forthcoming appearance in Leningrad and Moscow.

This trip to Russia, the first of its kind ever attempted by an American theatrical group, was to be the culmination of a four-year world tour for *Porgy and Bess.* It had come about after many months of complicated, in some areas still beclouded, negotiation between the U.S.S.R. and the producers of the Gershwin opera, Robert Breen and Blevins Davis, who operate under the name Everyman Opera, Incorporated.

Although the Russians had not yet delivered their actual visas, the enormous troupe, consisting of fifty-eight actors, seven backstage personnel, two conductors, assorted wives and office workers, six children and their schoolteacher, three journalists, two dogs and one psychiatrist, were all set to depart within the next forty-eight hours, traveling by train from East Berlin via Warsaw and Moscow to Leningrad, a distance of some eleven hundred miles, yet requiring, apparently, three days and nights.

On my way to the diplomatic briefing, I shared a taxi with Mrs. Ira Gershwin and a square-cut, muscular man called Jerry Laws, who was formerly a boxer and is presently a singer. Mrs. Gershwin is of course the wife of the lyricist who, aside from being the brother of its composer, is himself co-author of *Porgy and Bess*. Periodically, for the past four years, she has left her husband at home in Beverly Hills to accompany the opera on its around-the-world wanderings: "Ira's such a stick-in-the-mud. He hates to go from one room to the next. But I'm a gypsy, darling. I love wheels." Known to her friends as Lee, an abbreviation of Lenore, she is a small and fragile woman devoted to diamonds, and wears them, quite a few, at both breakfast and dinner. She has sun-streaked hair and a heart-shaped face. The flighty fragments of her conversation, delivered in a girlish voice that rushes along in an unsecretive whisper, are pasted together with terms of endearment.

"Oh, love," she said, as we rode through the dark drizzle along the Kurfurstendam, "have you heard about the Christmas tree? The Russians are giving us a Christmas tree. In Leningrad. I think that's so sweet of them. Since they don't *believe* in Christmas. They don't—do they, darling? Anyway, their Christmas comes much later. Because they have a different calendar. Darling, do you think it's true?"

"About whether they believe in Christmas?" said Jerry Laws.

"No, love," said Mrs. Gershwin impatiently. "About the microphones. And the photographs."

For several days there had been speculation among the company on the subject of personal privacy in Russia. It was based on the rumor that their letters would be censored, their hotel rooms wired and the walls encrusted with concealed cameras.

After a thoughtful moment, Laws said, "I believe it."

"Oh, darling, you don't!" Mrs. Gershwin protested. "It can't be true! After all, *where* are we going to gossip? Unless we simply stand in the bathroom and keep flushing. As for the cameras—"

"I believe that, too," said Laws.

Mrs. Gershwin settled into a musing silence until we reached the street where the rehearsal hall was located. Then, rather wistfully, she said, "I *still* think it's nice about the Christmas tree."

We were five minutes late, and had difficulty in finding seats among the folding chairs that had been set up at one end of the mirrored rehearsal hall. It was crowded and the room was well heated; nevertheless many of those present, as though they could feel already the cold winds of the steppes, sat bundled in the paraphernalia, the scarves and woolly coats, they'd specially acquired for their Russian journey. A competitive spirit had pervaded the purchasing of these outfits, of which more than several had a certain Eskimo-look.

The meeting was called to order by Robert Breen. In addition to being the co-producer of *Porgy and Bess,* he is also its director. After he'd introduced the representatives from the Moscow Embassy, Mr. Walmsley and Mr. Lowry, who were seated behind a table facing us, Mr. Walmsley, a stocky middle-aged man with a Mencken-style haircut and a dry, drawling manner, began by speaking of the "unique opportunity" the proposed tour offered and congratulating the company in advance on the "great success" he was sure they would have behind the iron curtain.

"Since nothing happens in the Soviet Union that isn't planned, and since it is *planned* that you should have a success there, I feel perfectly safe in congratulating you now."

As though sensing a faultiness in his colleague's presumed compliment, Mr. Lowry, a youngish man with the strait-laced façade of a schoolmaster, interposed to sug-

gest that while what Mr. Walmsley had said was perfectly
correct, it was also true that there was "a genuine excitement in Russia about your coming there. They know the
Gershwin music. In fact, a Russian acquaintance of mine
told me he was at a party the other night where three
friends of his sang 'Bess, You Is My Woman Now' all
the way through."

The cast smiled appreciatively, and Mr. Walmsley
resumed. "Yes, there are some nice Russians. Very nice
people. But they have a bad government," he said, in
slow spelling-it-out tones. "You must always bear in
mind that their system of government is basically hostile
to our own. It is a system, with rules and regulations,
such as you have never experienced before. Certainly in
my experience, which is a long one, I've never encountered anything like it."

A member of the cast, John McCurry, raised his
hand to ask a question. McCurry plays the villainous
part of Crown, and is, in his own appearance, high and
heavy and somewhat forbidding, as befits the role. He
wanted to know, "Suppose some of these people invite
us into their home? See, most places we go, people do
that. Now, is it all right for us to go?"

The two diplomats exchanged an amused glance.
"As you may well imagine," said Mr. Walmsley, "we at
the Embassy have never been bothered with that problem. We're never invited *any*where. Except officially. I
can't say *you* won't be. And if so, by all means take advantage of the opportunity. From what I understand,"
he continued, "your hosts plan an extensive program of
entertainment. Something every minute. Enough to wear
you out."

Some of the youngsters smacked their lips at this
prospect, but one of them complained, "I don't touch a
drop of nothing. So when they're making all these toasts
we've heard about, how do I get out of it gracefully?"

Mr. Walmsley shrugged. "You don't have to drink
if you don't want to."

"Sure, man," the worried one was advised by a

friend, "nobody's got to drink what they don't want to. And what you don't want, you hand to me."

Now the questions came quickly. The parents, for instance, were concerned about their children. Would there be pasteurized milk? Yes. Still, Mr. Lowry thought it advisable to take a supply of Starlac, which is what he fed his own two children. And the water, was it fit to drink? Perfectly safe. Mr. Walmsley often drank it from the tap. How does one address a Soviet citizen? "Well," said Mr. Walmsley, "I *wouldn't* call them Comrade. Mr. and Mrs. will do." What about shopping, was it expensive? "Outrageously," but it hardly mattered, since there was nothing much to buy anyway. How cold did it get? Oh, it *could* occasionally go to thirty-two below zero. In that case, would their hotel room be warm? Yes, indeed. Overheated, actually.

When these fundamentals had been gone through, a voice from the back raised itself to say, "There's been so much myth talk around here. We heard we're going to be trailed all the time."

"Trailed?" Mr. Walmsley smiled. "Perhaps. Though not in the manner you're thinking of. If they assign anyone to follow you, it will be for your own protection. You must, you see, expect to attract extraordinary attention, crowds wherever you go. It won't be like walking down a street in Berlin. For that reason you may be followed, yes."

"After all," said Mr. Lowry, "the Ministry of Culture has been so anxious to have you come there that you will probably receive very generous treatment, free of the niggling-naggling that a stray foreign visitor might expect."

The voice from the back persisted, somewhat in a key of disappointment. "We heard they going to trail us. And open our letters."

"Ah," said Mr. Walmsley, "*that* is another matter. Something you take for granted. I always assume my letters have been opened."

His audience shifted in their chairs, their eyes swerving with I-told-you-so's. Robert Breen's secretary, Nancy Ryan, stood up. Miss Ryan (Radcliffe '52) had been with the company three months, having taken the job because of an interest in the theatre. A New Yorker, she is blonde, very blue-eyed, tall, just under six feet in fact, and bears considerable resemblance to her mother, an often-photographed and celebrated beauty, Mrs. William Rhinelander Stewart. She wanted to make a suggestion. "Mr. Walmsley, if it's true our letters will be censored, then wouldn't it be better to do all our correspondence on postcards? I mean, if they didn't have to open it to read it, wouldn't that cause less of a delay in outgoing mail?"

Mr. Walmsley seemed not to think Miss Ryan's plan had much merit, as either a time-saving or trouble-saving device. Meanwhile, Mrs. Gershwin had been urging Jerry Laws into action. "Go on, darling. Ask him about the microphones."

Laws caught the diplomat's attention. "A lot of us," he said, "we've been worried about the possibility of wire-tapping in our rooms."

Mr. Walmsley nodded. "I should say it's more than a possibility. Again, it's the sort of thing you should assume. Of course, no one really *knows*."

There was a silent pause, during which Mrs. Gershwin, plucking at a diamond brooch, seemed to wait for Jerry Laws to bring up the matter of concealed cameras, but he hadn't the chance before McCurry regained the floor.

McCurry leaned forward, hunching his burly shoulders. He said he thought it was about time they stopped beating around the bush and came to grips with "the big problem. The big problem is, now what do we say when they ask us political stuff? I'm speaking of the Negro situation."

McCurry's deep voice made the question ride across the room like a wave, collecting as it went the complete interest of the audience. Mr. Walmsley hesitated, as though uncertain whether to ride over it or swim under; at all events, he seemed not prepared to meet it head on.

"You don't have to answer political questions, any more than they would answer questions of that nature put to them by you." Walmsley cleared his throat, and added, "It's all dangerous ground. Treading on eggs."

Mutterings in the audience indicated that they felt the diplomat's advice was inadequate. Lowry whispered in Walmsley's ear, and McCurry consulted his wife, a melancholy woman who was sitting beside him with their three-year-old daughter on her lap. Then McCurry said, "But they're bound to ask us about the Negro situation. They always do. Last year we were in Yugoslavia, and all the time we were there—"

"Yes, I know," said Walmsley peremptorily. "That's what this whole thing is about. That's the point, isn't it?"

Walmsley's statement, or possibly the manner in which it was made, seemed to rub several people the wrong way; and Jerry Laws, a legend in the company for his fighting quick temper, jumped to his feet, his body stiff with tension. "Then how do we handle it? Should we answer it the way it is? Tell the truth? Or do you want us to gloss it over?"

Walmsley blinked. He took off a pair of horn-rimmed glasses and polished them with a handkerchief. "Why, tell the truth," he said. "Believe me, sir, the Russians know as much about the Negro situation as you do. And they don't give a damn one way or another. Except for statements, propaganda, anything they can turn to their own interests. I think you ought to keep in mind that any interviews you give will be picked up by the American press and reprinted in your home-town newspapers."

A woman, the first who had spoken, rose from her seat in the front row. "We all know there's discrimination back home," she said in a shy voice to which everyone listened respectfully. "But in the last eight years Negroes have made a lot of progress. We've come a long way and that's the truth. We can point with pride to our scientists, artists. If we did that (in Russia), it might do a lot of good."

Others agreed, and addressed the group in a similar vein. Willem Van Loon, a Russian-speaking son of the late historian, and one of the persons handling publicity for Everyman Opera, announced that he was "very, very glad this matter is being gone into so thoroughly. The other day I had a couple of the cast taping an interview for the American Service stations here in Germany, and touching on this point, this racial question, I knew we had to be very, very careful, because of being so near to East Berlin and the possibility of our being monitored—"

"Of course," said Walmsley, quietly interrupting. "I suppose you realize that we're being monitored right now."

Clearly Van Loon had not, nor had anyone else, to judge from the general consternation and gazing-round to see who could be the cause of Walmsley's remark. But any evidence, at least in the shape of mysterious strangers, was not apparent. Van Loon, however, didn't finish what he'd intended saying. His voice trailed away, as did the meeting itself, which shortly came to a meandering conclusion. Both of the diplomats blushed when the company thanked them with applause.

"Thank you," said Walmsley. "It's been a great pleasure to talk to you. Mr. Lowry and I don't often get into contact with the atmosphere of grease paint."

The director, Robert Breen, then called his cast to rehearsal, but before it began, there was much milling about and swapping of opinions on the "briefing." Jerry Laws restricted himself to one word, "Uninformative." Mrs. Greshwin, on the contrary, seemed to have found it too informative. "I'm stunned, darling. Think of living like that! Always assuming. Never *knowing*. Seriously, darling, where are we going to gossip?"

Downstairs, I was offered a return ride to the hotel by Warner Watson, production assistant to Mr. Breen. He introduced me to Dr. Fabian Schupper, who also shared the taxi. Dr. Schupper is an American student

at the German Psychoanalytic Institute. I was told he'd
been invited on the Russian tour to counteract any
"stresses" members of the company might experience.
At the last moment, much to his disappointment, Dr.
Schupper did not actually go, the management having
decided that a psychiatrist was perhaps, after all, not
necessary; though the fact that psychoanalysis and its
practitioners are not welcome in the Soviet Union may
well have been a contributing cause. But at the moment,
in the taxi, he was advising Warner Watson to "relax."

Watson, lighting a cigarette with hands that trembled noticeably, said, "Relaxed people do *not* get productions like this played on the samovar circuit."

Watson is in his late thirties. He has a graying
crew-cut, and timid, resigned brown eyes. There is about
his face, and his manner too, a blurred gentleness, a be-
yond-his-years fatigue. At one time an actor, he has been
associated with Everyman Opera since its inception in
1952. In his job, he is primarily concerned with what he
calls "fencing things in." During the past two weeks in
Berlin, he'd very nearly taken up residence at the Soviet
Embassy, attempting to get a few things fenced in. Despite
these efforts, there remained a multiplicity of matters
that had escaped corralling. Among them, there was the
situation over the company's passports, which, at this late
date, were still lurking in Russian hands waiting to be
visaed. Then, too, Watson was encountering trouble on
the subject of the train by which the troupe was to travel
to Leningrad. The production had requested four sleeping cars. The Russians had replied, quite flatly, that
they could only supply three second-class cars with "soft-
bed" (the Russian term for sleeping berth) accommodations. These, together with a baggage car and a car for
the show's scenery, would be attached to The Blue Express, a regularly scheduled Soviet train running between
East Berlin and Moscow. Watson's difficulty was that
he could not obtain from the Russians a plan of the
"soft-bed" cars, and so was unable to chart out sleeping
arrangements. He therefore imagined on the train a slap-

stick *Walpurgisnacht:* "More bodies than berths." He'd also not been able to learn at what hotels in either Leningrad or Moscow the troupe would be staying, and other details of that nature. "They'll never tell you the whole thing about anything. Not all at once. If they tell you A, they *might* tell you B, but between the two there's a long, long wait."

Apparently, though, the Russians themselves did not practice the same patience they required of others. Some hours earlier a cable had arrived from Moscow that Watson counted among the causes for his trembling hands. UNLESS ORCHESTRATIONS DELIVERED EMBASSY BERLIN TONIGHT WILL POSTPONE LENINGRAD OPENING REDUCE FEE. The Soviets had for weeks been demanding the orchestrations because they wanted their musicians to rehearse in advance of the company's arrival. Breen, fearing the orchestrations, his only copy, might be lost in transit, had refused to comply. But this ultimatum cable, with its two dire last words, seemed to have changed his mind, and now Watson was on his way to deliver the orchestrations to the Soviet Embassy.

"Don't worry," said Watson, wiping beads of moisture from his upper lip. *"I'm* not worried. We're going to get all this fenced in."

"Relax," said Dr. Schupper.

Back at my hotel, the Kempenski, where many of the company were staying, I stopped by Breen's suite to see his wife, Wilva. She'd just returned from an overnight flight to Brussels, where she'd gone to consult a doctor. For some while twinges of appendicitis had been troubling her, and when, the day before, she'd flown to Brussels, it was with the knowledge that she might have to undergo an immediate operation, thereby canceling her part in the trip to Russia. The previous October she'd spent ten days in Moscow discussing arrangements for the tour with the Ministry of Culture, a "fascinating" experience that had made her anxious to return.

"It's all right, the doctor says I can go. I didn't know

how much I wanted to until I thought I couldn't," she
said, smiling the smile that seems less an expression than
a circumstance of her eager, her anxious-to-please personality. Mrs. Breen has dimples and large brown eyes.
Her hair, a maple color, is worn upswept and held in
place by huge pins that could serve as weapons. At the
moment, she was wearing a dress of purple wool, the
color that dominates her wardrobe: "Robert's mad for
purple." She and Breen met at the University of Minnesota, where both were graduate students in the drama
department. They have been married eighteen years.
Though Mrs. Breen has played professionally on the
stage, once as Shakespeare's Juliet, her real devotions,
in the words of one of their associates, are to "Robert
and Robert's career. If she could find enough paper, she'd
wrap up the world and hand it to him."

On the surface of it, a shortage of paper would not
appear to be one of Mrs. Breen's problems, for she lives
with a traveling mountain of letters and clippings and
files. The international correspondence for Everyman
Opera is among her principal responsibilities; that, and
seeing that the company is "kept happy." In the latter
role, she'd brought back from Brussels a parcel of toys
to be distributed among the children of the cast at
Christmas time in Leningrad. *"If* I can get them away
from Robert long enough to pack them again," she said,
pointing to a bathroom where an armada of mechanical
boats floated in a filled tub. "Robert's mad for toys.
Really," she sighed, "it's dreadful to think of getting all
this into suitcases." Several of the objects on view, in
the bedroom and in the living room which doubled as
an office, presented obvious packing difficulties, especially a large seesaw-like apparatus known as a Relaxer Board. "I don't see why I can't take it to Russia.
I've taken it everywhere else. It does me a world of
good."

Mrs. Breen asked if I were looking forward to
boarding The Blue Express, and was exaggeratedly
pleased to hear that I was. "Oh, Robert and I wouldn't

miss this train ride for the world! Everybody in the cast is so darling. I know it's going to be the kind of fun you'll never stop talking about. But," she said, with a sudden sorrow in her voice that sounded not altogether sincere, "Robert and I have decided to go by plane. Of course we'll see you off at the station here—and be right there on the platform when you pull into Leningrad. At least I *hope* we will. Only I can't believe it. That it's really going to happen." She paused; for an instant a frown marred her immaculate enthusiasm. "Someday I'll tell you the real story behind it all. The people who didn't want this to happen! Oh, we've had such blows." She struck her breast. "Real body blows. And they're still coming. Right up to the last minute," she said, glancing at a sheaf of cables on a desk.

A few of the Breens' tribulations were already common knowledge. For instance, it seemed an accepted fact, in the rumor and publicity surrounding the Soviet venture, that the Russians had, on their own initiative, and out of a Geneva-spirit impulse, invited *Porgy and Bess* to tour their country. The truth of the matter is, Everyman Opera had invited itself. Breen, having long considered a trip to Russia the logical extension of his company's "good will" travels, sat down and wrote a letter to the Soviet Premier, Marshal Bulganin, saying, in effect, that *Porgy and Bess* would be pleased to undertake the journey if the U.S.S.R. was willing to have them. The appeal must have impressed Bulganin favorably, for he forwarded the letter to the Ministry of Culture, the government monopoly which, under the direction of Nikolai Mikhailov, controls every facet of artistic life inside the Soviet Union. Theatre, music films, publishing, painting, each of these activities comes under the specific, not always lenient, supervision of the Ministry of Culture, whose headquarters are in Moscow. Therefore, with the implied blessings of Bulganin, the Ministry began negotiations with Everyman Opera, though to do so could not have been a casual decision. Casual, say, as the decisions might have been in the case of the Comédie Française, whose company had appeared in Moscow a year earlier, or a British production of *Hamlet,* which had been given a Moscow première in the autumn of 1955. Both of these troupes had enjoyed whole-hearted success. But from any point of view, whether that of the visiting artists or their hosts, the risks involved were merely aesthetic. Molière and Shakespeare do not lend themselves to the intentions of modern political propaganda.

The same cannot be said of *Porgy and Bess.* Here, either side of the curtain, American or Soviet, had much to concern them, for the Gershwin opera, when slipped under the dialectical microscope, proves a test tube brimming with the kind of bacteria to which the present Russian regime is most allergic. It is extremely erotic, a serious cause for dismay in a nation with laws so prim, persons can be arrested for kissing in public. It is God-fearing; over and again it stresses the necessity of faith in a world above the stars rather than below, demonstrates in song and dialogue the comforts to be derived from religious belief ("the opium of the people"). Furthermore, it discourses, in an uncritical vein, on the subject of superstition, i.e., "The Buzzard Song." As if this weren't anathema enough, it also sings out loud that people can be happy with plenty of nothin', an unwelcome message indeed.

Certainly the Ministry of Culture must have taken these drawbacks into account, and then reflected that, though the pill was definitely there, at least it was sugar-coated. After all, and despite its accent on folkish fun, the situation of the American Negro as depicted in *Porgy and Bess,* an exploited race at the mercy of ruthless Southern whites, poverty-pinched and segregated in the ghetto of Catfish Row, could not be more agreeably imagined if the Ministry of Culture had assigned one of their own writers to the job. And so, midsummer of 1955, the Ministry informed Everyman Opera they were prepared to roll out the red carpet.

Assured of a welcome in Russia, Breen then faced

the problem of getting there, and that required money, an estimated $150,000. The first newspaper announcements of the Russian "invitation" to *Porgy and Bess* more or less suggested that the American State Department would not only be the spiritual heart of this "unprecedented project," as Breen occasionally called it, but would also provide its financial backbone. Breen believed so, and with good reason. Over the last several years the State Department had received universal praise for its moral and financial sponsoring of *Porgy and Bess,* which the *New York Times,* among others, frequently summarized as the "best ambassador" the State Department had ever sent abroad. But Breen soon discovered, after a series of pleading trips to Washington, that he could no longer rely on the patronage of his Potomac friends. Apparently they thought his project too unprecedented, or, in their own phrase, "politically premature." In other words, not one cent.

In New York, theatrical circles theorized that the State Department had withdrawn its support because they feared the opera too vulnerable to the purposes of Soviet propaganda. Defenders of the enterprise considered this attitude nonsensical. In their opinion, the fact that such social-critical aspects as the opera contained could be freely presented in the American theatre counteracted the possibilities of effective propaganda on that score. A further argument was that in Russia the very presence of the Negro cast, their affluent appearance, their so obviously unoppressed outspokenness, their educated, even worldly manner ("Why," said Mrs. Breen, "some of our cast speak three and four languages. Perfectly.") would impress on the Russian people a different image of the American Negro from the stereotype that continues to make Harriet Beecher Stowe one of the Soviet's best-selling authors.

Variety, the theatrical trade paper, reported as rumor a more straightforward explanation for the State Department's reversal. According to them, the International Exchange Program, a branch of the American

National Theatre and Academy (ANTA), whose advice on theatrical matters carries great weight in Washington, had registered opposition on the grounds that the State Department had already spent enough money on *Porgy and Bess,* and that the funds at their disposal should be more evenly spread to allow a larger catalogue of events in cultural exchange.

Nonetheless, ANTA and the State Department wished Everyman Opera the best of luck. They were not disowning, simply disinheriting. But well-wishers added little to Breen's bank account, and as he pondered the possibilities of raising the needed amount by private subscription, there was an unexpected development. The Russians stepped forward and offered to pick up the tab themselves. While the feeblest linguist could translate the meaning of this gesture, designed, as it was, to embarrass the State Department, American partisans of Breen's venture welcomed it for the very reason it was offered. They felt it would shame Washington into taking a less miserly position. They were mistaken.

Consequently, with time growing short, Breen had the choice of abandoning his plan or permitting the Soviet to capitalize it. A contract, dated December 3, 1955, was drawn up in Moscow between the Ministry of Culture of the U.S.S.R. ("designated hereinafter under the name of the 'Ministry' ") and Everyman Opera, Inc. ("hereinafter under the name of the 'Company' "). The contract consists of three and a half closely typed pages, and contains several quaint items—the Ministry agrees to supply a Russian member of the cast, namely, "one domesticated she-goat." But the burden of it is set forth in Article 5. When the writhings of language in this long clause are disentangled, it emerges that, during their stay in the Soviet Union, the company would receive weekly payments of $16,000, a figure quite below their customary fee, especially so since the payments were to be made half "in U. S. Dollars in a bank check in New York, the remainder in cash Rubles at the official rate." (As everyone knows, the official rate is an arbitrary four rubles to the dollar. Opinion wavers on what a fair exchange would be, but on the Moscow black market it is possible to get ten to one, and if a person were willing to take a chance on transporting currency out of the country, thereby risking Siberian detention, he could obtain in Switzerland only one dollar for every fifteen rubles.) In addition to these monetary agreements Article 5 also promised that the Ministry would supply the Company with: "Free lodging and food in first-class hotels or, when traveling, with sleeper accommodations and food in a dining car. Furthermore, it is understood and agreed that the Ministry pay all expenses for traveling of all members of the Company and the transportation of its scenic equipment to and through the Soviet Union and back to a European border of the Soviet Union."

All told, the Russians were investing approximately $150,000. This should not be construed as cultural philanthropy. Actually, for them it was a sound business proposition. If every performance sold out, as was almost certain to happen, the Ministry would double its investment, that is, have a total box-office gross the equivalent of $300,000. Whereas, on the basis of the Ministry-Company contract, and by applying the laws of income versus operating cost, it could be calculated that Everyman Opera would lose around $4,000 a week. Presumably Breen had devised a formula for sustaining such a loss. "But don't ask *me* what it is, darling," said Mrs. Gershwin. "It's an absolute mystery."

While Mrs. Breen was still on the theme of "body blows," her husband returned from the studio where he'd been rehearsing the cast after the diplomatic briefing. She asked him if he'd like a drink. He said he would, very much. Straight brandy, please.

Breen is around forty-five, a man of medium height. He has an excellent figure and one is kept aware of it by the fit of his clothes, for he is partial to trim Eisenhower jackets and those close-cut, narrow-legged trousers known as frontier pants. He wears custom-made shirts, preferably in the colors black and purple. He has thinning blond hair and is seldom indoors or out without a black beret. Depending on the expression, whether solemn or smiling, his face, pale and with a smoothly gaunt bone structure, suggests altogether opposite personalities. In the solemn moments, which can last hours, his face presents a mask of brooding aloofness, as though he were posing for a photographer who had warned him not to move a muscle. Inevitably, one is reminded that Breen, like his wife, has acted Shakespeare—and that the part was Hamlet, which he played in a production that, soon after the war, toured Europe and was even staged at Elsinore itself. But when Breen relaxes, or when something succceds in catching his interest, he has a complete physical altering in the direction of extreme liveliness and boyish grinning good humor. A shyness, a vulnerable, gullible look replaces the remote and seeming self-assurance. The dual nature of Breen's appearance may explain why an Everyman Opera employee could complain in one breath, "You never know where you stand with Mr. Breen," and say in the next, "Anybody can take advantage of him. He's just too kind."

Breen took a swallow of brandy and beckoned me into the bathroom, where he wanted to demonstrate how one of the toy boats operated. It was a tin canoe with a windup Indian that paddled. "Isn't that wonderful?" he said, as the Indian paddled back and forth across the tub. "Did you ever see anything like that?" He has an actor's trained voice, "placed" in a register so very deep that it makes for automatic pomposity, and as he speaks his manicured hands move with his words, not in an excitable, Latin style, but in a gracefully slow ritualistic manner, rather as though he were saying Mass. Indeed, Breen's earliest ambitions *were* ecclesiastical. Before his interest turned toward the stage, he spent a year training to become a priest.

I asked him how the rehearsal had gone. "Well, it's a good cast," he said. "But they're a little spoiled, they take it too much for granted. Curtain calls and ovations. Rave reviews. I keep telling them, I want them to understand going to Russia isn't just another engagement. We've got to be the best we've ever been."

If Breen expected the wish contained in this last sentence to come true, then, in the estimation of some observers, he had his work cut out for him. In 1952, when Breen and his co-producer, Blevins Davis, revived the Gershwin opera, which had been a box-office and somewhat of a critical failure in its original (1935) Theatre Guild presentation, the program listed William Warfield as Porgy, Leontyne Price as Bess, and Cab Calloway in the role of Sportin' Life. Since then, these stars had been replaced, and even their replacements replaced, not always with artists of comparable quality. To maintain a high level in performance of any long-run production, doubly so if the show is on tour where the strain of overnight hops, the dreamlike flow of rooms and restaurants, the electric emotional climate surrounding groups who continuously live and work together, are factors creating an accumulative fatigue that the show often reflects. Horst Kuegler, a Berlin theatre critic who, when he'd reviewed *Porgy and Bess* three years earlier (it was then appearing in Germany as part of the Berlin Music Festival), had been so enthusiastic he'd gone to see it five times, now felt, seeing it again, that it was "still full of energy and charm, though the production has deteriorated greatly." For the past week, Breen had rehearsed his cast to the limit Actors Equity permits; but whether or not the show could be whipped into prime shape, Breen had no qualms about its reception at the Leningrad première. It was going to be a "bombshell"! The Russians would be "stunned"! And, what was an unarguable prediction, "They'll never have seen anything like it!"

As Breen was finishing his brandy, his wife called from the next room. "You'd better get ready, Robert. They'll be here at six, and I've reserved a private dining room."

"Four Russians from the Embassy," Breen explained, showing me to the door. "They're coming over for dinner. You know, get friendly. It's friendship that counts."

When I arrived back in my own room in the Kempenski, I found waiting on my bed a large package wrapped in plain brown paper. My name was on it, the name of the hotel and the number of my room, but nothing to identify the sender. Inside, there were half a dozen thick anti-Communist pamphlets, and a handwritten card, without signature, which said, *Dear Sir— You can be saved*. Saved, one presumed, from the fates described in the accompanying literature, most of which purported to be the case histories of individuals, primarily Germans, who had gone behind the iron curtain, either voluntarily or as the result of force, and had not been heard from again. It was absorbing, as only case histories can be, and I would have read through the lot uninterruptedly if the telephone hadn't rung.

The caller was Breen's secretary, Nancy Ryan. "Listen," she said, "how would you like to sleep with me? On the train, I mean. The way it works out, there are going to be four in a compartment, so I'm afraid we'll have to do as the Russians do. They always put boys and girls together. *Anyway,* I'm helping assign the berths, and what with all the affections and frictions and those who want to be together and those who definitely do *not,* well, really, it's *frighten*ing. So it would simplify the situation if you and I shared a compartment with the lovebirds."

The so-called "lovebirds" were Earl Bruce Jackson, one of three alternates in the role of Sportin' Life, and Helen Thigpen, a soprano who plays the part of Serena. Jackson and Miss Thigpen had been engaged for many months. According to Everyman Opera's publicity releases, they planned to be married in Moscow.

I told Miss Ryan the arrangement sounded satisfactory. "That's brilliant," she said. "Well, see you on the train. If our visas ever come through . . ."

On Monday, the nineteenth of December, passports and visas were still in abeyance. Regardless, around three o'clock that afternoon a trio of chartered buses began circling through Berlin to collect, from the hotels and pensions where they were staying, the personnel of Everyman Opera and transport them to the railway station in East Berlin where the Soviet train, The Blue Express, was scheduled to depart at four or six or midnight, no one seemed to know for certain.

A small group, spoken of by Warner Watson as "our distinguished guests," waited together in the lobby of the Hotel Kempenski. The distinguished guests were persons who had no direct connection with *Porgy and Bess,* but had, nevertheless, been invited by the management to travel with the troupe into Russia. They amounted to: Herman Sartorius, a New York financier and close friend of Breen's; a newspaper columnist, Leonard Lyons, who was described to the Soviets in Everyman Opera's official dossier as "Company Historian," neglecting to mention that he would be mailing his history to the *New York Post;* another journalist, a Pulitzer Prize winner, Ira Wolfert, accompanied by his wife, Helen. Mr. Wolfert is on the staff of the *Reader's Digest,* and the Breens, who keep extensive scrapbooks, hoped he would do an article on their Russian adventures for that publication. Mrs. Wolfert is also an author, a poet. "A *modern* poet," she emphasized.

Mr. Lyons paced the lobby, impatient for the bus to arrive. "I'm excited. I can't sleep. Just before I left New York, Abe Burrows called me up. We live in the same building. He said you know how cold it is in Moscow? He heard on the radio it was forty below. That was day before yesterday. You got on your long underwear?" He hiked up his trouser leg to flash a stretch of red wool. Ordinarily a trim-looking man of average size, Lyon had so well prepared himself for the cold that, resplendent in a fur hat and fur-lined coat and gloves and shoes, he seemed to bulge like a shoplifter. "My wife, Sylvia, bought me three pairs of these. From Saks. They don't itch."

The financier, Herman Sartorius, attired in a conservative topcoat and business suit, as though he were setting off for Wall Street, said that no, he was not wearing long underwear. "I didn't have time to buy anything. Except a map. Did you ever try to buy a road map of Russia? Well, it's the damnedest thing. Had to turn New York upside down before I found one. Good to have on the train. Know where we are."

Lyons agreed. "But," he said, lowering his voice, and with his alert black eyes snapping from side to side, "better keep it out of sight. They might not like it. A map."

"Hmn," said Sartorius, as though he could not quite follow the drift of Lyons' thought. "Yes, well, I'll keep that in mind." Sartorius has gray hair, a height, a weight, a gentlemanly reserve that inspires the kind of confidence desirable in a financier.

"I had a letter from a friend," continued Lyons. "President Truman. He wrote me I'd better be careful in Russia because he was no longer in any position to bail me out. Russia! What a dateline!" he said, glancing around as if hunting some evidence that his elation was shared by the others.

Mrs. Wolfert said, "I'm hungry."

Her husband patted her on the shoulder. The Wolferts, who are the parents of grown children, resemble each other in that both have pink cheeks and silvering hair, a long-married, settled-down calm. "That's all right, Helen," he said, between puffs on a pipe. "Soon as we get on the train, we'll go right to the dining car."

"Sure," said Lyons. "Caviar and vodka."

Nancy Ryan came racing through the lobby, her blond hair flying, her coat flapping. "Don't stop me! There's a crisis!" She stopped, of course; and, rather as though she enjoyed imparting the bad news, said, *"Now* they tell us! Ten minutes before we leave! That there *isn't* a dining car on the train. And there *won't* be, not until we reach the Russian border. Thirty hours!"

"I'm hungry," said Mrs. Wolfert plaintively.

Miss Ryan hurried onward. "We're doing the best we can." By which she meant the management of Everyman Opera were out scouring the delicatessens of Berlin.

It was turning dark, a rain-mist was sifting through the streets when the bus arrived and, with a joking, shouting full load of passengers, rumbled off through West Berlin toward the Brandenburg Gate, where the Communist world begins.

In the bus I sat behind a couple, a young pretty member of the cast and an emaciated youth who was supposed to be a West German journalist. They had met in a Berlin jazz cellar, presumably he had fallen in love, at any rate he was now seeing her off, amid whispers and tears and soft laughter. As we neared the Brandenburg Gate, he protested that he must get off the bus. "It would be dangerous for me to go into East Berlin." Which, in retrospect, was an interesting remark. Because several weeks later who should turn up in Russia, grinning and swaggering and with no plausible explanation of how he'd got there, but this selfsame young man, still claiming to be a West German and a journalist and in love.

Beyond the Brandenburg Gate, we rode for forty minutes through the blackened acres of bombed-out East Berlin. The two additional buses, with the rest of the company, had arrived at the station before us. We joined the others on the platform where The Blue Express waited. Mrs. Gershwin was there, supervising the loading of her luggage onto the train. She was wearing a nutria coat and, over her arm, carried a mink coat zippered into a plastic bag. "Oh, the mink's for Russia, darling. Darling," she said, "why do they call it The Blue Express? When it's not blue at all?"

It was green, a sleek collection of dark green cars hitched to a Diesel engine. The letters CCCP were

painted in yellow on the side of each car, and below
them, in different languages, the train's cities of destination: Berlin-Warsaw-Moscow. Soviet train officers, elegantly turned out in black Persian lamb hats and flaring
princess-cut coats, were stationed at the entrances to
every car. Sleeping-car attendants, more humbly dressed,
stood beside them. Both the officers and the attendants
were smoking cigarettes in long vamp-style holders. As
they watched the confusion around them, the excited
milling about of the troupe, they managed to preserve a
stony uninterest despite the bold attentions of those
Americans who approached and stared at them as though
amazed, and rather peeved, to discover Russians had
two eyes correctly located.

A man from the cast walked over to one of the officers. "Tell me something, kid," he said, indicating the
lettering on the side of the train, "what's that mean,
CCCP?"

The Russian pointed his cigarette holder at the
man. Frowning, he said, *"Sie sind Deutsch?"*

The actor laughed. "I'd make a kind of funny-
looking German. Seems to me I would."

A second Russian, a car attendant, spoke up. *"Sind
sie* nicht *Deutsch?"*

"Man," said the actor, "let's us settle this misery."
He glanced down the platform and beckoned to Robin
Joachim, a young Russian-speaking New Yorker whom
Everyman Opera had hired to go along on the trip as a
translator.

The two Russians smiled with pleasure when Joachim began to talk to them in their own language;
pleasure gave way to astonishment as he explained that
the passengers boarding their train were not Germans,
but "Amerikansky" on their way to perform an opera in
Leningrad and Moscow.

"Isn't that peculiar?" said Joachim, turning to a
group of listeners that included Leonard Lyons. "Nobody
told them a thing about us being on the train. They never
heard of *Porgy and Bess*."

Lyons, the first of the Americans to recover from the shock of this news, whipped out a notebook and pencil. "Well, what do they think? What's their reaction?"

"Oh," said Joachim, "they couldn't be happier. They're delirious with joy."

It was true that the Russians were nodding and laughing. The officer gave the attendant a hearty slap on the back and shouted an order.

"What did he say?" asked Lyons, pencil poised.

Joachim said, "He told him to go put some tea on the samovar."

A station clock said six-five. There were signs of departure, whistle sounds, a clanging of doors. In the corridors of the train a radio began blaring martial music, and the company, now all aboard, were hanging out the windows waving at dispirited German luggage porters, none of whom had received the "capitalist insult," as we'd been warned the People's Democracies consider it, of a tip. Suddenly, at every window, a cheer went up. It was for the Breens, Robert and Wilva, who were plunging along the platform, followed by a wagonload of food supplies, cardboard cases of beer and wine, frankfurters, rolls and sweet buns, cold cuts, apples and oranges. There was only time to carry the cases onto the train before the radio's military fanfare reached a crescendo, and the Breens, watching with brave parental smiles, saw their "unprecedented project" slide away from them into the night.

The space to which I'd been assigned was in Car 2, Compartment 6. It seemed larger than an ordinary wagon-lit compartment, and had a certain prettiness about it, despite the presence of a radio loud-speaker that could not be completely turned off, and a blue light bulb, burning in a blue ceiling, that could never be extinguished. The walls were blue, the window was framed with blue plush curtains which matched the seat upholstery. There was a small table between the seats, and on it a lamp with a rosy silk shade.

Miss Ryan introduced me to our companions in Compartment 6, Earl Bruce Jackson and his fiancée, Helen Thigpen, whom I'd not met before.

Jackson is tall and lean, a live-wire with slanting eyes and a saturnine face. He affects a chin goatee, and his hands are radiant with rings, diamonds and sapphires and rubies. We shook hands. "Peace, brother, peace. That's the word," he said, and resumed peeling an orange, letting the hulls drop on the floor.

"No, Earl," said Miss Ryan, "that's *not* the word. The word is, keep things tidy. Put your orange hulls in the ash tray. After all," she said, looking out the window where the lonely last lights of East Berlin were fading, "this is going to be our home for a hell-uva long time."

"That's right, Earl. Our home," said Miss Thigpen.

"Peace, brother, peace. That's the word. Tell the boys back in New York," said Jackson, and spit out some seed.

Miss Ryan began to distribute part of the last-minute picnic the Breens had provided. With a sigh, Miss Thigpen refused a bottle of beer and a salami sandwich. "I don't know what I'll eat. There's nothing goes with my diet. Since I met Earl, I went on a diet and lost fifty-six pounds. Five tablespoons of caviar add up to one hundred calories."

"*This* isn't caviar. For God's sake," said Miss Ryan, her mouth full of salami sandwich.

"I'm thinking of the future," said Miss Thigpen glumly. She yawned. "Anybody object if I slip into my negligee? Might as well make ourselves comfortable."

Miss Thigpen, a concert artist before she joined *Porgy and Bess* four years ago, is a small, plump woman, lavishly powdered. She wears the highest heels, the tallest hats, and generous sprinklings of Joy ("The World's Costliest Perfume").

"Hi there, good-lookin'," said Jackson, admiring his fiancée's efforts to make herself comfortable. "The number to play is seven seven three, and peace is the word. Ooble-ee-do!"

Miss Thigpen ignored these compliments. "Earl," she said, "it *was* São Paulo, honey?"

"Was what?"

"Was where we got engaged."

"Yeah. São Paulo. Brazil."

Miss Thigpen seemed relieved. "That's what I told Mr. Lyons. He wanted to know. He's the one writes for the paper. You met him?"

"Yeah," said Jackson. "I rubbed palms with that cat."

"Maybe you heard?" said Miss Thigpen, looking at me. "About us being married in Moscow. 'Twas Earl's idea. I didn't even know we were engaged. I lost fifty-six pounds, but I didn't know we were engaged until Earl had this idea about us being married in Moscow."

"Bound to be a big story," said Jackson, and though he snapped his glittering fingers, his tone was serious, slow, as though thinking long thoughts. "The first couple of Negro Americans married in Moscow. That's front page. That's TV." He turned to Miss Thigpen. "And I don't want you to go telling that cat Lyons anything about it. Not till we're sure the magnetic vibrations are right. With a big thing like this, you got to feel the right vibrations."

Miss Thigpen said, "You ought to see Earl's wedding suit. He had it made in Munich."

"Crazy, man, crazy," said Jackson. "Brown tails with champagne satin lapels. Shoes to match, natch. And on top of that, I've got a brand-new overcoat with a—how d'ya call it—Persian lamb collar. But man, nobody's going to see *none* of it, not till The Day."

I asked when that would be, and Jackson admitted that no exact date had been set. "Mr. Breen's handling all the arrangements. He's talking to the Russians. It'll be a big thing for them, too."

"Sure," said Miss Ryan, retrieving orange hulls off the floor. "Put Russia on the map."

Miss Thigpen stretched out in her negligee and prepared to study a musical score; but she seemed troubled, unable to concentrate. "What bothers me, it won't be legal. Back home, in several states, they don't consider it legal, people married in Russia."

"What states?" said Jackson, as though resuming with her a tedious argument.

Miss Thigpen thought. "Several," she said finally.

"It's legal in Washington, D.C.," he told her. "And that's your home town. So if it's legal in your home town, what have you got to worry about?"

"Earl," said Miss Thigpen wearily, "why don't you go find your friends and have a game of Tonk?"

Tonk, popular with some elements among the cast, is a five-card variation of ordinary rummy. Jackson complained that it was useless for him to try getting up a game. "There's nowhere for us to play. All the sharps (gamblers) are bunked in with a lot of squares (non-gamblers)."

The door of our compartment was open, and Ducky James, a boyish, blond Englishman who is prop man for the production, passed by announcing, in his cockney accent. "Anybody wants a drink, we've set up a bar in our place. Martinis . . . Manhattans . . . Scotch . . ."

"That Ducky!" said Miss Thigpen. "If *he's* not the lucky one! I don't wonder he's handing out drinks. You know what happened to him? Just before we got on the train along comes this telegram. His aunt died. Leaving him ninety thousand pounds."

Jackson whistled. "How much is that in real money?"

"Two hundred and seventy thousand dollars, thereabouts," said Miss Thigpen. Then, as her future husband stood up to leave the compartment, "Where you going, Earl?"

"Just thought I'd find out if Ducky plays Tonk."

Presently we had a visit from Twerp, an all-white boxer puppy who gaily trotted into the compartment and promptly proved herself unhousebroken. She belonged to the company's wardrobe mistress, a young woman from Brooklyn named Marilyn Putnam. Miss Putnam appeared, calling, "Twerp! Twerp! Oh, *there* you are, you little bitch. Isn't she a little bitch?"

"Yes," said Miss Ryan, down on her hands and knees scrubbing at the carpet with wadded newspaper. "We have to live in here. For God's sake."

"The Russians don't mind," said Miss Putnam defensively. She scooped up her puppy and kissed its forehead. "Twerp's been being naughty up and down the corridor—haven't you, angel? The Russians just smile. *They* understand she's only a baby." She turned to leave and almost collided at the door with a girl who stood there crying. "Why, Delirious," she said to the girl, "darling, what's the matter—are you sick?"

The girl shook her head. Her chin trembled, her large eyes quivered with fresh tears.

"Delirious, honey, don't take on so," said Miss Thigpen. "Sit down. Say what's wrong."

The girl sat down. Her name was Dolores Swann; but, like many of the cast, she had acquired a nickname, in this case the descriptive Delirious. A singer in the chorus, she has red poodle-cut hair. Her pale gold face is as round as her eyes, and has the same quality of show-girl innocence. She swallowed and wailed, "I lost both my coats. Both of them. My fur coat and the blue one, too. I left them back there in the station. Not insured or anything."

Miss Thigpen clucked her tongue. "Only *you* could do a thing like that, Delirious."

"But it wasn't my fault," said Miss Swann. "I was so scared. You see, I got left behind. I missed the bus. And it was terrible, running around trying to find a taxi to take me to the station. Because none of them wanted to go to *East* Berlin. Well, finally this man spoke English and he felt sorry for me and he said he would. Well, it was terrible. Because police kept stopping us and asking questions and wanting to see papers and, oh—I was sure I was going to be left there in the pitch-black with police

and Communists and whatall. I was sure I'd never see
any of you again."

The reliving of her ordeal brought on more tears.
Miss Ryan poured her a brandy, and Miss Thigpen
squeezed her hand, saying, "It's all right, honey."

"But you can imagine how I felt, how relieved I
was when I got to the station—and there everybody was.
You hadn't left without me. I wanted to hug everybody.
I put down my coats to hug Ducky. I hugged Ducky and
forgot about my coats. Until just now."

"Think of it like this, Delirious," said Miss Thigpen,
as though searching for a comforting phrase, "just remember, you're the only person who ever went to Russia without a coat."

"I know a more unique claim that we can *all* make,"
said Miss Ryan. "Not only unique, but nuts. I mean,
here we are—rattling off to Russia without our passports.
No passports, no visa, no nothin'.."

Half an hour later, Miss Ryan's claim became less
valid, for when the train stopped at Frankfurt-am-Oder,
which marks the German-Polish border, a delegation of
officials boarded the train and, quite literally, dumped
the company's long-absent passports into Warner Watson's lap.

"I don't understand it," said Watson, parading
through the train delivering the passports to their individual owners. "This very morning the Russian Embassy told me the passports had gone to Moscow. Now
they suddenly turn up at the Polish border."

Miss Ryan quickly rifled through her passport and
found blankness on those pages where the Russian visa
should have been stamped. "For God's sake, Warner.
There's nothing here."

"They've issued a collective visa. They have, or
they're going to, don't ask me which," said Watson, his
timid, tired voice skidding to a hoarse whisper. His skin
was gray, and under his eyes purple bruises of fatigue
were prominent as paint.

"But, Warner . . ."

Watson held up a protesting hand. "I'm not human," he said. "I've got to go to bed. I'm going to go to bed and stay there until we get to Leningrad."

"Well, it's a pity," said Miss Ryan as Watson fled, "a damned shame we can't have a stamp in our passports. I like souvenirs."

The train was scheduled to stay at the border forty minutes. I decided to get off and look around. At the end of the car, I found the exit door open and started down the small iron steps leading onto the tracks. Far ahead I could see the lights of a station, and a misty red lantern swinging back and forth. But it was dark where I was, except for the yellow squares cast by the train's windows. I walked along the tracks, liking the fresh feel of the cold and wondering whether I was in Germany or Poland. Suddenly I noticed figures running toward me, a set of shadows that, drawing nearer, turned into three soldiers, pale flat-faced men with awkward ankle-length coats and bayoneted rifles strapped to their shoulders. They stared at me in silence. Then one of them pointed to the train; he grunted and motioned for me to get back on it. We marched along together, the four of us, and I said in English that I was sorry, I hadn't realized passengers were not allowed off the train. There was no response, merely another grunt and an urging forward. I climbed the train steps and turned to wave at them. They didn't wave back.

"Darling, you haven't been *out,*" said Mrs. Gershwin, whose compartment I passed in returning. "Well, you shouldn't. It isn't safe." Mrs. Gershwin was one of the two people occupying compartments to themselves. (The other was Leonard Lyons, who had obtained privacy by threatening to leave the train unless his erstwhile roommates, Herman Sartorius and Warner Watson, were removed. "It's nothing personal," he said, "but I'm a working man. I've got to turn out a thousand words a day. I can't write with a lot of characters sitting around." Sartorius and Watson had therefore been forced to move in with the Ira Wolferts. As for Mrs. Gershwin, she'd been allotted her solo status because, in the view of the management, "She deserves it. She's a Gershwin.") Without discarding her diamonds, Mrs. Gershwin had changed into slacks and a sweater; she'd tied ribbons in her hair and slippered her feet in bits of fluff. "It must have been freezing out there. I see snow on the ground. You ought to have some hot tea. Mmmmm, it's lovely," she said, sipping dark, almost black tea from a tall glass set in a silver holder with a silver handle. "That darling little man is brewing it on his samovar."

I went to look for the tea-maker, who was the attendant for Car 2; but when I found him, at the end of the corridor, he was contending with more than a blazing samovar. Twerp, the boxer puppy, was yapping between his legs and snapping at his trousers. Moreover, he was undergoing an intense interview, Lyons asking the questions and Robin Joachim acting as translator. Small and haggard, the Russian had a pushed-in, Pekingese face creased with wrinkles that seemed to indicate nutritional defects rather than age. His mouth was studded with steel teeth, and his eyelids drooped, as though he were on the verge of sleep. Between dispensing tea and fending off Twerp, he answered Lyons' quick-fire queries like a wilted housewife talking to the censor. He said he was from Smolensk. He said his feet hurt him, his back hurt him, that he always had a headache from overwork. He said he only made two hundred rubles a month ($50, but much less in actual buying power) and considered himself underpaid. He said yes, he'd very much appreciate a tip.

Lyons paused in his notetaking and said, "I didn't know they were allowed to complain like this. The way it sounds, I get the impression this guy is a discontent."

The attendant gave me my tea, and at the same time offered me, from a crumpled pack, one of his own cigarettes. It was two-thirds filter and one-third tobacco, good for seven or eight harsh puffs, though I didn't enjoy that many, for as I started back to my compartment the train lurched forward with an abruptness that sent both tea and cigarette flying.

Marilyn Putnam poked her head into the corridor. "Holy mackerel," she said, surveying the wreckage, "did *Twerp* do that?"

In Compartment 6 the berths had been made for the night, indeed for the whole journey, since they were never remade. Clean coarse linen, a crunchy pillow that smelled of hay, a single thin blanket. Miss Ryan and Miss Thigpen had gone to bed to read, having first turned the radio as low as it would go and opened the window a finger's width.

Miss Thigpen yawned, and asked me, "Did you see Earl, honey?"

I told her that I had. "He's teaching Ducky to play Tonk."

"Oh," said Miss Thigpen, giggling sleepily, "that means Earl won't be home till dawn."

I kicked off my shoes, and lay down in my berth, thinking in a moment I'd finish undressing. Overhead, in the berth above mine, I could hear Miss Ryan muttering to herself, as though she were reading aloud. It developed that she was studying Russian, using for the purpose an old English-Russian phrase book the U. S. Army had issued during the war for the benefit of American soldiers who might come in contact with Russians.

"Nancy," said Miss Thigpen, like a child asking for a bedtime story, "Nancy, say us something in Russian."

"The only thing I've learned is *Awr-ga-nih-ya ra-neen* . . ." Miss Ryan faltered. She took a deep breath. ". . . *V-pa-lavih-yee.* Wow! I only wanted to learn the alphabet. So I can read street signs."

"But that was nice, Nancy. What does it mean?"

"It means, 'I have been wounded in the privates.' "

"Really, Nancy," said Miss Thigpen, bewildered, "why on earth would you care to memorize something like that?"

"Go to sleep," said Miss Ryan, turning off her reading light.

Miss Thigpen yawned again. She pulled the covers up to her chin. "I'm about ready to."

Soon, lying there, I had a sense of stillness traveling through the train, seeping through the cars like the wintry color of the blue light bulb. Frost was spreading at the corners of the window; it seemed like a web-weaving in reverse. On the muted radio an orchestra of balalaikas made shivery music; like an odd and lonely counterpoint, someone somewhere nearby was playing a harmonica.

"Listen," whispered Miss Thigpen, calling attention to the harmonica. "That's Junior," she said, meaning Junior Mignatt, a member of the cast still in his teens. "Don't you know that boy is lonesome? He's from Panama. He's never seen snow before."

"Go to sleep," said Miss Ryan. The northern roar of wind at the window seemed to echo her command. The train shrieked into a tunnel. For me, fallen asleep fully clothed, the tunnel lasted all night long.

Coldness woke me. Snow was blowing through the window's minute opening. Enough had settled at the foot of my berth to scoop into a snowball. I got up, glad I'd gone to bed with my clothes on, and closed the window. It was blurred with ice. I rubbed a part of it until I could peer out. There were hints of sunrise on the rim of the sky, yet it was still dark, and the traces of morning color were like goldfish swimming in ink. We were on the outskirts of a city. Rural lamplighted houses gave way to cement blocks of forlorn, look-alike apartment dwellings. The train rumbled over a bridge that spanned a street; below, a frail streetcar, jammed with people on their way to work, careened round a curve like a rickety bobsled. Moments later we pulled into a station, which by now I realized must be Warsaw. On a dim, snow-deep platform gangs of men stood clustered together stamping their feet and slapping their ears. I noticed our

car attendant, the tea-maker, join one of the groups. He
gestured toward the train and said something that made
them laugh. An explosion of breath-smoke filled the air.
Still laughing, several of the men approached the train.
I slipped back into bed, for it was obvious that they
intended to peek in the windows. One after another, distorted faces mashed themselves against the glass. Presently I heard a short scream. It came from a compartment further ahead and sounded like Dolores Swann.
Screams were understandable if she'd wakened to see,
looming at the window, one of these frosty masks.
Though it roused none of my own companions, I waited,
expecting a commotion in the car, but quietness resumed,
except for Twerp, who started barking with a regular
rhythm that sent me off to sleep again.

At ten, when I opened my eyes, we were in a wild,
crystal world of frozen rivers and snowfields. Here and
there, like printing on paper, stretches of fir trees interrupted the whiteness. Flights of crows seemed to skate
on a sky hard and shiny as ice.

"Man," said Earl Bruce Jackson, just awake and
sleepily scratching himself as he stared out the window.
"I'm telling you. They don't grow oranges here."

The washroom in Car 2 was a bleak unheated
chamber. There was a rusty washbasin with the customary two faucets, hot and cold. Unfortunately, they both
leaked a frigid trickle. That first morning a long queue
of men waited at the washroom door, toothbrushes in
one hand, shaving tackle in the other. Ducky James had
the notion of asking the attendant, who was busily
stoking the little coal fire under his samovar, to part
with some of his tea water and "gives us blokes a
chance at a decent shave." Everyone thought this a
splendid idea except the Russian, for when the request
was translated to him he looked at his samovar as
though it were bubbling with melted diamonds. Then he
did a curious thing.

He stepped up to each man and brushed his fingertips against their cheeks, examining their beard stubble. There was a tenderness in the action that made it memorable. "Boy," said Ducky James, "he sure is affectionate."

But the attendant concluded his researches with a headshake. Absolutely no, *nyet,* he would not give away his hot water. The condition of the gentlemen's beards did not justify such a sacrifice, and besides, when traveling, the "realistic" man should expect to go unshaven. "My water is for tea," he said. "Hot and sweet and good for the spirit."

A steaming glass of it went with me into the washroom. I used it for brushing my teeth, and then, combining it with soap, transformed it into a shaving cream. Rather sticky, but not bad at all.

Afterwards, feeling spruce, I commenced a round of visits. The occupant of Compartment 1, Leonard Lyons, was having a professional tête-à-tête with Earl Bruce Jackson. Clearly Jackson had overcome his fear that Lyons might not possess the "right vibrations," for he was describing to him the details of his forthcoming Moscow marriage.

"That's great. Just great, Earl," said Lyons, scribbling away. "Brown tails. Champagne satin lapels. Now —who's going to be your best man?"

Jackson told him he'd invited Warner Watson to serve in that capacity. Lyons seemed reluctant to approve the choice. "Listen," he said, tapping Jackson on the knee, "did you ever think of asking somebody, well, important?"

"Like you, you mean?"

"Like *Khrushchev,*" said Lyons. "Like *Bulganin.*"

Jackson's eyes narrowed, as though he couldn't decide whether Lyons' suggestion was serious or a leg pull. "But I already ask Warner. But maybe, under that kind of circumstance . . ."

"Sure," said Lyons, "Warner would understand."

Still, Jackson had one last vestige of doubt. "You think Mr. Breen can arrange it, to get me one of those cats?"

"He could try," said Lyons. "And just trying, see, that could land you on the front page."

"*C'est* ooble-ee-do," said Jackson, gazing at Lyons with perfect admiration. "Really crazy, man. Gone."

Further along the corridor, I called on the Wolferts, who were sharing their compartment with Herman Sartorius and Warner Watson, the pair Lyons had evicted, the latter in more ways than one. But Watson was still asleep, unaware of his impending dismissal as Jackson's best man. Sartorius and Ira Wolfert were sitting with an immense map spread across their collective lap, and Mrs. Wolfert, bundled in a fur coat, was hunched over a manuscript. I asked if she were keeping a journal.

"I *do*. Only this is a poem. I've been working on it since last January. I thought I might finish it on the train. But the way I feel . . ." she said dismally. "I didn't sleep a wink last night. My hands are cold. My head's whirling with impressions. I don't know where I am."

Sartorius placed a fastidious finger on his map. "I'll tell you where we are. We've passed Liedce. Now we've got about five more hours of Poland before Brest Litovsk."

Brest Litovsk was to be the first stop in Russia. A good deal was scheduled to happen there. The wheels of the train would be changed to fit Russia's wide-gauge tracks; a dining car would be attached, and, most importantly, representatives from the Ministry of Culture were to meet the company and travel on with them to Leningrad.

"Know what this reminds me of," said Ira Wolfert, pointing a pipe at the severe landscape. "Parts of America. The West."

Sartorius nodded. "Wyoming in the winter."

Returning to the corridor, I encountered Miss Ryan, still wearing her bed costume, a red flannel nightshirt. She was hopping on one foot, her other foot having made contact with a sample of Twerp's misbehavior.

I said, "Good morning."

She said, *"Don't speak to me,"* and hopped away toward the washroom.

Next, I went to Car 3, where the family groups, children and their parents, were installed. School had just let out; that is, the children had finished their morning lessons and were consequently in sportive spirit. Paper planes sailed through the air. Caricatures were being finger-drawn on the frosted windows. The Russian attendant, who looked even more mournful and harassed than his colleague in Car 2, was kept at such a hop protecting Soviet property that he hadn't noticed what was happening to his samovar. Two little boys had taken it over and were roasting hot dogs. One of them, Davy Bey, offered me a bite. "Good, huh?" I told him it was indeed. Well, he said, if I liked it that much, then I could have the rest of it; he'd already eaten fifteen.

"You see the wolves?" he asked.

An older friend, Gail Barnes, told him, "Stop making stories, Davy. They weren't wolves. They were plain dogs."

"Was wolves," said Davy, who has a snub nose and a wicked tilt to his eyes. "Everybody saw them. Out the window. They *looked* like dogs. Police dogs, only littler. And what they were up to, they were chasing each other round and round in the snow. Like they were having a grand time. I coulda killed one dead. Woooooolves," he howled, and poked me in the stomach with a cowboy pistol.

Gail said that she hoped I understood. "Davy's only a child." Gail, whose father, Irving Barnes, alternates in the role of Porgy, is eleven, the oldest of the company's six children, most of whom play minor parts in the show. Because of her seniority, she has developed a sense of big-sister responsibility toward all the children, and handles them with mature good nature, a firm politeness that could set any governess an example. "Excuse me," she said, glancing down the corridor where several of her charges, by managing to open a window, were letting in blasts of Arctic wind. "I'm afraid I'll have to put a stop to that."

But before she had completed her mission, Gail herself was swept away into being a child again. "Oh, look," she cried, hanging out the very window she'd gone to close. "Look, kids . . . *People!*"

The people were two small children ice-skating on a long ribbon of pond at the edge of a white wood. They skated fast as they could, trying to keep up with the train, and as it sped beyond them they stretched out their arms, as though to catch the shouted greetings, the blown kisses of Gail and her friends.

Meanwhile, the Russian attendant had discovered smoke billowing from his samovar. He snatched charred hot dogs off the fire, and tossed them on the floor. Then, sucking blistered fingers and employing a vocabulary that must have been, to judge from its tone, on the blistery side itself, he rushed to pry the children away from the window and slam it shut.

"Aw, dont' be a sorehead," Davy told him. "We're just having a grand time."

The remnants of a cheese and fruit lunch were scattered on the table (and the carpet) of Compartment 6. Midafternoon sunlight sparkled in a glass of Chianti Miss Ryan was revolving in her hand. "I adore wine," she said fervently. "I began drinking it when I was twelve. Heavily. It's a wonder I'm not a wino." She sipped and sighed with a contentment that reflected the general mood. Miss Thigpen and her fiancé, who'd had their share of Chianti, were nestled together in a corner of their seat, her head resting on his shoulder. The drowsy, dreaming spell was broken by a knock at the door, and someone saying, "This is it. Russia."

"Places, please," said Miss Ryan. "Curtain going up."

The first signs of an approaching frontier came into

view: stark wooden guard towers, not unsimilar to those
that encircle Southern convict farms. Spread at wide in-
tervals, they marched across the wastes like giant telephone poles. In the nearest of them I could see a man
watching the train through binoculars. The train slowed
round a curve and slackened to a stop. We were in a
switch yard, surrounded by a maze of tracks and halted
freight cars. It was the Soviet border, forty minutes from
Brest Litovsk.

Along the tracks, herds of women with shawl-
wrapped heads, like a woolly version of purdah, were
swinging picks, shoveling snow, pausing only to blow
their noses into naked, raw-red hands. The few who
even glanced at The Blue Express risked sharp looks
from various militiamen lounging about with their hands
stuffed in their coat pockets.

"If that's not a *shame*," said Miss Thigpen. "Ladies
doing all the work, while the men just stand around. How
disgraceful!"

"That's what it is here, honey," said Jackson, puffing on one of his ruby rings, and polishing it against his
lapel. "Every man a Sportin' Life."

"I'd like to see somebody treat *me* that way," replied Miss Thigpen, warningly.

"But I must say," said Miss Ryan, "the men are
pretty divine." Her interest was fixed on a pair of officers
pacing below the window, tall-strong-silent types with
thin lips and rugged, windburned faces. One of them
looked up and, catching sight of Miss Ryan's blue eyes
and long golden hair, lost step with his partner. Miss
Ryan whimpered, "Oh, wouldn't it be awful!"

"Awful what, honey?" said Miss Thigpen.

"If I fell in love with a Russian," said Miss Ryan.
"Wouldn't that be the absolute *fin?* Actually, my mother's afraid that I might. She said if I fell in love with any
Russians I needn't bother coming home. But," she added,
her gaze again drifting toward the officer, "if they're all
like *that* . . ."

Quite suddenly Miss Ryan's admirer had no time

for flirtation. He became part of a small Russian army chasing round the yard after Robin Joachim. Joachim, an overly avid photographer, had broken the rules by getting off the train, then compounded that error by attempting to take pictures. Now he was racing zigzag across the tracks, narrowly avoiding the wrathful swipe of a woman worker's shovel, barely eluding the grasp of a guard.

"I hope they catch him," said Miss Ryan coldly. "Him and his goddam cameras. I knew he'd get us into trouble."

Joachim, however, turned out to be a resourceful young man. Slipping past his pursuers, he hurled himself onto the train, rushed into a compartment, threw his coat, his camera and cap under the seat, and to further alter his appearance, whipped off his horn-rimmed glasses. Seconds later, when the angry Soviets came aboard, he calmly assumed his role of company translator and helped them hunt the culprit, a search that included every compartment. Warner Watson, roused from his slumbers, was the person least amused by the situation. He promised Joachim a good talking to. "This," he said, "is *not* the way to begin a cultural exchange."

The incident caused the train to be delayed forty-five minutes and had other repercussions as well, one of them involving Twerp, for the Russians, in the course of their search, had been appalled by certain conditions in Car 2 attributable to the puppy. Twerp's owner, Marilyn Putnam, said later, "I put it to them straight. I said, since we're never allowed off the train, what the hell do you expect? That shut 'em up."

We reached Brest Litovsk in a luminous twilight. Statues of political heroes, painted cheap-silver like those souvenir figures sold at Woolworth's, saluted us along the last mile of track leading to the station. The station was on high ground that afforded a partial view of the city, dim and blue and dominated, far-off, by an Orthodox cathedral, whose onion-domes and mosaic towers still projected, despite the failing light, their Oriental colors.

Among the company it had been rumored that we would be allowed off the train here, and perhaps, while the wheels were changed and the dining car added, permitted to tour the city. Leonard Lyons was most anxious that this should happen. "I can't write a thousand words a day just sitting on a train. I need action." Lyons had gone so far as to discuss with the cast the kind of action he would like. He wanted them to traipse around Brest Litovsk singing spirituals. "It's a good story and it's a good showmanship. I'm surprised Breen didn't think of it." When the train stopped, the doors opened all right, but were immediately closed again, after admitting a five-man delegation from Moscow's Ministry of Culture.

One of these emissaries was a middle-aged woman with straying dishwater hair and, except for her eyes, what seemed a kind, motherly face. The eyes, dull gray and flecked with dots of milky white, had an embalmed glaze that did not blend with the cheerful contours of her expression. She wore a black cloth coat and a rusty black dress that sagged at the breasts from the weight of an ivory rose. In introducing herself and her colleagues, she ran the names together so that it sounded like a patter song. "You will please to meet SaschaMenashaTiomkenKerin-skyIvorsIvanovichNikolaiSavchenkoPlesitskyaGrutchen-koRickiSomanenko . . ."

In due time, the Americans were to sort and simplify these names until their owners became familiar as Miss Lydia. Henry, Sascha and Igor, the latter young underlings from the Ministry who, like the middle-aged Miss Lydia, had been assigned to the company as translators. But the fifth member of the quintet, Nikolai Savchenko, was not the man you call Nick. An important official in the Ministry, Savchenko was in charge of the *Porgy and Bess* tour.

The victim of a slightly receding chin, mildly bulging eyes and a tendency toward fat, he was nevertheless a formidable figure—well over six feet, with a stern, no-nonsense attitude and a handshake like a nutcracker.

Beside him, his young assistants looked like sickly children, though two of them, Sascha and Igor, were strapping boys whose shoulders were too broad for their fur-collared coats; and Henry, a spidery mite with huge ears so red they were purple, made up by personal vividness what he lacked in stature.

It seemed natural that Miss Lydia, and the young men should react awkwardly to this, their first encounter with Westerners; understandable that they should hesitate to test their English, so tediously learned at Moscow's Institute of Foreign Languages but never before practiced on bona-fide foreigners; forgivable that they should, instead, stare as though the Americans represented pawns in a chess problem. But Savchenko also gave an impression of being ill at ease, of preferring, in fact, a stretch in Lubyanka to his present chores. Which was excusable, too; though rather odd when you consider that for two years during the war he served as Counsel at the Soviet Embassy in Washington. Even so, he seemed to find Americans such a tongue-tying novelty that for the moment he affected not to speak English. He delivered a small speech of welcome in gruff Russian, then had it translated by Miss Lydia. "We hope each and all have had a pleasant journey. Too bad you see us in the winter. It is not the good time of year. But we have the saying, Better now than never. Your visit is a step forward in the march toward peace. When the cannons are heard, the muses are silent; when the cannons are silent, the muses are heard."

The muse-cannon metaphor, which was to prove a Savchenko favorite, the starring sentence of all future speeches, was an instant hit with his listeners ("A beautiful thing." "Just great, Mr. Savchenko." "That's cool cookin', man."), and Savchenko, warmed by success and beginning to relax, decided there was perhaps no reason to keep the company cooped up in the train. Why not step out on the platform and watch the changing of the wheels?

.   .   .

Outside, Lyons canvassed the group, trying to work up a song fest. But the temperature, ten below zero, was not conducive to a musical mood. Moreover, a large percentage of those who had been grateful to escape The Blue Express were, after the briefest exposure, shoving each other to get back in. The hearties who remained watched in the nightfall as workers of both sexes uncoupled the cars and jacked them to the height of a man. The old wheels, spraying sparks, were then rolled from under the train, while from the opposite direction the new wide-gauge wheels came gliding into place. Ira Wolfert called the operation "very efficient"; Herman Sartorius considered it "most impressive"; but Miss Ryan thought it was a "damned bore" and said that if I'd follow her into the station, she would buy me a vodka.

No one stopped us. We crossed a hundred yards of track, walked down a dirt lane between warehouses, and arrived at what appeared to be a combination of a parking lot and a market place. Brightly lighted kiosks circled it like candles burning on a cake. It was puzzling to discover that each of the kiosks sold the same products: cans of Red Star salmon, Red Star sardines, dusty bottles of Kremlin perfume, dusty boxes of Kremlin candy, pickled tomatoes, hairy slabs of raw bacon slapped between thick slices of grime-colored bread, weird liqueurs, cross buns (without the cross) that one somehow felt had been baked last July. And though the kiosks were attracting a brisk trade, the most sought-after item was not on sale at any of them. It was in the private hands of a peddler, an elderly Chinese who carried a tray of apples. The apples were as shriveled and miniature as himself, but his waiting line of customers appeared disconsolate when the last of them evaporated. At the far end of the area a flight of steps led to the main entrance of the station, and the Chinese, folding his empty tray, wandered over to them and sat down next to a friend. The friend was a beggar bundled in an old army coat and with a pair of crutches sprawled beside him like the wings of a wounded bird. Every third or fourth person going by dropped a coin into his hand. The Chinese gave him something, too. An apple. He'd saved one for the beggar, and one for himself. The two friends gnawed their apples and leaned against each other in the cutting cold.

The constant wailing of a train whistle seemed to fuse the apple-eaters and the kiosks and the batlike passings of fur-shrouded faces into a smoky, single image of its woeful sound. "I've never been homesick. Never in my life," Miss Ryan informed me. "But sometimes, for God's sake. Sometimes," she said, running up the steps and pushing open the doors of the station, "you do feel a long *way* from home."

Since Brest Litovsk is one of Russia's most strategic railroad centers, its station is among the country's largest. Looking for somewhere to buy a drink, we explored lofty corridors and a series of waiting rooms, the principal one furnished with handsome oak benches occupied by many passengers with very few suitcases. Children and paper bundles filled their laps. The stone floors, soggy with black slush, made slippery walking, and there was an odor in the air, a saturation so heavy it seemed less a smell than a pressure. Travelers to Venice often remark on the vivid scents of that city. The public places of Russia, terminals and department stores, restaurants and theatres, also have a reek instantly recognizable. And Miss Ryan, taking her first sniff of it, said, "Boy, I wouldn't want a bottle of this. Old socks and a million yawns."

In the search for a bar, we began opening doors at random. Miss Ryan sailed through one and out again. It was a men's room. Then, spotting a pair of dead-drunks as they emerged from behind a small red door, she decided, "That's the place we're looking for." The red door led into an extraordinary restaurant. The size of a gymnasium, it looked as if it had been done over for a school prom by a decorating committee with Victorian tastes. Plush crimson draperies were looped along the walls. Other-era chandeliers distributed a tropic glare that beat down on a jungle of borscht-stained tablecloths and withering rubber plants. The maître d'hôtel seemed appropriate to this atmosphere of grandeur gone to seed. He was at least eighty years old, a white-bearded patriarch with ferocious eyes that peered at us, through a sailor's-dive haze of cigarette smoke, as though questioning our right to be there.

Miss Ryan smiled at him and said, "Vodka, *pjolista*." The old man stared at her with more hostility then comprehension. She tried varying pronunciations, "Woedka . . . Wadka . . . Woodka," and even performed a bottoms-up pantomime. "The poor thing's deaf," she said, and shouted, *"Vodka. For God's sake."*

Although his expression remained unenlightened, the old man beckoned us forward and, following the Russian custom of seating strangers together, put us at a table with two men. They both were drinking beer, and the old man pointed at it, as if asking, was this what we wanted? Miss Ryan, resigning herself, nodded.

Our companions at the table were two very different specimens. One, a beefy boy with a shaved head and wearing some sort of faded uniform, was well on his way to being drunk, a condition shared by a surprising lot of the restaurant's clientele, most of whom were male, many of them either boisterous or slumped across their tables mumbling to themselves. The second man was an enigma. In appearance he might have been a Wall Street partner of Herman Sartorius, the kind of person better imagined dining at the Pavillon than sipping beer in Brest Litovsk. His suit was pressed, and one could see that he hadn't sewn it himself. There were gold cuff links in his shirt, and he was the only man in the room sporting a tie.

After a moment the shaven-headed soldier spoke to Miss Ryan. "I'm afraid I don't speak Russian," she told him. "We're Americans. *Amerikansky*." Her declaration had a somewhat sobering effect. His reddened eyes slowly came into semifocus. He turned to the well-dressed man and made a long statement, at the end of which the man answered him with several chiseled, cold-sounding sentences. There followed between them a sharp repartee, then the soldier took his beer and stalked to another table, where he sat glowering. "Well," said Miss Ryan, glowering back, "not *all* the men are attractive, that's for sure." However, she considered our apparent defender, the well-dressed man: "Very attractive. Sort of Otto Kruger. Funny, I've always liked older men. Stop staring. He'll know we're talking about him. Listen," she said, after calling attention to his shirt, his cuff links, his clean fingernails, "do you suppose there's such a thing as a Russian millionaire?"

The beer arrived. A quart bottle and two glasses. The maître d'hôtel poured an inch of beer into my glass, then waited expectantly. Miss Ryan saw the point before I did. "He wants you to *taste* it, like wine." Lifting the glass, I wondered if beer-tasting was a Soviet commonplace, or if it was a ceremony, some confused champagne-memory of Czarist elegance that the old man had revived to impress us. I sipped, nodded, and the old man proudly filled our glasses with a warm and foamless brew. But Miss Ryan said suddenly, "Don't touch it. It's dreadful!" I told her I didn't think it was that bad. "I mean, we're in dreadful trouble," she said. "I mean, my God, we can't pay for this. I completely forgot. We haven't any rubles."

"Please, won't you be my guests?" inquired a soft voice in beautifully accented English. It was the well-dressed man who had spoken, and though his face was perfectly straight, his eyes, a bright Nordic blue, wrinkled with an amusement that took full measure of our discomfort. "I am not a Russian millionaire. They *do* exist— I know quite a few—but it would give me pleasure to pay for your drink. No, please, there is no cause to apologize," he said, in response to Miss Ryan's stammered efforts, and openly smiling, "it's been the keenest enjoyment. Very unusual. Very unusual to run across Americans in this part of the world. Are you Communists?"

After disabusing him of that notion, Miss Ryan told him where we were going, and why. "You are fortunate that you go to Leningrad first. A lovely city," he said, "very quiet, really European, the one place in Russia I could imagine living, not that I do, but still . . . Yes, I like Leningrad. It's not the least like Moscow. I'm on my way to Warsaw, but I've just been two weeks in Moscow. That's equal to two months anywhere else." He told us that he was Norwegian, and that his business, lumber, had required him to visit the Soviet Union several weeks of every year, except for a gap during the war, since 1931. "I speak the language quite well, and among my friends I don't mind passing as a Russian authority. But to be honest, I can't say I understand much more about it now than I did in 1931. Whenever I go to your country —I've been there, oh, I guess a half dozen times—it always strikes me that Americans are the only people who remind me of Russians. You don't object to my saying that? Americans are so generous. Energetic. And underneath all that brag they have such a wishing to be loved, they want to be petted, like dogs and children, and told that they are just as good and even better than the rest of us. Well, Europeans are inclined to agree with them. But they simply won't believe it. They go right on feeling inferior and far away. Alone. Like Russians. Precisely."

Miss Ryan wanted to know the substance of his dialogue with the soldier who had left the table. "Oh, silly rot," he said. "Alcoholic bravado. For some foozled reason he thought you had insulted him. I told him he was being *nye kulturni*. Remember that: *nye kulturni*. You'll find it extremely useful, because when these chaps are rude and you feel obliged to tick them off, it means not a whit to call them a bastard, a son of a dog, but to tell him he's *uncultured,* that really strikes home."

Miss Ryan was growing anxious about the time. We shook hands with the gentleman and thanked him for the beer. "You've been very *kulturni,*" she said. "And by the way, I think you're *more* attractive than Otto Kruger."

"I shall certainly tell my wife," he said grinning. "*Dazvedanya.* Good luck."

An hour out of Brest Litovsk, the first call to the dining car was announced. It was an event the company had looked forward to with appetites excited by both genuine hunger and the conviction that the Soviet hosts were bound to make this, the company's first Russian meal, a "real spread"; or, as another of the cast forthrightly phrased it, " a bust-gut."

Miss Thigpen's desires were the most modest. "Five spoons of caviar and a piece of dry toast. That's one hundred and thirty calories." Calories were Mrs. Gershwin's last concern. "Don't think I'm not going to tear into the cavy, darling. It cost thirty-five dollars a pound in Beverly Hills." The dreams of Leonard Lyons centered around hot borscht and sour cream. Earl Bruce Jackson planned to "stone" himself with vodka and "slay" himself with shashlik. Marilyn Putnam hoped that everyone would save little tidbits for Twerp.

The first sitting, fifty strong, marched into the dining car and took their places at linen-covered tables, each seating four, that ran down either side of the aisle. The tables were set with white crockery and smoothly worn silver. The diner itself seemed as old as the silver, and the smell of cooking, a half-century's worth, hung in the air like a visible steam. Savchenko was absent, but Miss Lydia and the three young men from the Ministry played host at different tables. The young men kept gazing round, as though silently calling to each other from separate islands of exile and misery.

Miss Lydia shared a table with Lyons, Miss Ryan and myself. One sensed that for this middle-aged woman, who said that her ordinary life was translating articles and living in a room in Moscow, the unique experience, the one that brought such a flush to her cheeks, was not that she was talking to foreigners, but that she was sitting in a dining car riding on a train. Something about the silver and the clean cloth and a little basket of puckered apples, like those the Chinese man had sold, made her fuss with her ivory rose and tuck up the straying ends of her hair. "Ah, we eat!" she said, her eyes shifting toward a quartet of chunky waitresses who came waddling down the aisle with trayloads of the first course.

Those whose palates had been anticipating iced caviar and chilled carafes of vodka were a bit chagrined to see, set before them, yogurt accompanied by bottles of raspberry soda. Miss Thigpen, seated behind me, was the sole voice expressing enthusiasm: "I just could kiss them! More proteins than a steak and only half the calories." But across the aisle, Mrs. Gershwin warned Miss Putnam not to ruin her appetite by eating it. "Don't, darling, I'm sure the cavy will come along next." The next course, however, consisted of stiff noddles lying like sunken logs in a watery broth. The entree that followed featured breaded veal cutlets, boiled potatoes, and peas that rattled on the plate like gunshot; to wash this down, there were further provisions of raspberry soda. Miss Putnam said to Mrs. Gershwin, "It's not *my* stomach I'm worried about. It's Twerp's," and Mrs. Gershwin, sawing at her cutlet, said, "Do you suppose they could be saving the cavy for dessert? You know, with little pancakes?"

Miss Lydia's cheeks bulged, her eyes popped, her jaws pumped like pistons, a trickle of sweat ran down her neck. "Eat, eat," she urged, "it's good, yes?" Miss Ryan told her it was wonderful, and Miss Lydia, swabbing her plate with a quarter loaf of black bread, nodded vehemently: "You will not obtain better in Moscow itself."

During the lull between entree and dessert, she went to work on the basket of apples; as the cores piled up she paused occasionally to answer questions. Lyons was anxious to learn at what hotel the company would be staying in Leningrad. Miss Lydia was startled that he didn't know. "The Astoria. For weeks the rooms have been reserved," she said, and went on to describe the Astoria as "very old-fashion but exquisite." "Well," said Lyons, "what about the night life in Leningrad, any action there?" Miss Lydia replied by saying that perhaps her English was not all it should be, and proceeded, from her Muscovite point of view, to discuss Leningrad rather as a New Yorker might Philadelphia; it was "old-fashion," it was "provincial," it was "not the same like Moscow." At the end of this recital, Lyons said glumly, "Sounds like a two-day town to me." Miss Ryan thought to ask, when was the last time Miss Lydia had visited Leningrad? Miss Lydia blinked. "The last time? Never. I have never been there. It will be interesting to see, yes?"

Presently she had a qustion of her own. "I would appreciate you to explain to me. Why is Paul Robeson not in with the players? *He* is a colored person, yes?"

"Yes," said Miss Ryan; and so, she added, were sixteen million other Americans. Surely Miss Lydia didn't expect *Porgy and Bess* to employ them all?

Miss Lydia leaned back in her chair with a cunning, I'm-no-fool expression. "It is because *you*," she said, smiling at Miss Ryan, *"you* do not permit him his pass-port."

The dessert arrived. It was vanilla ice cream, and it was excellent. Behind me, Miss Thigpen said to her fiancé, "Earl, honey, I wouldn't touch it. Maybe it's not pasteurized." Across the aisle, Mrs. Gershwin observed to Miss Putnam, "It's my theory they send it all to California. It cost thirty-five dollars a pound in Beverly Hills."

Coffee followed, and with it an altercation. Jackson and several of his friends had taken over a table and were dealing out a game of Tonk. The two huskiest of the Ministry's young men, Sascha and Igor, converged on the card players and informed them, their voices struggling to sound firm, that "gambling" was illegal in the Soviet Union. "Man," said one of the players, "nobody's gambling here. We got to do *something*. We don't have a friendly game, we blow our stacks." Sascha insisted, "It's illegal. Not allowed." The men threw down their cards, and Jackson, tucking them into a case, said, "Old Squareville. Home for dead cats. The number to play is zero. Tell the boys back in New York."

"They are unhappy. We regret," said Miss Lydia.

"But we must remember our restaurant workers." Her stubby-fingered hand motioned elegantly toward the waitresses, whose blear-eyed, solid faces glistened with perspiration as they shambled down the aisle balancing a hundred pounds of dirty dishes. "You understand. It would not look well for them to see the laws disenforced." She gathered the last few apples, and stuffed them into a cloth handbag. "Now," she said cheerfully, "we go to dream. We unravel the sleeve of care."

On the morning of December 21, The Blue Express was twenty-four hours from Leningrad, another day and night, though the difference between the two seemed, as the train crawled deeper into Russia, tenuous indeed, so little did the sun, a gray ghost rising at ten and returned to its grave by three, help to divide them. The fragile span of daylight continued to reveal winter at its un-crackable hardest: birches, their branches broken from the weight of snow; a log-cabin village, not a soul in sight and the roofs hung with icicles heavy as elephant tusks. Once, a village cemetery, poor plain wooden crosses, wind-bent and all but buried. But here and there haystacks, standing in deserted fields, were evidence that even this harsh ground could, in distant spring, grow green again.

Aboard, among the passengers, the emotional pen-dulum had settled at that nirvana point between the strains of departure and the tensions of arrival. An on and on timeless nowhere that one accepted as perhaps lasting forever, like the wind that swept white cauldrons of snow-spray against the train. At last, even Warner Watson relaxed. "Well," he said, lighting a cigarette with hands that scarcely trembled, "I guess maybe I've got my nerves fenced in." Twerp snoozed in the corridor, pink stomach upturned, paws awry. In Compartment 6, by now a welter of unmade berths, orange peelings, spilled face powder and cigarette butts floating in cold tea, Jack-son practiced card-shuffling while his fiancée buffed her nails, and Miss Ryan, pursuing her Russian studies, memorized a new phrase out of the old army textbook;

"SLOO-*sha eess-ya ee-lee ya* BOO-*doo streel*-YAHT! Obey or I'll fire!" Lyons alone stayed faithful to the pressures of a workaday world. "Nobody gets in my tax bracket looking at scenery," he said, sternly typing the heading for a new column: *"Showtrain to Leningrad."*

At seven that evening, when the others had gone off to the day's third round of yogurt and raspberry soda, I stayed in the compartment and dined on a Hershey chocolate bar. I thought Twerp and I had the car to ourselves until I noticed one of the Ministry's interpreters, Henry, the child-sized young man with the large ears, pass my door, then pass again, each time giving me a glance that quivered with curiosity. It was as though he wanted to speak but caution and timidity prevented him. When finally, after another reconnoiter, he did come into the compartment, the approach he'd designed was official.

"Give me your passport," he said, with that bluntness shy people often assume.

He sat on Miss Thigpen's berth, and studied the passport through a pair of spectacles that kept sliding to the tip of his nose; like everything he wore, from his shiny black suit with its bell-bottom trousers to his brown worn-down shoes, they were much too big for him. I said if he would tell me what he was looking for, possibly I could help him. "It is necessary," he mumbled, his red ears burning like hot coals. The train must have traveled several miles while he fingered through the passport like a boy poring over a stamp album; and though he carefully examined the mementos left on its pages by immigration authorities, his attention lingered longest on the data that states one's occupation, height and color, date of birth.

"Here is correct?" he said, pointing to my birth date. I told him it was. "We are three years apart," he said. "I am youngest—*younger?*—I am younger, thank you. But you have seen much. So. I have seen Moscow." I asked him if he would like to travel. His answer began as a physical action, a queer sequence of shrugs and flutterings, shrinking inside his fat man's suit that seemed to mean yes and no, perhaps. He pushed up his spectacles, and said, "I have not the time. I am a worker like him and him. Three years, it could also happen my passport has many imprimaturs. But I am content with the scenic—no, *scenery*—scenery of the mind. The world is the same, but here," he tapped his forehead, struck it really, *"here,"* he spread a hand over his heart, "are changefuls. Which is correct; chang*ings* or change*fuls?"* I said either one; as used, they both made sense.

The effort of shaping these sentences, and an excess of feeling behind them, had left him breathless. He leaned on his elbow and rested a spell before suddenly observing, "You resemble Shostakovich. That is correct?" I told him I wouldn't have thought so, not from the photographs of Shostakovich that I'd seen. "We have discuss it. Mr. Savchenko has also the opinion," he said, as though this were final, for who were we, either of us, to challenge Savchenko? Shostakovich's name led to mention of David Oistrakh, the great Soviet violinist who had recently played concerts in New York and Philadelphia. He listened to my report of Oistrakh's American triumphs as if I were praising him, Henry; his hunched shoulders straightened, all at once he seemed to fill out his flapping suit, and the heels of his shoes, dangling over the side of the berth, swung together and clicked, clicked and swung, as though he were dancing a jig. I asked him if he thought *Porgy and Bess* would have a success in Russia comparable to Oistrakh's American reception. "It is not my ability to say. But we at the Ministry hope more than you hope. A real man's job for us, that *Porgy-Bess.*" He told me that although he'd worked at the Ministry for five years, this was the only time his job had taken him outside Moscow. Usually, he said, he spent six days a week at a desk in the Ministry ("I have my own telephone"), and on Sundays he stayed home reading ("Among your writers, the powerful one is A. J. Cronin. But Sholikov is more powerful, yes?").

Home was an apartment on the outskirts of Moscow where he lived with his family and, as he was unmarried ("My stipend is not yet equal to the aspiration"), shared a bedroom with his brother.

The conversation moved with an increasing ease; he ate a piece of Hershey, he laughed, his heels clicked; and then I offered him some books. They were stacked on the table, and his eyes continually strayed toward them, a gaudy collection of twenty-five-cent thrillers mixed in with Edmund Wilson's *To the Finland Station,* a history of the rise of Socialism, and Nancy Mitford's biography, *Madame de Pompadour.* I told him he could have them, if he liked.

At first, he was pleased. Then, as he reached for the books, his hands hesitated, withdrew, and his personal tic started; more shrugs, shrinkings, until he was swallowed again in the looseness of his clothes. "I have not the time," he said regretfully. Afterwards, there seemed nothing left to say. He informed me that my passport was in order, and left.

Between midnight and two in the morning, The Blue Express stood still in a railroad siding near Moscow. The exterior coldness had stolen into the cars, forming lenses of ice on the inside surface of the windowpanes; looking out, one saw merely spectral diffusions, as if your vision were deformed by cataracts. As soon as the train left Moscow, a restless mood rippled through the compartments; those who had been asleep wakened, began to flutter about like chickens tricked by a false dawn. The stay-ups poured another drink and breathed a second wind. Already, the pendulum was swinging toward the tensions of arrival.

Miss Thigpen woke up, calling, "Earl! Earl!" as though she'd had a bad dream.

"Gone," said Miss Ryan, who was curled in her berth nursing a brandy and reading Mickey Spillane. "He's out defying the law. Somebody's running a bootleg Tonk in the next car."

"That's no way to do. Earl ought to be getting his rest," said Miss Thigpen grouchily.

"Give him hell," Miss Ryan advised her. "He's *got* to marry you."

"Nancy, *quelle heure est-il?*"

"Twenty to four." At four Miss Thigpen again inquired the time; and again at ten past. "For God's sake, Helen. Either get a watch or take an *Oblivon.*"

Miss Thigpen kicked back her covers. "No sense trying. I'm better off dressed." It took her an hour and twenty-five minutes to select her costume and apply the right proportions of cosmetics and perfume. At five thirty-five she put on a feathered hat with a veil and sat down on her berth, completely clothed except for stockings and shoes. "I'm worried sick what to wear on my legs. I don't want to be poisoned," she said. Her fear was founded on a memo the Russians had issued to the ladies of the company on the subject of nylon hosiery. In conditions of severe cold, nylon, they announced, had a tendency to disintegrate, which might cause nylon poisoning. Miss Thigpen rubbed her naked legs and groaned. "What kind of place *is* this we're going? Where a lady's stockings fall to pieces on the street and maybe kill her?"

"Forget it," said Miss Ryan.

"But the Russians . . ."

"How the hell would they know? They don't have any nylons. That's why they say it."

It was eight in the morning before Jackson returned from his Tonk game. "Earl," said Miss Thigpen, "is this how you're going to do after we're married?"

"Sweet-girl," he said, wearily climbing into his berth, "the cat has howled his last. He's zero point zero. Ooble-ee-dood out."

Miss Thigpen was unsympathetic. "Earl, don't you dare go to sleep now. We're almost there. Go to sleep for such a little bit and you'll wake up an ugly mess."

Jackson muttered and drew a blanket over his head.

"Earl," said Miss Ryan softly, "I suppose you know they're going to make newsreels at the station?"

Very shortly afterwards, Jackson had shaved, changed shirts, and arrayed himself in a caramel-colored fur coat. He owned a hat of the same fur that he'd had "custom-made" fedora-style. While working his hands into a pair of gloves with holes along the fingers to reveal his rings, he gave his fiancée instructions on how to handle the expected cameras: "See, honey, we don't want to get stuck with a lot of still-men. That's a waste of time when they're busting out the flicker stuff." He scratched at the window with his jeweled fist, and squinted out; it was nine-five and still pitch-black, not the ideal color for photography. But half an hour later the darkness had turned to steel-gray mist and one could see the blueness of lightly falling snow.

One of the Ministry's representatives, Sascha, passed through the car, knocking at compartment doors. "Ladies and gentlemen, in twenty minutes we are arriving Leningrad."

I finished dressing and squeezed my way into the crowded corridor, where an excitement was moment by moment accelerating like the wheels of the train. Even Twerp, shawl-wrapped and hugged in Miss Putnam's arms, was prepared to disembark. Mrs. Gershwin was more prepared then Twerp. She bristled with mink, was frosted with diamonds, and her curls peeked charmingly from under a rich soft sable hat. "The hat, darling? I bought it in California. I've been saving it for a surprise. You do, love? How sweet of you, darling. *Darling . . .*" she said, an abrupt silence adding volume to her voice, "we're *there!*"

A stunned instant of disbelief, then a collective pushing toward the vestibule. The sad-eyed car attendant, stationed there to receive his tips, found himself not only ignored but also crushed against the wall. Alert as horses at the starting gate, Jackson and John McCurry jockeyed by the exit for position. McCurry is the heftier of the two, and when the door opened, he was the first man out.

He stepped straight into a gray throng, and a flash

bulb's pop. "Bless you," said McCurry, as women vied to thrust bouquets into his hand. "Bless your little pointed heads."

"As we arrived, there were many birds flying about —black and white," wrote Warner Watson, as he later recorded the scene in his diary. "The white ones are *sakaros*. I write it down for my bird-watching friends. We were greeted by many friendly Russians. The women and men (of the company) were given bouquets of flowers. I wonder where they got them this time of year. Pathetic little bouquets like those made by a child."

Miss Ryan, also the keeper of a diary, wrote: "Official welcoming party of giant men and shabby ladies dressed more to meet a coffin than a theatrical company (black clothes, gray faces) but perhaps that's what they *were* doing. My useless plastic galoshes kept falling off, making it impossible to elbow efficiently through the press of microphones, cameras, and those battling to get at them. The Breens were on hand, Robert still half asleep but Wilva smile-smiling. At the head of the quay, dull brass letters spelled out LENINGRAD—and then I knew it was true."

The poet, Helen Wolfert, composed for her journal a lengthy description. Here is an excerpt: "As we advanced along the platform to the exit, two columns of people stood on either side, applauding. When we reached the street a press of spectators closed in on us. Policemen pushed them away to let us pass but the people in return pushed them with equal vigor. The actors responded to the warmth and bustle and welcome with grace, graciousness, expansiveness and flare. If the Russian people fell in love with them, they weren't alone. I fell in love with them myself."

Perhaps a few footnotes should be added to these entries. The persons Miss Ryan refers to as "giant men and shabby ladies" were a hundred or more of Leningrad's leading theatrical artists who had been organized to meet the train. Remarkably, none of them had known in advance that *Porgy and Bess* had a Negro cast, and before the committee could rearrange their bewildered faces into expressions of positive welcome, the company were halfway out of the station. The "press of spectators" noted by Mrs. Wolfert consisted of ordinary citizens whose presence was the result of an item printed in the local edition of the previous day's *Izvestia*. "A touring American opera company will arrive by train tomorrow morning in Leningrad. It is expected they will perform here." These two lines were, by the way, the first publicity the Soviet press had given Breen's venture; but, despite its meager detail, the announcement had proved sufficiently intriguing to attract the at least one thousand Leningraders who lined the length of the station, cascaded down a flight of stairs and spilled into the street. I was less aware of the "warmth and bustle" that impressed Mrs. Wolfert. Except for light sprinklings of applause, the crowd, so it seemed to me, watched the exiting cast with immense silence, an almost catatonic demeanor that provided few clues as to what they thought of the American parade—Mrs. Gershwin, loaded with more bouquets than a bride; small Davy Bey, dancing an impromptu Suzy-Q; Jackson dispensing royal waves, and John McCurry walking with his hands clenched above his head like a prize fighter.

While the Russian reaction may have been inscrutable, the official Company Historian, Leonard Lyons, had a very definite opinion of his own. Taking professional note of the scene, he shook his head. "It hasn't been handled right. No showmanship. Why, if Breen knew his business," he said, passing through the door of the station, "we would've come out singing!"

Part II
THE MUSES ARE HEARD

THE LENINGRAD PREMIÈRE OF *Porgy and Bess,* an event expected to reap international publicity, was planned for the evening of Monday, December 26, which gave the company five days to prepare and rehearse, a sufficient time considering that the show had been touring the world nearly four years. But Robert Breen, the production's director, was determined that the audience at the Leningrad première would see the finest possible rendering of the Negro opera. Breen, and his energetic partner-wife, Wilva, and their chief assistant, the gentle, yet highly strung Warner Watson, were confident that the Russians would be "stunned" by the musical folk tale, that they would "never have seen anything like it." Several observers, though sympathetic, were not as sure. However looked at, by the Americans or by their Russian sponsors, the opening night promised to be one of the most suspenseful in theatrical annals. But that event was, on the morning of arrival, over a hundred hours away; and after the company had been driven in chartered buses from the Leningrad terminal to the Hotel Astoria, their feelings of suspense were centered around room accommodations.

The Astoria, situated on the impressive expanse of St. Isaac's Square, is an Intourist hotel, which means that it is run by the Soviet agency in control of all hotels where foreigners are permitted to stay. The Astoria justifiably claims to be the best hotel in Leningrad. Some think it the Ritz of all Russia. But it contains few concessions to Western ideas of a deluxe establishment. Of these, one is a room off the lobby that advertises itself as an *Institut De Beauté,* where guests may obtain *Pedicure,* and *Coiffeur pour Madame.* The *Institut,* with its mottled whiteness, its painful appurtenances, resembles a charity clinic supervised by not too sanitary nurses, and the coiffeur that Madame receives there is liable to leave her hair with a texture excellent for scouring pans. There is also on the lobby floor a trio of restaurants, each leading into the other, cavernous affairs cheerful as airplane hangars. The center one is Leningrad's smartest restaurant, and in the evenings, from eight till midnight, an orchestra plays Russian jazz for a local *haut monde* who seldom dance but sit morosely counting the bubbles in syrupy glasses of Georgian champagne. The hotel's Intourist office is located behind a low counter in the main lobby; its dozen desks are so arranged that the employees have a broad view, which simplifies their task of keeping tabs on the comings and goings of the guests. It is a job they have made still simpler, or foolproof, by stationing dormitory matrons on each of the residential floors, vigilantes who are on duty from dawn to dawn, never allowing anyone to leave his room without giving him the key, and constantly, like human punch-clocks, recording ins and outs in a bulky ledger. Perhaps Houdini could've eluded them, but it is hard to see how, since they sit at desks that face both the staircase and the elevator, an ancient bird cage that creaks on its cables. Actually, there is a rear, unguarded staircase connecting the upper floors with a remote side-lobby; and for the clandestine visitor, or the resident wishing to depart unnoticed, this would make the ideal route. Would, except that it is barricaded top to bottom with wooden fences reinforced by old settees and armoires. It might be that the management can find nowhere else to stash these pieces of furniture. Certainly there is no more room in the rooms. For the average Astoria abode is like the annex in a Victorian attic where some poor relation lives buried among the family discards: a miasma of romantic marble statuary, weak-bulbed lamps with tulle shades like ballerina skirts, tables, several of them, covered with Oriental carpeting, chairs galore, plush settees, armoires that could store steamer trunks, flower-papered walls kaleidoscopic with gilt-framed paintings of fruit and country idylls, beds concealed in cavelike alcoves behind dank velvet curtains: all this crammed into a tomb-dark, unventilated area (you can't open the windows in winter, and wouldn't want to if you could) quadruple the size of a train compartment. The hotel has grander quarters, of course, suites with five and six rooms, but the effect of the décor is the same, merely more abundantly so.

Nevertheless, the majority of the *Porgy and Bess* company were most approving of the Astoria, many because they had anticipated "something so much *worse*" and, instead, found their rooms "cozy," "kind of atmospheric" or, as the production's sophisticated publicist, Willem Van Loon, put it, "Full of art-nouveau charms. Really me!" But when the troupe first entered the lobby of the hotel, already milling with Chinese dignitaries and high-booted Cossacks, actual occupancy of these rooms was, in some instances, distant and debatable.

The Astoria's assigning of the rooms and, particularly, the suites seemed to be governed by a protocol, or lack of one, that embittered rather a few. Nancy Ryan volunteered a theory that the Russians had arrived at their system of room distribution by consulting Everyman Opera's payroll: "The less you get the more they give you." Whatever the reason, several of the leading players and prominent personalities, who were traveling as guests of the company, thought it "grotesque" and "crazy, man, crazy" that stagehands and wardrobe mistresses, carpenters and electricians were being led straight-away to the V.I.P. apartments, while they, the "real people," were supposed to content themselves with the hotel's backwater leftovers. "Are they kidding?" said Leonard Lyons. Another company guest, the New York financier, Herman Sartorius, had valid cause to complain; he'd been assigned no room at all. Nor had Mrs. Gershwin, who sat on her luggage in the lobby being soothed by Wilva Breen and Warner Watson.

"Don't you worry, baby," said Mrs. Breen, who had

arrived the night before by plane and was ensconced with her husband in six rooms of Astorian splendor. "The Russians may be slow, they may get things a little mixed up, but everything comes out straight in the end. Look what happened when I went to Moscow," she added, referring to a visit she had made to Moscow the previous October in connection with the present tour. "It took me nine days to do two hours' work. But everything came out fine in the end."

"Sure, Lee," said Warner Watson, brushing down his graying crew-cut with an agitated hand. "Sure, honey, we'll get this room business fenced in."

"Darling, I'm perfectly happy, darling," Mrs. Gershwin assured them. "I just think it's so wonderful *being* here."

"To think we really made it," said Mrs. Breen, beaming round her. "And what sweet, kind, adorable people. Wasn't that adorable when the train arrived?"

"Adorable," said Mrs. Gershwin, glancing at the mass of wilting bouquets that had been given her at the station.

"And the hotel's simply beautiful, isn't it?"

"Yes, Wilva," said Mrs. Gershwin blankly, as though her friend's enthusiasm was beginning to tire her.

"You'll have a beautiful room, Lee," said Mrs. Breen, and Warner Watson added, "If you don't like it, you can change it. Anything you want, Lee, we'll get it fenced in."

"Darling, please. It's not important, Not the tiniest bit. If they'll just put me *some*where, I wouldn't dream of moving," said Mrs. Gershwin, who was destined, in the course of the next few days, to insist on changing her accommodations three times.

The Ministry of Culture's delegation, headed by Nikolai Savchenko, the businesslike, formidable six-footer, were now in a whirl of pacifying, rectifying, promising everyone they would get the rooms they deserved. "Patience," pleaded one of them, the middle-aged Russian interpreter called Miss Lydia. "Do not contribute to the misery. We have plenty rooms. No one will stride the streets." Nancy Ryan said she wouldn't mind striding the streets, and suggested to me that we escape the confusion in the lobby by taking a walk.

St. Isaac's Square is hemmed on one side by a canal stemming from the Neva, a river that in winter threads through the city like a frozen Seine, and on the other by St. Issac's Cathedral, which is now an antireligious museum. We walked toward the canal. The sky was sunless gray, and there was snow in the air, buoyant motes, playthings that seethed and floated like the toy flakes inside a crystal. It was noon, but there was no modern traffic on the square except for a car or two and a bus with its headlights burning. Now and then, though, horse-drawn sleds slithered across the snowy pavement. Along the embankments of the Neva, men on skis silently passed, and mothers aired their babies, dragging them in small sleds. Everywhere, like darting blackbirds, black-furred school children ice-skated on the sidewalks. Two of these children stopped to inspect us. They were twins, girls of nine or ten, and they wore gray rabbit coats and blue velvet bonnets. They had divided a pair of skates between them, but by holding hands and pushing together, they managed very well on one skate apiece. They looked at us with pretty brown puzzled eyes, as though wondering what made us different: Our clothes? Miss Ryan's lipstick? The soft waves in her loose blond hair? Most foreigners in Russia soon become accustomed to this: the slight frown of the passer-by who is disturbed by something about you that he can't at once put his finger on, and who stops, stares, keeps glancing back, even quite often feels compelled to follow you. The twins followed us onto a footbridge that crossed the Neva, and watched while we paused to look at the view.

The canal, no more than a snow ditch, was a sporting ground for children whose laughing shrillness combined with a ringing of bells, both sounds carrying on the strong, shivery winds that blow from the Bay of Finland. Skeleton trees, sheathed in ice, glittered against the austere fronts of palaces that lined the embankments and stretched to the distant Nevsky Prospekt. Leningrad, presently a city of four million, the Soviet Union's second largest and northernmost metropolis, was built to the taste of the Czars, and Czarist taste ran to French and Italian architecture, which accounts not only for the style but also for the coloring of the palaces along the Neva and in other old quarters. Parisian blacks and grays predominate, but suddenly, here and there, the hot Italian palette intervenes: a palace of bitter green, of brilliant ochre, pale blue, orange. A few of the palaces have been converted into apartments, most are used for offices. Peter the Great, who is given high marks by the current regime because he introduced the sciences to Russia, would probably approve the myriad television aerials that have settled like a swarm of metal insects on the roofs of his once Imperial city.

We crossed the bridge and wandered through opened iron gates into the deserted courtyard of a blue palace. It was the beginning of a labyrinth, an arctic Casbah where one courtyard led into another via arcades and tunnels and across narrow streets snow-hushed and silent except for sleigh horses stamping their hooves, a drifting sound of bells, an occasional giggle from the twins, still trailing behind us.

The cold was like an anesthetic; gradually, I felt numb enough to undergo major surgery. But Miss Ryan refused to turn back. She said, "This is St. Petersburg, for God's sake. We're not just walking anywhere. I want to see as much as I can. And I'd better. From now on, you know where *I'll* be? Locked in a room typing a lot of nonsense for the Breens." But I saw that she couldn't last much longer, her face was drunkard-red, a frostbite spot whitened the tip of her nose. Minutes later, feeling its first sting, she was ready to seek the Astoria.

The trouble was, we were lost. It amused the twins greatly to see us rotating round the same streets and courtyards. They screeched and hugged each other with laughter when we came on an old man chopping wood

and begged him for directions by swinging our arms like
compass needles and shouting, *Astoria! Astoria!* The
woodchopper didn't understand; he put down his axe
and accompanied us to a street corner, where we were
required to repeat our pantomime for three swarthy
friends of his, none of whom got the point, but nevertheless beckoned us up another street. On the way, out of
curiosity, we were joined by a gangly boy carrying a
violin case, and a woman who must have been a butcher,
for over her coat she was wearing an apron splattered
with blood. The Russians babbled and argued; we decided they were taking us to a police station, and neither
of us cared, as long as it was heated. By now, the moisture in my nose had frozen, my eyes were unfocused
with cold. Still, I could see well enough to know that
abruptly we were back at the Neva Canal footbridge. I
wanted to grab Miss Ryan's hand and run. But she felt
our entourage had been so faithful they deserved to see
the mystery solved. From woodchopper to violinist, the
procession, led by the twins who skated ahead like pied
pipers, convoyed us across the square and straight to the
Astoria's entrance. While they surrounded one of the
Intourist limousines that stay parked in front of the hotel,
and began to question its chauffeur about us, we rushed
inside, collapsed on a bench and sucked the warm air
like divers who have been too long underwater.

Leonard Lyons walked by. "Looks like you've been
out," he said. Miss Ryan nodded, and Lyons, lowering
his voice, asked, "Anybody follow you?"

"Yes," said Miss Ryan, *"crowds."*

A company bulletin board had been installed in the
lobby. Attached to it were announcements concerning the
company's rehearsal schedule, and a list of entertainments their Soviet hosts had planned for them, which
included, in the days before the première, ballet and
opera performances, a ride on the new Leningrad subway,
a visit to the Hermitage Museum, and a Christmas party.
Under the heading PROMPTLY, the dining hours had also

been posted, and these, influenced by the fact that in the Russian theatre matinées start at noon and evening performances at eight, were listed as: Breakfast 9:30 A.M., Lunch 11:00 A.M., Dinner 5 P.M., Evening snack 11:30 P.M.

But at five on that first evening, I was enjoying a hot tub too much to bother about dinner. The bathroom, which belonged to the third-floor room assigned to me, had peeling sulphur walls, a cold radiator, and a broken toilet that rumbled like a mountain brook. The tub itself, circa 1900, was splotched with rust stains, and the water that poured from its taps was brown as iodine; but it was warm, it made a wonderful steam, and I basked in it, idly wondering if downstairs in the bleak dining room the company were at last being treated to caviar and vodka, shashlik, blinis and sour cream. (Ironically, as I learned later, they were receiving the same menu that had been served at every meal on the train: yogurt and raspberry soda, broth, breaded veal cutlets, carrots and peas.) My water-logged drowsing was interrupted when the telephone rang in the outer room. I let it go awhile, the way you might if you were sitting in a bath at home. Then I realized I wasn't home, remembered that, looking at the telephone earlier, I'd thought what a dead object it was to me in Russia, as useless as if the wires were cut. Naked and dripping, I picked up the receiver to hear the interpreter, Miss Lydia, telling me I had a call from Moscow. The telephone was on a desk next to the window. In the street below, a regiment of soldiers marched by singing a military song, and when Moscow came through I could hardly hear for the robust boom of their voices. The caller was someone I'd never met, Henry Shapiro, a United Press correspondent. He said, "What's going on there? Anything'd make a story?" He told me he'd been intending to travel to Leningrad for "the big story," the *Porgy and Bess* première, but now he couldn't, because he had to cover "another opening," the Supreme Soviet, which was happening in Moscow the same night. He would therefore appreciate it if he could call again on Monday after the première and have me report to him "how it went, what really happened." I said all right, I'd try. The call, and the shock of standing unclothed in a cold room, had brought me back to life. The company were expected to attend a ballet, and I started to get dressed for it. There was a problem here. The Breens had decreed that the men should wear black-tie, and the ladies short evening dresses. "It's more respectful," said Mrs. Breen, "and besides, Robert and I like everything to be gala." There was an opposing clique who felt that the Breens' pronouncement would, if obeyed, make them look "ridiculous" in a country where no one dressed formally for any occasion whatever. I compromised by putting on a gray flannel suit *and* a black tie. While dressing, I moved around the room straightening some of the fruit and flower paintings that clotted the walls. They were rather atilt, owing to an inspective visit from Leonard Lyons, who was convinced the Astoria's rooms were wired for sound. Lyons' theories were shared by most of the company, which was not remarkable, considering that the two American diplomats from the Moscow Embassy had told them at a briefing in Berlin that, during their Russian visit, they should "assume" their rooms would be wired and their letters opened. Even Breen, who called the diplomatic advice "a lot of blah," had unwittingly encouraged the company's suspicions by declaring that, regardless of what anyone might individually feel, he hoped in correspondence they simply would write how "interesting" Russia was and what a "good time" they were having; this, some pointed out, was a contradiction, for why would Breen make such a request if he, too, didn't believe they were living in an atmosphere of microphones and steam kettles?

On my way out, I stopped at the floor desk and handed my key to the guardian, a plump pale woman with a kewpie-doll smile who wrote in her ledger *224-1900:* the number of my room and hour of departure.

. . .

Downstairs, there was a row in progress. The company, dressed and ready to leave for the ballet, stood around the lobby like mortified figures in a tableau, while one of the cast, John McCurry, a husky bull-like man, stomped about yelling, "Goddam if I will. I'm not gonna pay any goddam crooked somebody seven bucks fifty to baby sit anybody." McCurry was complaining of the price a Russian baby sitter was charging to stay with his four-year-old daughter while he and his wife went to the ballet. At a cost of thirty rubles per sitter, Intourist had supplied a batch to all the parents of the troupe's six children; they had even arranged one for Twerp, the boxer puppy belonging to the production's wardrobe mistress. Thirty rubles, at the exchange of four to one, amounts to $7.50, a stiff tariff; but actually to the Russian, thirty rubles has a buying power equivalent to $1.70, and the Russians, who had only this modest fee in mind, couldn't fathom why McCurry was causing such a scene. Savchenko, head man from the Ministry of Culture, was rosy with indignation, Miss Lydia white. Breen spoke sharply to McCurry, and McCurry's wife, a shy woman whose eyes are usually downcast, told him if he would please be quiet she would remain home with the child. Warner Watson and Miss Ryan hustled everyone out of the lobby and onto the two buses that had been chartered for the duration of their Leningrad stay.

Later, Breen apologized to Savchenko for the "conduct" of a few members of the company. The apology was intended to cover more than the McCurry incident. Free liquor was not included in the contract that had been drawn up between the Ministry of Culture and Everyman Opera, Inc. Savchenko was distressed because several persons had ordered drinks brought to their rooms and refused to pay for them, fought and insulted the waiters. Further, it had come to Savchenko's attention that many of the Americans were referring to him and his staff as "spies." Breen, too, felt that this was "unwarranted and outrageous," and Savchenko, in accepting his apologies, said, "Well, of course, in a company this size, we must expect some who will fall below the mark."

The ballet was at the Mariinsky theatre, which has been renamed, though no one calls it that, the Kirov, after the old revolutionary and friend of Stalin's whose assassination in 1934 is said to have initiated the first of the Moscow trials. Galina Ulanova, the Bolshoi's prima ballerina, made her debut in this theatre, and the Leningrad Opera and Ballet Company, which is now installed there on a repertorial basis, is considered first-class by Soviet critics. Except for the Fenice in Venice, a theatre it somewhat resembles in its eighteenth-century size and style and heating system, I think it the most beautiful theatre I've seen. Unfortunately, the old seats have been replaced by wooden ones, rather like those in a school auditorium, and their harsh, natural color makes too raw a contrast against the subtle grays and silvers of the Mariinsky's simplified rococo interior.

Despite the chilliness of the theatre, everyone, ladies included, were required to leave their coats at the cloakroom; even Mrs. Gershwin was forced to part with her mink, for in Russia it is thought uncultured, *nye kulturni* at its extremest, to enter a theatre, restaurant, museum, any such place, wearing a coat or wrap. At the moment, the principal sufferer from the ruling was Miss Ryan. A tall, striking blonde, Miss Ryan was wearing a low strapless dress that hugged her curves cleverly; and as she swayed down the aisle, masculine eyes swerved in her direction like flowers turning toward the sun. For that matter, the entrance of the entire company was creating a mass stir in the crowded audience. People were standing up to get a better view of the Americans and their black ties, silks and sparkles. Much of the attention was centered on Earl Bruce Jackson and his fiancée, Helen Thigpen. They were sitting in the Royal Box, where a hammer-and-sickle blotted out the Imperial crest. Jackson, lolling his hand over the edge of the box so that his jewelry, a ring on every finger, could be seen to advantage, was slowly inclining his head right and left, like Queen Victoria.

"I'd be freezing, if I weren't so embarrassed," said Miss Ryan, as an usher seated her. "Just look, they think I'm *indecent*." One couldn't deny that there was a touch of criticism in the glances Miss Ryan's bare shoulders were receiving from surrounding Russian women. Mrs. Gershwin, who was wearing a becoming green cocktail dress, said, "I *told* Wilva Breen we shouldn't get all dressed up. I knew we'd look ridiculous. Well, darling, never again. But really, what *should* we wear?" she asked, looking about as if hunting fashion hints among the audience's melancholy, shapeless attire. "I didn't bring anything that wasn't pretty."

Sitting in the row ahead, there was one girl whose hair was neither plaited nor a sour bundle of string; she had an urchin-cut, which suited her curious, wild-faun face. She was wearing a black cardigan, and a pearl necklace. I pointed her out to Miss Ryan.

"But I *know* her," said Miss Ryan excitedly. "She's from Long Island, we went to Radcliffe together! *Priscilla* Johnson," she called, and the girl, squinting near-sighted eyes, turned around. "For God's sake, Priscilla. What are you doing here?"

"Gosh. Gee whiz, Nancy," said the girl, rubbing back her tomboy bangs. "What are *you* doing here?"

Miss Ryan told her, and the girl, who said that she too was staying at the Astoria, explained that she had been granted a lengthy visa to live in the Soviet Union and study Russian law, a subject that had interested her since Radcliffe, where she'd also learned the Russian language.

"But, darling," said Mrs. Gershwin, "how can anyone study Russian law? When it changes so often?"

"Gosh. Ha ha," said Miss Johnson. "Well, that's not the *only* thing I'm doing. I'm making a kind of Kinsey report. It's great fun, gosh."

"I should think," said Miss Ryan. "The research."

"Oh, that's easy," Miss Johnson assured her. "I just

keep steering the conversation toward sex; and gee whiz, you'd be surprised what Russians think about it. Gosh, Nancy, the number of men who have mistresses! Or wished they did. I'm sending articles to *Vogue* and *Harper's Bazaar*. I thought they might be interested."

"Priscilla's a sort of genius," Miss Ryan whispered to me, as chandeliers dimmed and the orchestra conductor raised his baton. The ballet, in three acts with two intermissions, was called *Corsair*. The average Soviet ballet is far less concerned with dancing than with stupendous production, and *Corsair,* though a minor work in their repertory, involves as much change of scenery as the extravagant vaudevilles at Radio City Music Hall or the Folies Bergère, two theatres where *Corsair* would feel quite at home, except that the choreography and its execution are not up to the standards of the former, and the latter would never tolerate a scene of dancing slave girls swathed to the neck. The theme of *Corsair* is very similar to *The Fountains of Bahchisarai,* a poem of Pushkin's that the Bolshoi ballet has taken and swollen into one of its prize exhibits. In *Fountains,* an aristocratic girl is kidnaped by a barbaric Tartar chieftain and hauled off to his harem where, for three hours of playing time, many vile adventures befall her. In *Corsair,* this girl's twin sister undergoes somewhat the same ordeal; here she is the victim of a shipwreck (brilliantly simulated on stage with thunder, lightning, torrents of water crashing against the stricken vessel) who is captured by pirates, after which, for three hours, ditto. Both these tales, and countless like them, reflect a tendency in the contemporary Soviet theatre to rely on fantasy and legend; it would seem that the modern author who wishes to roam beyond the propagandist garden finds that the only safe path is the one that leads him into the forest of fairy stories. But even fantasy needs realistic underpinning, reminders of the recognizable, the human; without them, the power of life is not there, nor is art, a dual absence that occurs too often in the Soviet theatre, whose practitioners appear to believe that trick effects and technical wizardry can be made to supplant them. The Ministry of Culture frequently boasts that Russia is the sole country to have produced an art-culture *en rapport* with its population. The reaction of the audience to *Corsair* was nothing to disprove the claim; every set, every solo brought chandelier-shaking rounds of applause.

The Americans were enthusiastic too. "Magnificent, a dream," Mrs. Breen told Mrs. Gershwin during an intermission spent in the Mariinsky's café-salon. The opinion was seconded by her husband. Yet while praising the ballet, Breen, a dapper man whose facial expressions alternate between boyish beamings and Buster Keaton calm, had a troubled flickering in his eyes, as though perhaps he was comparing the physical elaborateness of *Corsair* with *Porgy and Bess'* three simple changes of scenery; if lavish effects were the criterion, then Soviet audiences were certain to be disappointed with his production.

"Well, *I* don't like it," said Mrs. Gershwin rebelliously, as the Breens moved on to another group. "I can hardly keep awake. And I'm not going to say I like it if I don't. They (the Breens) would put the words in your mouth if they could." That, of course, was the difficulty of the Breens' position. Like parents who have taken their children on a visit to the neighbors, they lived in dreadful anticipation of *gaffes,* of breakage and misconduct.

Refreshments were on sale in the Mariinsky's café-salon: beer, liqueurs, raspberry soda, sandwiches, candy and ice cream. Earl Bruce Jackson said he was starving: "But, man, that ice cream costs a dollar a lick. And guess what they want for a little bitty piece of chocolate not big as your toe? Five-fifty." Ice cream, advertised by the Soviets to be a delicacy of their own contriving, started to become a national passion in the U.S.S.R. in 1939, when American machinery was imported for its making. Most of the customers jammed into the salon stood spooning it out of paper cups while watching the

Americans pose for photographs, informal ones, balancing beer bottles on their foreheads, demonstrating the shimmy, doing imitations of Louis Armstrong.

At the second interval, I looked for Miss Ryan and found her backed into a corner, haughtily smoking a cigarette in a long holder and trying to pretend she was not the cynosure of puffy girls and leaden-faced women gathered to giggle and comment on her clinging gown and naked shoulders. Leonard Lyons, standing with her, said, "See, now you know how Marilyn Monroe feels. Would she be a wow here! She ought to get a visa. I'm going to tell her."

"Ohhhh," moaned Miss Ryan, "if *only* I could get my coat."

A man in his late thirties, clean-shaven, dignified, an athletic figure with a scholar's face, stepped up to Miss Ryan. "I should like to shake your hand," he said respectfully, "I want you to know how much my friends and I are looking forward to *Porgy and Bess*. It will be a powerful event for us, I can assure you. Some of us have obtained tickets for the first night. I," he said, smiling, "am among the fortunate." Miss Ryan said she was pleased to hear that, and remarked on the excellence of his English, which he explained by saying that he'd spent several of the war years in Washington as part of a Russian Purchasing Commission. "But can you really understand me? It's been so long since I've had the opportunity of speaking—it makes my heart pound." One sensed, in the admiring intensity of his attitude toward Miss Ryan, that the pounding of his heart was not altogether due to the English language. His smile slackened as a fluttering light signaled the end of intermission; and urgently, as though spurred by an impulse he couldn't resist, he said, "Please let me see you again. I'd like to show you Leningrad." The invitation was directed to Miss Ryan, but by polite necessity included Lyons and myself. Miss Ryan told him to call us at the Astoria, and he jotted our names on a program, then wrote out his own and handed it to Miss Ryan.

"Stefan Orlov," Miss Ryan read, as we returned for the last act. "He's quite sweet."

"Yeah," said Lyons. "But he won't call. He'll think it over and get cold feet."

Arrangements had been made for the company to go backstage and meet the ballet artists. The final scene of *Corsair* is partly played on the deck of a ship hung with rope nets, and at the end of the performance, when the Americans came behind the curtain, there was such a congestion on stage that half the dancers had to stand on the ship's deck or climb the rope nets to get a glimpse of the Western colleagues whose entrance they cheered and applauded a full four minutes before enough quiet could be summoned for Breen to make a speech, which began, "It is *we* who should applaud *you*. Your thrilling artistry has produced an evening none of us will ever forget, and we only hope on Monday evening we can a little repay you for the pleasure you have given us." While Breen finished his speech, and the director of the Mariinsky made another, the little ballerinas, sweat seeping through their make-up, crept close to the American performers, and their painted eyes rolled, their lips ohd-ahd as they gazed at the visitors' shoes, shyly, then boldly, touched the dresses, rubbed bits of silk and taffeta between their fingers. One of them reached out and put her arm around a member of the company named Georgia Burke. "Why, precious-child," said Miss Burke, a warm, happy-natured woman, "hug me all you like. It's good to know somebody loves you."

It was nearer one than midnight when the company started the bus ride back to the Astoria. The buses, rolling refrigerators, had the same seating plan as those that operate on Madison Avenue. I sat on the long back seat between Miss Ryan and the interpreter, Miss Lydia. Street lamps, yellowing the snows of empty streets, flashed at the windows like wintry fireflies, and Miss Ryan, looking out, said, "The palaces are so beautiful in the lamplight."

"Yes," said Miss Lydia, stifling a sleepy yawn, "the private homes are beautiful." Then, as though suddenly awake, she added, "The *former* private homes."

The next morning I went shopping on the Nevsky Prospekt with Lyons and Mrs. Gershwin. Leningrad's principal street, the Nevsky is not a third the length of Fifth Avenue, but it is twice as wide; to get across its skidding aisles of traffic is a perilous chore and a rather pointless one, for the stores on either side of the street are all government-owned emporiums selling, in their different classifications, the same stock at the same prices. Bargain hunters, buyers on the lookout for "something a little different" would find shopping on the Nevsky a discouraging experience.

Lyons had set out with starry hopes of picking up "a nice piece of Fabergé" to take home to his wife. After the revolution, the Bolsheviks sold to French and English collectors almost all the jeweled eggs and boxes that Fabergé had created for the royal amusement; the few known examples of his work left in Russia are on display in Leningrad's Hermitage Museum and in the Armory at the Kremlin. Today, on the international market, the beginning price of a small Fabergé box is over two thousand dollars. None of this information impressed Lyons, who felt he was going to locate his Fabergé quickly and quite cheaply at a Commission Shop. Which was right thinking as far as it went, for if such an item existed, then a Commission Shop, a state-controlled pawn brokerage where a comrade can turn the last of his hidden heirlooms into spot cash, is probably the only place you would discover it. We visited several, drafty establishments with the going-gone sadness of auction halls. In one, the largest, a glass cabinet ran the length of the room, and the spectacle its contents presented, the conglomeration of spookily diverse objects, seemed a dadaist experiment. Rows of second-hand shoes, so worn the spectral shape of the previous owner's foot could be pathetically discerned, were neatly set forth under glass like treasures, which indeed they were at $50 to $175 a pair; a selection of headgear flanked the shoes, flapper cloches and velvet cartwheels; after the hats, the surrealistic variety and value of the cabinets' contents spiraled: a shattered fan ($30), a soiled powder puff ($7), an amber comb with broken teeth ($45), tarnished mesh handbags ($100 and up), a silver umbrella handle ($340), an unexceptional ivory chess set with five pawns missing ($1,450), a celluloid elephant ($25), a pink plaster doll cracked and flaked as though it had been left in the rain ($25). All these articles, and yards more, were placed and numbered with a care that suggested an exhibition of mementos, the possessions of some dead beloved figure, and it was this, the reverence of the display, that made it poignant. Lyons said, "Who do you s'pose *buys* this stuff?" But he had only to look around him to see that there were those who, in lieu of anything else, found the moth-nibbled fan and the silver umbrella handle still fetching, still desirable, quite worth their quoted costs. According to the Russian calendar, Christmas was two weeks off, but Russians prefer to give gifts at New Year's, and the Commission Shops, like all the stores along the Nevsky, were packed with spenders. Though Lyons failed to flush any Fabergé, one pawnbroker came up with a unique nineteenth-century snuffbox, an immense topaz, hollowed and split in half. But the price, $80,000, was more than the customer had in mind.

Mrs. Gershwin, who intended giving a "really good" Christmas present to every member of the *Porgy and Bess* cast ("After all, darling, it's the company's fourth Christmas together, and I do want to show the darlings my appreciation"), still had a few odds and ends to finish off, though she'd carted a trunkload of gifts from Berlin. And so, struggling through the Nevsky crowds ("You can't deny there's a lot of vitality around here," said Lyons), we visited a furrier where the cheapest sable was a short jacket selling, or rather not selling, for $11,000. Then we stopped at an antique shop declared by Intourist to be Leningrad's most "elegant." The antiques turned out to be used television sets, an icebox, an old American electric fan, some battered pieces of Biedermeier, and a colossal number of oil paintings depicting scenes of historical event if not value. "What did you expect, darling?" said Mrs. Gershwin. "There's no such thing as Russian antiques. If there are, they're French." Inquiring for caviar, we went to two fancy-food stores, the local Vendômes; there were pineapples from Africa, oranges from Israel, fresh lichee nuts from China; but no caviar. "Where, *where* did I get the idea it was the butter on the workingman's bread?" lamented Mrs. Gershwin, who said she'd settle for a cup of tea, a desire that shortly drove us into a Soviet version of Schrafft's. It was in a cellar, a dungeon where waitresses, wearing knee boots and tiaras made of doily paper, waded across slush-flooded floors carrying trays of ice cream and improbable pastry to gloomy groups of middle-aged women. But Mrs. Gershwin had to do without her tea, for there were no tables available, nor even space to stand.

So far, no one had made a single purchase. Mrs. Gershwin decided to try a department store. On the way, Lyons, who had a camera, paused often to take photographs, of match women and cherry-cheeked girls dragging Christmas trees, of street-corner flower stalls that in winter sell artificial roses, paper tulips stuck in flowerpots, as though they were real. Each of his photographic forays caused pedestrian traffic jams, a gallery of silent spectators who smiled, and sometimes scowled, when he took their pictures, too. Presently I noticed that there was one man who continuously showed up among the onlookers, yet did not seem part of them. He always stood at the rear, a chunky man with a crooked nose. He was bundled in a black coat and astrakhan cap and half his face was hidden behind the kind of windshield dark glasses skiers wear. I lost track of him before we reached the department store.

The store was reminiscent of a carnival alley, consisting, as it did, of counters and alcoves whose shelves seemed mostly stocked with shooting gallery prizes, the cheap familiar dolls, ugly urns, plaster animals, the toilette set bedded in a crumpling of white casket silk. Mrs. Gershwin, overcome by an odor of rancid glue, felt swift necessity to leave the "leather-goods" department, a swifter one to flee the perfume counter. A crowd began trailing us through the store, and when, in an alcove devoted to hats, I started trying on caps of ersatz Persian lamb, a good thirty grinning, jostling Russians ganged around demanding I buy this one, that one, themselves whisking models on and off my head and ordering the clerk to bring more, more, until hats were toppling off the counter. Someone bent to retrieve one from the floor; it was the man wearing ski glasses. The hat I bought, chosen at desperate random, proved later not to fit. A fake astrakhan, it cost $45; and, because of the complicated payment system that operates in all Soviet stores, from the humblest grocery to GUM's in Moscow, it required another forty minutes to complete the transaction. First, the clerk gives you a sales slip, which you carry to a cashier's booth, where you cool your heels while the cashier does her computations on an abacus, an efficient method no doubt, still some clever Soviet should invent the cash register; when the money has been paid, the cashier stamps the sales slip, and this you take back to the clerk, who by now is attending five other people; eventually, though, the clerk will accept the slip, go to check it with the cashier, come back, hand over your purchase, and direct you to a wrapping department, where you join another queue. At the end of this process, I was given my hat in a green box. "Please, darling," Mrs. Gershwin begged Lyons, who was tempted to buy a hat himself, *"Don't* make us go through all that again."

Ski-glasses was nowhere in sight when we left the store. He turned up soon enough, however, at the edge of a group watching Lyons photograph peddlers selling Christmas trees in a snowy courtyard. It was there in the courtyard that I left the hatbox; I must have put it down to slap my numbed hands together. I didn't realize it was missing until many blocks later. Lyons and Mrs. Gershwin were game to go back and look for it. But that wasn't necessary. For as we turned around, we saw ski-glasses coming toward us, and dangling in his hand was the green hatbox. He gave it to me with a smile that twitched his crooked nose. Before I could think to say thank you, he'd tipped his cap and walked away.

"Well, ho ho—call that a coincidence?" crowed Lyons, a joyous shine livening his shrewd eyes. "Oh, I've had *him* spotted!"

"So have I," admitted Mrs. Gershwin. "But I think it's darling. Adorable. Simply adorable of them to take such good care of us. It makes you feel so protected. Well, darling," she said, as though determined Lyons should be persuaded to adopt her view, "*isn't* it a comfort to know you can't *lose* anything in Russia?"

At the Astoria, after lunch, I rode up in the elevator with Ira Wolfert, the former war correspondent who supposedly intended writing an article on Everyman Opera's tour for the *Reader's Digest*. "But I'm still looking for a story. What it seems to me is, is repetitious," Wolfert told me. "And you can't talk to anybody around here. Russians, I mean. It's giving me claustrophobia, every time I get into a political talk I keep getting the same old line. I was talking to Savchenko, he's supposed to be an intelligent guy, and I said to him, since this is a private talk, do you *honestly* believe all these things you're saying about America? You know, he was saying how Wall Street runs the country. But you can't talk to them. There's no realism in this social realism. Yesterday I was talking to a Russian—I won't define him, one of the guys we've met around here—and he slips me a note. This note asking me to call his sister in New York. He has a sister living there. Later on I see this on the street. I pull him down a side street and say, 'What the hell goes on here?' And he says, 'Everything's fine. Only it's better to be careful.' Everything's fine, but the guy's slipping me notes!" Wolfert bit hard on his pipe, and shook his head. "There's no realism. I'm getting claustrophobia."

Upstairs, I could hear the telephone ringing inside my room as I unlocked the door. It was the man I'd met during an intermission at the ballet, Miss Ryan's admirer, Stefan Orlov. He said he'd been calling Miss Ryan but there was no answer. I suggested he try the Breen's suite, one room of which Miss Ryan was using as an office. "No," he said, sounding nervously apologetic. "I must not call again. So soon. But when may I see Nancy? *And* you?" he added, tactfully. I asked him if he would like to come by the hotel for a drink. There was a pause that lasted until I thought we'd been disconnected. Finally, he said, "That would not be convenient. But could you meet me, say, in an hour?" I said yes, where? He told me, "Walk around the cathedral. St. Isaac's. Keep walking. I will see you." He rang off without saying good-bye.

I went down to the Breens' suite to tell Miss Ryan of the invitation. She was delighted, "I knew he'd call," but crestfallen, "I'm stuck with six copies of a rush item," she said, inserting layers of paper and carbon into a portable typewriter. The rush item was a two-page letter written by Robert Breen and addressed to Charles E. Bohlen, the American Ambassador to Russia. It began by expressing gratitude over the fact that Ambassador and Mrs. Bohlen were coming to Leningrad for the *Porgy and Bess* première; but the bulk of the letter was in a tone of grieving complaint. Although the production's Soviet tour had the blessings of the U. S. State Department, it was not, contrary to the popular impression, under their official sponsorship. Indeed, the trip had been made financially possible by Russia's own Ministry of Culture. Nevertheless, Breen felt it was "a crying shame" no member of Ambassador Bohlen's staff had been permanently assigned to the company to observe "the day-to-day and minute-to-minute happenings, the individual contacts, and the spontaneous, warm incidents" that Breen considered necessary if the Embassy intended to "prepare properly the sort of full and valid report which rightfully should be expected on this unprecedented project." Breen wrote, "The need for such documentation concerns not only this good-will tour, important as it is, but also possible future cultural exchanges. No one can imagine the extreme lengths to which we have gone to provide smooth running—or the infinite amount of details which have to be foreseen and arranged if this type of exchange is to bear the fruit of its promise. The documentation should record not only our successes, but also those facets of public relations which might be improved, and the possible failures."

"Give my love to Stefan," Miss Ryan instructed, as I left to keep the appointment. "And if it turns out to be a spontaneous, warm incident be sure and tell me so I can put it in the *Porgy and Bess* log," she said, referring to an official journal of that title maintained by her employers.

It's a stone's throw from the Astoria to the semi-Gothic mass of St. Isaac's Cathedral. I left the hotel at exactly three-thirty, the time Orlov had said he would meet me. But on stepping out the door, I found myself confronting a pair of ski glasses. There was an Intourist Ziv parked at the curb, and the man was sitting in the front seat talking to a chauffeur. For a moment I thought of returning to the hotel; it seemed the sensible course if Orlov was concerned that his rendezvous be off the record. But I decided to stroll past the car and see what happened; as I went by, nerves and an unreliable sense of etiquette prompted me to nod at the man. He yawned and averted his face. I didn't look back until I'd crossed the square and was in the shadows of St. Isaac's. By then, the car was gone. I walked slowly around the cathedral, pretending to admire the architecture, though

there was no reason to pretend anything, for the sidewalks were deserted. Still, I felt conspicuous, and not
quite lawful. Night swept the sky like the black crows
that wheeled and cawed overhead. On the third lap
around, I began to suspect Orlov had changed his mind.
I tried to forget the cold by counting my steps, and had
ticked off two hundred and sixteen when, turning a corner, I came on a scene that made the flow of numbers
stop like the hands of a dropped watch.

It was this: four men in black had a fifth man
backed against the cathedral wall. They were pounding
him with their fists, pushing him forward and hitting him
with the full weight of their bodies, like football players
practicing on a dummy. A woman, respectably dressed
and carrying a pocketbook tucked under her arm, stood
on the sidelines as though she were casually waiting
while some men friends finished a business conversation.
Except for the cawing of crows, it was like an episode
from a silent film; no one made a sound, and as the
four attackers relinquished the man, leaving him spread-
eagled on the snow, they glanced at me indifferently,
joined the woman and walked off without a word between them. I went over to the man. He was fat, too
heavy for me to lift, and the drink on his breath would
have killed scorpions. He was not bleeding and he was
not unconscious, but he wanted to speak and couldn't;
he gazed up at me like a deaf-mute attempting to communicate with his eyes.

A headlighted car pulled alongside the curb. The
strip of black and white checks bordering its frame
identified it as a taxi. The rear door opened, and Stefan
Orlov called my name. Leaning in the door, I tried to
explain what had happened and ask him to help the
man, but he was impatient, he didn't want to listen, he
kept saying, "Get in," and, "Will you *please* get in";
and at last, with a fury that shocked me, "You're an
idiot!" he said, yanking me onto the seat. As the taxi
swung in a U-turn, its headlights exposed the man
sprawled on the sidewalk, his lifted hands plowing the

air, like the claws of an insect cruelly tumbled on its back.

"I'm sorry," said Orlov, regaining a civil voice that also managed to sound sincerely remorseful. "But other people's quarrels. They are not so much interesting, you understand. Now, enjoy yourself. We are going to the Eastern." He commented on Miss Ryan's absence and regretted "deeply" that she'd been unable to accept his invitation. "The Eastern is where you want to take a girl like Nancy. Very good food. Music. A bit of Oriental atmosphere." After the clandestine nature of our meeting, it struck me as curious that we were now proceeding anywhere as gay and public as he described; and I said so. He was hurt. "I have no fears, but I'm not an idiot either. The Astoria is a sensitive place. You understand? It's a nuisance to go there. Why shouldn't I see you if I like?" he said, asking himself the question. "You are a singer, I'm interested in music." He was under the impression that both Miss Ryan and myself were singers in the cast of *Porgy and Bess*. When I corrected him, and told him I was a writer, he seemed upset. He had lighted a cigarette, and his lips, pursed to blow out the match, tautened. "Are you a correspondent?" he asked, letting the flame burn. I said no, not what he meant by a correspondent. He blew on the match. "Because I hate correspondents," he said, rather warningly, as though I'd best not be lying to him. "They're filthy. And Americans, it's too bad to say, are the worst. The filthiest." Now that he knew I was a writer, I thought perhaps he saw the situation in a different, less harmless perspective, and so suggested that if the taxi would take me within walking distance of the Astoria, we could amicably part company then and there. He interpreted this as a protest to his opinion of American correspondents. "Please, you misunderstand. I admire so much the American *people*," he said, and told me that the years he'd spent in Washington "were of a happiness I never forget. The Russians who lived in New York were always very snobbish about the Russians who had to live in Washington;

they said, 'Oh, my dear, Washington is so *boring* and provincial.' " He laughed at his grande-dame imitation. "But for me, I liked it there. The hot streets in the summer. Bourbon whiskey. I liked so much my flat. I open my windows and pour myself a bourbon," he said, as though reliving these actions. "I sit in my underwear and drink the bourbon and play the Vic loudly as I like. There is a girl I know. Two girls. One of them always comes by."

The so-called Eastern is a restaurant attached to the Hotel Europa, just off the Nevsky Prospekt. Unless a few desiccated potted-palms connote the Orient, I am at a loss to explain Orlov's contention that the place had a slant-eyed atmosphere. The atmosphere, if any, was a discouraging one of yellow-walled drabness and sparsely occupied tables. Orlov was self-conscious, he picked at his tie and smoothed his dark hair. While we crossed an empty dance floor, an ensemble, four musicians as spidery as the palms they stood among, were scratching out a waltz. We climbed a flight of stairs that led to a balcony where there were discreet dining booths. "I'm sure you think the Astoria is more elegant," he said, as we were seated. "But that is for foreigners and large snobs. Here is for smaller snobs. I am *very* small snob."

It worried me that he probably couldn't afford the Eastern at all. His overcoat featured a luxurious sable collar and he had a hat of gleaming sealskin. Still his suit was a poor, thin plaid and the laundered freshness of his white shirt somehow made more apparent its frayed cuffs and collar. But he gave sumptuous instructions to the waiter, who brought us a 400-gram carafe of vodka and a huge helping of caviar heaped in silver ice-cream dishes, toast and slices of lemon on the side. With a passing thought for Mrs. Gershwin, I dispatched every soft, unsalted, gray, pearly bead of it, and Orlov, marveling at the speed of my accomplishment, asked if I would like another serving. I said no, I couldn't possibly, but he saw that I could, and sent the waiter for more.

Meanwhile, he proposed toasts in honor of Miss Ryan. "To Nancy," he said, draining his glass, then, with a refill, "To Nancy. She is a beautiful girl"; and, again pouring, "That beautiful Nancy. Beautiful girl. Beautiful."

The succession of fast-gulped vodka flushed his pale, almost handsome face. He told me he could drink "a fool's fill" and not get drunk, but a gradual dimming of intelligence in his fine blue eyes belied the boast. He wanted to know if I thought Miss Ryan was partial to him. "Because," he said, leaning forward in an attitude of excessive confidence, "she is a beautiful girl, and I like her." I said yes, I gathered he considered her highly. "But you think I'm an idiot? Because I'm nearly forty and I'm married five years?" He spread his hand on the table to show me a plain gold wedding ring. "I would never do harm to my marriage," he said piously. "We have two babies, little girls." He described his wife as "not beautiful, but my principal friend," and told me that, aside from the children, the mutual interests they shared made the marriage "a serious composition." Among professional classes in Russia, it can be observed that persons seldom make alliances with anyone outside their own field of work. Doctors marry doctors; lawyers, lawyers. The Orlovs, it seemed, were both mathematicians who taught at the same Leningrad school. Music and the theatre formed their main pleasures; they had taken turns, he said, waiting in line to buy tickets for the *Porgy and Bess* first-night, but in the end they had been allowed just one ticket. "Now my wife pretends she doesn't want to go. That is so I can go." The previous year they had bought a television set as a New Year's present to each other, but now they regretted having spent the money on something "so boring and childish." He expressed himself with equal harshness on the subject of Soviet films. His wife, however, was fond of going to the *kino,* but he himself would only be enthusiastic if ever again they showed American pictures. ("I should like to know. What has happened to that beautiful girl, Joan Bennett? And the other one, Ingrid Bergman? And George Raft? What a wonderful actor! Is he still alive?") Apart from this disagreement on the merits of movie going, his wife's tastes coincided with his at every point; they even, he said, enjoyed the same sport, "boating," and for several years had been saving to buy a small sailboat, which they intended docking at a fishing village near Leningrad where each summer they spent two months' vacation. "That is what I live for—guiding a boat through the poetry of our white nights. You must come back when the white nights are here. They are a true reward for nine months' dark."

The vodka was exhausted, and Orlov, after calling for a replenishment, grumbled that I wasn't keeping pace with him. He said it "disgusted" him to watch me "just tasting," and demanded that I "drink like a decent fellow or leave the table." I was surprised how easy it was to empty a glass in one swallow, how pleasant, and it appeared not to affect me except for a tickling warmth and a feeling that my critical faculties were receding. I began to think that after all Orlov was right, the restaurant did have an Oriental atmosphere, a Moorish coziness, and the music of the orchestra, scraping like cicadas among the palms, seemed to acquire a beguiling, nostalgic lilt.

Orlov, at the stage of repeating himself, said, "I'm a good man and I have a good wife," three times before he could reach the next sentence, which was, "But I have strong muscles." He flexed his arms. "I'm passionate. A lusty dancer. On hot nights, with the window open, and the Vic playing loud as we like . . . and the Vic playing loud as we like. One of them always comes by. And we dance like that. With the window open on hot nights. That's all I want. To dance with Nancy. Beautiful. A beautiful girl. You understand? Just to dance. Just to . . . Where is she?" His hand swept the table. Silverware clattered on the floor. "Why isn't Nancy here? Why won't she sing for us?" With his head tilted back he sang, "Missouri woman on the Mississippi with her apron strings Missouri woman drags her diamond rings by her apron strings down the bad Missouri on the Mississippi blues . . ." His voice grew louder, he lapsed into Russian, a hollering still obscurely associated with the tune of "St. Louis Blues." I looked at my watch. To my astonishment it was nine o'clock. We'd been sitting in the Eastern almost five hours, which meant I couldn't be as sober as I reckoned. The realization and the proof of it struck simultaneously, like a pair of assassins who had been lying in wait. The tables seemed to slide, the lights swing, as though the restaurant were a ship riding a rough sea. At my request, insistence, Orlov asked for the check, but he went on singing while he counted out his rubles, sang his way down the stairs and waltzed by himself across the dance floor, ignoring the orchestra for his own accompaniment, "Missouri woman you're a bad Missouri woman on the Mississippi blues . . ."

In front of the Eastern there was a vendor selling rubber animals. Orlov bought a rabbit and handed it to me. "Tell Nancy from Stefan." Then he pulled me along a street that led away from the Nevsky Prospekt. As mud lanes replaced pavement it became clear that our destination was not the Astoria. For this was no neighborhood of palaces. Instead it was as though I were walking again through the slums of New Orleans, a district of dirt streets and broken fences, sagging wooden houses. We passed an abandoned church where wind wailed round the domes like a widow at the grave. Not far from the church, sidewalks resumed, and, with them, the city's imperial façade. Orlov headed toward the lighted windows of a café. The cold walk had quietened, somewhat sobered him. At the door, he said, "Here it is better. A workingman's place."

It was as if one had fallen into a bear pit. The body heat and beery breath and damp-fur smell of a hundred growling, quarreling, pawing customers filled the bright-lighted café. Ten and twelve men huddled around each of the room's half-dozen tables.

The only women present were three look-alike waitresses, brawny girls, wide as they were tall, and with faces round and flat as plates. In addition to waiting, they did duty as bouncers. Calmly, expertly, with an odd absence of rancor and less effort than it takes to yawn, they could throw a punch that knocked the stuffings out of men double their size. Lord help the man who fought back. Then all three girls would converge on him, beat him to his knees, literally wipe the floor with him as they dragged his carcass to the door and pitched it into the night. Some men, would-be customers decidedly persona non grata, never got into the café, for as soon as any of these undesirables appeared at the door the ladies of the establishment formed a flying, flailing wedge to drive him out again. Yet they could be courteous. At least they smiled at Orlov, impressed, I think, by his sable collar and expensive hat. One of them showed us to a table where she told two men, young jut-jawed bruisers wearing leather coats, to get up and give us their chairs. One was willing, the other argued. She settled his objections by snatching his hair and twisting his ear.

For the most part, only upper-strata restaurants are licensed to sell vodka, and since the café was not in that category, Orlov ordered Russian cognac, a brackish liquid that came in large tea glasses overflowing their brim. With the blitheness of a man blowing foam off a beer, he emptied a third of his glass and asked if the café "pleased" me, or did I think it "rough." I answered yes, and yes. "Rough, but not hooligan," he differentiated. "On the waterfront, yes, that is hooligan. But here is just ordinary. A workingman's place. No snobs." We had eight companions at the table and they took an interest in me, picked at me like magpies, plucked a cigarette lighter out of my hand, a scarf from around my neck, objects they passed from one to the next, glaring at them, grinning over them, and showing, even the youngest, rows of rotted teeth, wrinkles for which age could not account. The man nearest was jealous and wanted all my attention. It was impossible to guess how old he was, anywhere from forty to seventy. He had an eye missing and this circumstance enabled him to do a trick, which he kept forcing me to watch. It was meant to be a parody of Christ on the Cross. Taking a swallow of beer he would stretch his arms and droop his head. In a moment a trickle of beer came crying out the gaping redness of his hollow eye socket. His friends at the table thought it was an uproarious stunt.

Another favorite of the café was a boy who roamed around with a guitar. If you bought him a drink he'd sing you a song. He played one for Orlov, who translated it to me, saying it was the kind of song "we" like. It was the lament of a sailor longing for the village of his youth and a lost love called Nina. "The green of the sea is the green of her eyes." The boy sang well, with plaintive flamenco waverings in his voice. I sensed, though, that he was not concentrating on the lyrics. His thoughts and his gaze too were directed toward me. His white face had a sadness that seemed to be painted on, like a clown's. But it was his eyes that bothered me. Then I knew why. It was because they reminded me of the expression, the deaf-mute pleadings, in the eyes of the man left lying on the cathedral sidewalk. When he stopped playing, Orlov told him to sing another song. Instead the boy tried to speak to me.

"I . . . you . . . mother . . . man." He knew about ten words of English and he struggled to pronounce them. I asked Orlov to interpret, and as they talked together in Russian it was as though the boy were singing again. While his voice wove some sorrowful prose melody, his fingers tinkered with the strings of the guitar. Tears sprang to his eyes, and he rubbed them away with the flat of his palm, leaving grimy smudges like a child. I asked Orlov what he was saying. "It's not so much interesting. I'm not interested in politics." It seemed inconceivable the boy was talking politics, and when I persisted, Orlov was annoyed. "It's nothing. A nuisance. He wants you to help him."

Help was a word the boy understood. "Help," he said, nodding vigorously. "Help."

"Isn't he a nuisance?" said Orlov. "He says his father was English and his mother Polish, and because of this he says he's very badly treated in our country. He wants you to write the British Ambassador. Something like that. He wants to go to England."

"English man," said the boy, pointing at himself proudly. "Help." I didn't see how I could, and as he looked at me despair began to shade the hopeful shine of his wet eyes. "Help," he repeated reproachfully. "Help. Help."

Orlov gave him a coin and told him the name of a song he wanted to hear. It was a comedy song with unending choruses, and though the boy drudged through it listlessly, even the waitresses laughed and roared out the key lines, which everybody seemed to know. The one-eyed man, angry that there should be such laughter for anything except his trick, climbed on his chair and stood like a scarecrow Jesus, beer oozing from the empty socket and dribbling down his cheek. At five minutes to midnight, closing time, the waitresses began to switch the lights on and off, warningly. But the customers kept the song going, clung to these last minutes, as though they loathed to trade the café's camaraderie for cold streets, the fierce lonely journeys homeward. Orlov said he'd walk me to St. Isaac's Square. But first, a final toast. He proposed, "To a long life and a merry one. Is that what they say?" Yes, I told him, that's what they say.

The boy with the guitar blocked our path to the door. Exiting customers were still warbling his song; you could hear their voices echoing down the street. And in the café the waitresses were shooing out the last diehards, darkening the lights in earnest. "Help," said the boy, gently catching hold of my sleeve. "Help," he said, his eyes full on me, as a waitress, at Orlov's request, pushed him aside to let us by. "Help, help," he called after me, a door between us now, and the words a muted sound fading into nothing like the night-falling snow.

"I think he's a crazy person," said Orlov.

"New York could've been bombed, for all we know," said Leonard Lyons to the financier, Herman Sartorius, who was sitting next to him in a bus that was taking the company on a morning visit to the Hermitage Museum. "I've never been in a place I couldn't read a newspaper, find out what's going on in the world. A prisoner, that's how I feel." Sartorius, a tall, graying, solemnly courteous man, confessed that he too missed Western newspapers and wondered aloud if it would seem "not quite the correct thing" if he inquired at a Leningrad bank for the current New York Stock Exchange quotations.

As it happened there was a passenger seated behind them who could have supplied any information they wanted. It was his business to know what went on beyond the iron curtain, especially in America. A Russian, his name was Josef ("Call me Joe") Adamov, and he was in Leningrad to tape-record interviews with the *Porgy and Bess* cast for Radio Moscow, the station that beams broadcasts to countries outside the Soviet orbit. Adamov's talents are devoted to programs intended for American, or English-speaking, consumption. The programs consist of news reports, music, and soap operas sudsy with propaganda. Listening to one of these plays is a startling experience, not for the content, which is crude, but for the acting, which isn't. The voices pretending to be "average" Americans seem precisely that: one has absolute belief in the man who says he's a Midwest farmer, a Texas cowhand, a Detroit factory worker. Even the voices of "children" sound familiar as the crunch of Wheaties, the crack of a baseball. Adamov bragged that none of these actors had ever left Russia, their accents were manufactured right in Moscow. Himself a frequent actor in the plays, Adamov has so perfected a certain American accent that he fooled a native of the region, Lyons, who

said, "Gee, I'm dumfounded, I keep wondering what's
he doing so far from Lindy's." Adamov indeed seems to
belong on the corner of Broadway and Fifty-first, a copy
of *Variety* jammed under his arm. Although his slang
needs dusting off, it is delivered with a bizarrely fluent
side-of-the-mouth technique. "Me, I'm no museum-type
guy," he said, as we neared the Hermitage. "But if you go
in for all that creepy stuff, they tell me this joint's okay,
really loaded." Swart, moon-faced, a man in his middle
thirties with a jumpy, giggling, coffee-nerves animation,
his shifty eyes grow shiftier when, under duress, he admits that his English was learned in New York, where he
lived from the ages of eight to twelve with an émigré
grandfather. He prefers to skate over this American episode. "I was just a kid," he says, as though he were saying, "I didn't know any better." A foreign resident in
Moscow, who knows Adamov well, described him to me
as "no fool. An opportunist with two fingers in every pie."
And an Italian correspondent, another old Moscow hand,
said, "Ah, si. Signor Adamov. The smiler with the knife."
In short, Adamov is a successful man, which means, as it
does elsewhere, though far more so in Russia, that he
enjoys privileges unknown to the ordinary citizen. The
one he values most is a two-room bachelor apartment in
Moscow's Gorky Street, where he lives, to hear him tell
it, the life of a Turk in his seraglio. "Gimme a buzz you
come to Moscow, you wanta meet some cute kids."
Meanwhile, he thought some members of the *Porgy and
Bess* company were "pretty cute kids," particularly the
saucer-eyed singer in the chorus named Dolores ("Delirious") Swann. At the museum, when the sightseers were
separated into battalions of twelve, Adamov made a
point of joining Miss Swann in a group that included,
among others, the Wolferts, Mrs. Gershwin, Nancy Ryan,
Warner Watson and myself.

The Hermitage is part of the Winter Palace, which
in recent years has been repainted the Imperial color, a
frosty chartreuse-*vert*. Its miles of silvery windows over-
look a park and a wide expanse of the Neva River. "The

Winter Palace was started working 1764 and took sev-
enty-eight years to finish," said the guide, a mannish girl
with a brisk, whip-'em-through attitude. "It consists of
four buildings and contains, as you see, the world's greatest museum. This where we are standing is the Ambassadorial Staircase, used by the ambassadors mounting to
see the Czar."

In the ectoplasmic wake of those ambassadors our
party followed her up marble stairs that curved under a
filigree ceiling of white and gold. We passed through a
splendid hall of green malachite, like a corridor under
the sea, and here there were French windows where a
few of us paused to look across the Neva at a misty-hazy
view of that celebrated torture chamber, the Peter-Paul
fortress. "Come, come," the guide urged. "There is much
to see and we will not accomplish our mission if we lin-
ger at useless spectacles."

A visit to the treasure vault was the mission's immediate objective. "That's where they keep the ice, the *real*
stuff: crown jools, all that crap," Adamov informed Miss
Swann. A dragoon of stunted Amazons, several of them
in uniform and wearing pistols strapped round their
waists, guard the vault's bolted doors. Adamov, jerking
a thumb toward the guards, told Warner Watson, "I'll bet
you don't have any female cops in America, huh?"

"Sure," said Watson timidly. "We have police-
women, sure."

"But," said Adamov, his moist moon-face going
scarlet with laughter, "not as fat as these, huh?"

While the vault's complicated steel doors were being
unlocked, the guide announced, "Ladies will please
leave their pocketbooks with the custodians." Then, as
though to circumvent the obvious implication, "It is a
matter of ladies causing damage dropping their pocketbooks. We have had that experience."

The vault is divided into three small, chandelier-
lighted rooms, the first two entirely occupied by the
museum's most unique display, a sophisticated panorama
of Scythian gold, buttons and bracelets, cruel weapons,

papery leaves and wreath garlands. "First-century stuff," said Adamov. "B.C. A.D. all that crap." The third room is intellectually duller, and much more dazzling. A dozen glass-enclosed cabinets (bearing the metal marker of their maker, Holland and Sons, 23 Mount Street, Grosvenor Square, London) afire with aristocratic souvenirs. Onyx and ivory walking sticks, musical birds that sing with emerald tongues, a lily bouquet made of pearls, another of ruby roses, rings and boxes that give off a trembling glare like heat waves.

Miss Swann sang, "But dee-*imonds* are a girl's best friend," and someone who shouted, "Where's that Earl Jackson?" was told, "Oh Earl, you know that cat wouldn't be up this hour of the day. But he's sure going to be sorry he missed this. Him feeling the way he does about sparkles."

Adamov planted himself in front of the cabinet containing one of the collection's few examples of Fabergé, a miniature version of the Czar's symbols of power: crown, scepter and orb. "It's gorgeous," sighed Miss Swann. "Don't you think it's gorgeous, Mr. Adamov?" Adamov smiled indulgently. "If *you* say so, kid. Personally, I think it's junk. What good does it do anybody?"

Ira Wolfert, chewing on an unlit pipe, was rather of Adamov's opinion. At least, "I hate jewelry," he said, glowering at a tray of blazing froufrou. "I don't know the difference between a zircon and a diamond. Except I like zircons better. They're shinier." He put an arm around his wife, Helen. "I'm glad I married a woman who doesn't like jewelry."

"Oh, I like *jewelry,* Ira," said Mrs. Wolfert, a comfortable-looking woman prone to expressing decisive notions in a tentative tone. "I like *creations.* But *this,* this is all trickery and show-off. It makes me ill."

"It makes me ill, too," said Miss Ryan. "But in quite a different way. I'd give anything for that ring—the tiger's eye."

"It makes me ill," Mrs. Wolfert repeated. "I don't call these things creations. This," she said, indicating a brooch of her own, a straightforward design in Mexican silver, "is what *I* call a creation."

Mrs. Gershwin was also making comparisons. "I wish I'd *never* come here," she said, forlornly fingering her diamonds. "I feel so dissatisfied, I'd like to go home and crack my husband on the head." Miss Ryan asked her, "If you could have any of this you wanted, what would you take?"

"All of it, darling," replied Mrs. Gershwin.

Miss Ryan agreed. "And when I got it home, I'd spread it on the floor and rip off my clothes and just *roll.*"

Wolfert desired nothing, he simply wanted to "get the hell out of here and see something interesting," a wish he conveyed to the guide, who acquiesced by herding everyone to the door and counting them as they left. Some six kilometers later, the group, its ranks thinned by fatigue cases, stumbled into the last exhibit hall, weak-legged after two hours of inspecting Egyptian mummies and Italian Madonnas, craning their necks at excellent old masters excruciatingly hung, poking about the sarcophagus of Alexander Nevsky, and marveling over a pair of Peter the Great's Goliath-large boots. "Made," said the guide, "by this progressive man with his *own* hands." Now, in the last hall, the guide commanded us to "go to the window and view the hanging garden."

"But where," bleated Miss Swann, "where *is* the garden?"

"Under the snow," said the guide. "And over here," she said, directing attention to the final item on the agenda, "is our famous The Peacock."

The Peacock, an exotic mechanical folly constructed by the eighteenth-century clockmaker, James Cox, was brought to Russia as a gift for Catherine II. It is housed in a glass cage the size of a garden gazebo. The focus of the piece is a peacock perched among the gilded leaves of a bronze tree. Balanced on other branches are an owl, a cock rooster, a squirrel nibbling a nut. At the base of the tree there is a scattering of mushrooms, one of which forms the face of a clock. "When the hour strikes, we have here a forceful happening," said the guide. "The peacock spreads her tail, and the rooster cackles. The owl blinks her eyes, and the squirrel has a good munch."

Adamov grunted. "I don't care what it does. It's dopey." Miss Ryan took him to task. She wanted to know why he should feel that way about an object of such "imaginative craftsmanship." He shrugged. "What's imaginative about it? A lot of jerks going blind so milady can watch a peacock fan her tail. Look at those leaves. Think of the work went into that. All for nothing. A nonutilitarian nothing. What'cha up to, kid?" he said, for Miss Ryan had started scribbling in a notebook. "What-'cha doing? Putting down all the dumb things I say?" Actually, as Miss Ryan was surprised into explaining, she was writing a description of the clock. "Uh huh," he said, his voice not as genial as his smile, "you think I'm pretty dumb, don't you? Well, put this down. I'll tell you a good reason I don't like it. Because that peacock's gonna go on fanning her tail when I'm dust. A man works all his life, he ends up dust. That's what museums are, reminders of death. Death," he repeated, with a nervous titter that expanded into mirthless guffaws.

A gang of soldiers, part of another tour, approached The Peacock just as the hour chimed, and the soldiers, country boys with their heads shaved bald, their drab uniforms sagging in the seat like diapers, had the double enchantment of gaping at foreigners and watching the golden-eyed winkings of an owl, a peacock flash its bronze feathers in the wan light of the Winter Palace. The Americans and the soldiers crowded close to hear the rooster crow. Man and art, for a moment alive together, immune to old mortality.

It was Christmas Eve. The translators from the Ministry of Culture, under the supervision of their chief, Savchenko, had personally set up a skinny fir tree in the center of an Astoria dining room and decorated it with hand-colored paper cards, wisps of tinsel. The members of the company, sentimental over their fourth Christmas together, had gone on spending sprees: a razzledazzle of cellophane and ribbon spread in a knee-deep, twenty-foot circle round the tree. The presents were to be opened at midnight. Long past that hour, Miss Ryan was still in her room wrapping packages and rummaging through suitcases selecting from her possessions trinkets to take the place of gifts she'd neglected to buy. "Maybe I could give the bunny to one of the kids," she said, meaning the rubber rabbit sent her by Stefan Orlov. The rabbit nestled among her bed pillows. She'd inked whiskers on its face and on its side printed, STEFAN—THE BUNNY. "I guess not," she decided. "If I gave him away no one would ever believe I'd snagged a Russian beau. *Almost* did." Orlov had not telephoned again.

I helped Miss Ryan carry her presents down to the dining room, where she was just in time for the end of the gift-distributing. The children had been allowed to stay up for the party, and now, hugging new dolls and squirting water pistols filled with raspberry soda, they cycloned through the gaudy wrapping-paper debris. The grownups danced to the music of the Russian jazz band, which could be heard playing in the connecting main restaurant. Mrs. Breen whirled by, a bit of holiday ribbon floating round her neck. "Isn't it bliss?" she said. "Aren't you happy? After all, we don't spend *every* Christmas in Leningrad!" The waitresses, young English-language students who had volunteered to tend table for the American troupe, demurely refused invitations to dance. "Oh, come on, honey," one waitress was urged, "let's you and me melt that curtain together." Vodka, abetting the spirit of the occasion, had already melted the reserve of the Ministry of Culture representatives. They each had received presents from the company, and Miss Lydia, who had been given a compact, wanted to kiss everyone in sight. "It is too kind, so kind," she said, tirelessly examining her pudgy face in the compact's mirror.

Even the aloof Savchenko, a dour, glacial Santa Claus, or Father Frost, as the fellow is known in Russia, seemed after a while willing to forget his dignity, at any rate was unprotesting when a girl in the cast plumped herself on his lap, threw her arms around him and, between kisses, told him, "How come you want to look like a grumpy old bear when you're just a doll? A living doll, that's what you are, Mr. Savchenko." Breen, too, had affectionate words for the Ministry of Culture executive. "Let's all drink to the man we can thank for this wonderful party," he said, hoisting a tumbler of vodka, "one of the best friends we have in the world, Nikolai Savchenko." Savchenko, wiping away lipstick, responded by proposing another toast. "To the free exchange of culture between the artists of our countries. When the cannons are heard, the muses are silent," he continued, quoting his favorite maxim. "When the cannons are silent, the muses are heard."

The radio man from Moscow, "Joe" Adamov, was busily tape-recording aspects of the party on a portable machine. Eight-year-old Davy Bey, solicited for a comment, said into Adamov's microphone, "Hello, everybody, happy Christmas. Daddy wants me to go to bed, but we're all having a grand time, so I'm not going. Well, I got a gun and a boat, only what I wanted was an airplane and not so many clothes. Any kids would like it, why don't they come over and play with us. We got bubble gum, and I know some good places to hide." Adamov also recorded "Silent Night, Holy Night," which the cast, gathered round the tree, sang with a volume that drowned the next-room thumping of the dance band. Ira Wolfert and his wife added their voices to the choir. The Wolferts, parents of adult children, had booked a telephone call to America. "All our children will be together tonight; tomorrow they go different ways," said Mrs. Wolfert when the caroling ended. "Oh, Ira," she squeezed her husband's hand, "that's the only present I want. For our call to come through." It never did. They waited till two, then went to bed.

After two, the Christmas party infiltrated the adjoining room, the Astoria's "night club," which is permitted to operate later than twelve on Saturdays, the only night of the week when patrons outnumber personnel. The Soviet habit of seating strangers together does not encourage uninhibited conversation, and the cavernous restaurant, occupied to near capacity by Leningrad's elite, was unreasonably subdued, the merest few, mostly young army and naval officers with their sweethearts, taking advantage of the orchestra's respectable rhythms. The rest, artists and theatrical personalities, groups of military Chinese, jowly commissars accompanied by their uncorseted, gold-toothed wives, sat around bored and uncaring as castaways on a Pacific atoll.

Earl Bruce Jackson took one look, and said, "Whatcha say, cats, let's get the snakes crawlin', put some hotcha in the pot, skin the beast and sprinkle pepper in his eyes." Whereupon five members of the company commandeered the bandstand. The hotel musicians had not the least objection to being ousted. They all were fans of American jazz, and one of them, a devotee of Dizzy Gillespie, had accumulated a large record collection by listening to foreign broadcasts and recording the music on discs made from old x-ray plates. Junior Mignatt spit into a trumpet, banana-fingered Lorenzo Fuller struck piano chords. Moses Lamar, a powerhouse with sandpaper lungs, stomped his foot, opened his mouth wide as an alligator. "Grab yo' hat 'n grab yo' coat, leave yo' worry on de do' step . . . It was as though the castaways had sighted rescue on the horizon. Smiles broke out like an unfurling of flags, tables emptied onto the dance floor. ". . . just direct yo' feet . . ." A Chinese cadet tapped his foot, Russians packed close to the bandstand, riveted by Lamar's scratchy voice, the drumbeat riding behind it. ". . . to de sunny *sunny* SUNNY . . ." Couples rocked, swayed in each other's arms. ". . . side ah de streeeet!"

"Look at them zombies go!" said Jackson, and shouted to Lamar, "They're skinned, man, skinned. Throw on the gasoline and burn 'em alive. Ooble-ee-do."

Mrs. Breen, a smiling shepherd gazing at her flock,

turned to Leonard Lyons. "You see. We've broken through. Robert's done what the diplomats couldn't." A skeptical Lyons replied, "All I say is, fiddles play while Rome burns."

At one of the tables I noticed Priscilla Johnson, the college friend of Miss Ryan's who was studying Russian law, and writing, so she said, articles on Soviet love life. She was sitting with three Russians, one of whom, a gnarled unshaven gnome with frothy black hair, splashed champagne into a glass and thrust it at me. "He wants you to sit down, and, gosh, you'd better," Miss Johnson advised. "He's a wild man, sort of. But fascinating." He was a Georgian sculptor, responsible for the heroic statuary in the new Leningrad subway, and his "wild man" quality came out in sudden rash assertions. "You see that one with the green tie?" he asked in English, pointing at a man across the room. "He's a rotten coward. An MVD. He wants to make me trouble." Or, "I like the West. I have been to Berlin, and met Marlene Dietrich. She was in love with me."

The other couple at the table, a man and wife, were silent until Miss Johnson and the sculptor left to dance. Then the woman, a death-pale brunette with Mongolian cheekbones and green almond eyes, said to me, "What an appalling little man. So dirty. A *Georgian,* of course. These people from the South!" She spoke English with the spurious elegance, the strained exactness of Liza Doolittle. "I am Madame Nervitsky. You of course know my husband, the crooner," she said, introducing me to the gentleman, who was twice her age, somewhere in his sixties, a vain, once-handsome man with an inflated stomach and a collapsing chin line. He wore makeup, powder, pencil, a touch of rouge. He knew no English, but told me in French, *"Je suis* Nervitsky. Le Bing Crosby de Russie." His wife was startled that I'd never heard of him. "No? *Nervitsky?* The famous *crooner?"* Her surprise was justified. In the Soviet Union, Nervitsky is a considerable celebrity, the idol of young girls who swoon over his interpretations of popular ballads. During the

twenties and thirties he lived in Paris, enjoying a minor
vogue as a cabaret artist. When that faltered, he went on
a honkytonk tour of the Far East. Though of Russian
parentage, his wife was born in Shanghai, and it was
there that she met and married Nervitsky. In 1943, they
moved to Moscow, where she launched a not too pros-
perous career as a film actress. "I am a painter really.
But I can't be bothered ingratiating all the right people.
That is necessary if you want your pictures shown. And
painting is so difficult when one travels." Nervitsky
spends most of the year making personal appearances
throughout Russia. He was currently engaged for a series
of concerts in Leningrad. "Nervitsky is more sold out
than the Negroes," his wife informed me. "We are going
to the Negro première," she said, and added that she was
sure it would be a "delightful" evening because "the
Negroes are so amusing and there is so little amusing
here. Nothing but work, work. We're all too tired to be
amusing. Don't you find Leningrad absolutely dead? A
beautiful corpse? And Moscow. Moscow is not quite as
dead, but so ugly." She wrinkled her nose and shuddered.
"I suppose, coming from New York, you find us very
shabby? Speak the truth. You think *me* shabby?" I
didn't think that, no. She wore a simple black dress, some
good jewelry, there was a mink stole slung over her
shoulders. In fact, she was the best-dressed, best-looking
woman I'd seen in Russia. "Ah, you're embarrassed to
say. But I know. When I look at your friends, these
American girls, I *feel* shabby. There are no nice things
next to my skin. It isn't that I'm poor. I have
money . . ." She hesitated. Miss Johnson and the sculptor were returning to the table. "Please," she said, "I
would like to say something to you privately. Do you
dance?"

The band was smooching its way through "Somebody Loves Me," and the crowd on the floor listened to
Lamar rasp out the lyrics with transfixed, transfigured
faces. ". . . who can it be oh *may*-be *ba*-by *may*-be it's
you!" Madame Nervitsky danced well, but her body

was tense, her hands icy. *"J'adore le musique des Negres.* It's so wicked. So vile," she said, and then, in the same breath, began to whisper rapidly in my ear, "You and your friends must find Russia very expensive. Take my advice, don't change your dollars. Sell your clothes. That is the way to get rubles. Sell. Anyone will buy. If it can be done discreetly. I am here in the hotel, Room 520. Tell your friends to bring me shoes, stockings, things for close to the skin. Anything," she said, digging her nails into my sleeve, "tell them I will buy *anything.* Really," she sighed, resuming a normal voice and raising it above the shriek of Mignatt's trumpet, "the Negroes are so delightful."

Somewhat set back from the Nevsky Prospekt, there is an arcaded building bearing a marked resemblance to St. Peter's. This is the Kazin Cathedral, Leningrad's largest antireligious museum. Inside, in an atmosphere of stained-glass gloom, the management has produced a Grand Guignol indictment against the teachings of the church. Statues and sinister portraits of the Popes follow each other down the galleries like a procession of witches. Everywhere ecclesiastics leer and grimace, make, in captioned cartoons, satyr suggestions to nunlike women, revel in orgies, snub the poor to cavort with the decadent rich. Ad infinitum the museum demonstrates its favorite thesis: that the church, the Roman Catholic in particular, exists solely as a protection to capitalism. One caricature, an enormous oil, depicts Rockefeller, Krupp, Hetty Green, Morgan and Ford plunging ferocious hands into a mountainous welter of coins and blood-soaked war helmets.

The Kazin Cathedral is popular with children. Understandably so, since the exhibition is liberally sprinkled with horror-comic scenes of brutality and torture. The schoolteachers who herd daily swarms of pupils through the place have difficulty dragging them away from such attractions as The Chamber of the Inquisitors. The Chamber is a real room peopled with the life-sized wax figures of four Inquisitors relishing the agonies of a heretic. The naked victim, chained to a table, is being branded with hot coals by a pair of masked torturers. The coals are electrically lighted. Children, even when pulled away, keep sneaking back for a second look.

Outside the cathedral, on the many columns supporting its arcades, there is another kind of display. Coarse chalk drawings, the usual men's room graffiti, scarcely worth mentioning, except that it seems on first thought an odd place to find it; and on second it doesn't. In a way it belongs.

Antireligious museums were not among the sightseeing projects their hosts had lined up for the *Porgy and Bess* cast. Quite the contrary, on Sunday, Christmas Day, the Soviets provided the choice of attending a Catholic Mass or a Baptist service. Eleven members of the company, including Rhoda Boggs, a soprano playing the part of the Strawberry Woman, went to the Baptist Evangelical Church, whose Leningrad parishioners number two thousand. Afterwards, I saw Miss Boggs sitting alone in the Astoria dining room. She is a round, honey-colored, jolly-faced woman, always carefully groomed, but now her little Sunday best hat was slightly askew, the handkerchief she kept dabbing at her eyes was wet as a washcloth.

"I'm tore to pieces," she told me, her breasts heaving. "I've been going to church since I can walk, but I never felt Jesus like I felt Jesus today. Oh, child, he was *there*. He was out in the open. He was plainly written on every face. He was singing with us, and you never heard such beautiful singing. It was old people mostly, and old people can't sing like that without Jesus is helping them along. The pastor, there was a sweet old man, he asked us colored people would we render a spiritual, and they listened so quiet, all those rows and rows and rows of old faces just looking at us, like we were telling them nobody's alone when Jesus is everywhere on this earth, which is a fact they know already, but it seemed to me like they were glad to hear it. Anybody doubts the presence of Our Saviour, he should've been there. Well, it came time to go. To say good-bye. And you know what happened? They stood up, the whole congregation. They took out white hankerchiefs and waved them in the air. And they sang, 'God Be With You Till We Meet Again.' The tears were just pouring down our faces, them and ours. Oh, child, it churned me up. I can't keep nothing on my stomach.''

That evening, with the première less than twenty-four hours away, the windows of the Astoria stayed lighted late. All night footsteps hurried along the corridors, doors slammed and telephones rang, as though a calamity were happening.

In Suite 415, Ambassador Bohlen and his wife entertained a small group of aides and friends who had just arrived with them by train from Leningrad. The gathering, which included Roye L. Lowry, Second Secretary at the Embassy and one of the two diplomats who had "briefed" the company in Berlin, was exceptionally quiet, since the Bohlens didn't want their presence in the hotel known until the last possible moment. They concealed themselves so successfully that the next morning Warner Watson, believing the diplomatic contingent were coming by plane, set out for the Leningrad airport with a bouquet for Mrs. Bohlen. Directly below the ambassadorial apartment, in Suite 315, Mrs. Breen was seesawing on a Relaxer Board, while her husband polished the pre-curtain speech he planned to deliver. It had been suggested to him that he might circumvent the Communist propaganda potential in *Porgy and Bess* by pointing out that its picture of American Negroes concerned the long ago, not today, and so he added the line, *"Porgy and Bess* is set in the past. It no more reflects the present than if it were about life under the Czars in Russia." In Room 223, Leonard Lyons was at his typewriter outlining the opening-night column he intended cabling his newspaper, the *New York Post*. "On stage were the flags of both nations, the U.S.S.R. and the U.S.A." he wrote, previewing the event. "The last time an American flag was displayed here was when there were only forty-five states in the union. A representative of the Ministry of Culture phoned to inquire how many states are united now. Yesterday a wardrobe mistress sewed three more stars on the old flag." The item finished a page. Lyons inserted a new sheet with fresh carbons. Instead of throwing the old carbon in a wastebasket, he took it to the bathroom and flushed it into oblivion. It was safer, he felt, to destroy used carbons, otherwise the Soviets, or perhaps rival correspondents, might ferret them out and decipher what he was writing. And indeed, the hotel was seething with journalistic competitors. The *Saturday Evening Post* was there in the person of Charles R. Thayer, Ambassador Bohlen's brother-in-law. Thayer, and C. L. Sulzberger of the *New York Times,* had arrived with the Bohlen party. The *Saturday Review* was sending Horace Sutton, *Time* and *Life* already had a photographer-reporting team on hand, and Mrs. Richard O'Malley, of AP's Moscow bureau, was speeding toward Leningrad aboard the crack Red Arrow Express, the same train which had, the night before, brought CBS correspondent Dan Schorr.

Now, on the second floor, in Room 111, Schorr, a heavy-set bachelor in his middle thirties, was simultaneously trying to correct a manuscript, keep a pipe lighted, and dictate on the telephone to a stenographer in Moscow. "Okay. Here's the story. You put in the slugs. Let's go," he barked, and began to read from typed pages. "*The Porgy and Bess Company comma believed to be the first American theatrical troupe ever to appear in Russia comma will open its Soviet engagement tomorrow night before a selected audience of two thousand two hundred* I repeat two two oh oh *at Leningrad's Palace of Culture comma but off-stage the Negro actors and singers have already scored a smash hit period The sixty members of the cast comma just by being themselves comma have had a tremendous impact on this comma the second largest city in the Soviet Union* . . . that's right, isn't it? It is the second largest?" For twenty min-

utes more Schorr droned out anecdotes and fact. Long
lines of Leningraders had waited all night in the snow
to buy tickets at a top-scale of sixty rubles ($15), a price
doubled and tripled on the black market. "Hey, what's
a synonym for black market that we can get past the
censors? Okay, make it curb price." Toward the end,
he was saying, *"They have given Leningrad a Christmas
probably unlike any in history period Until four o'clock
this morning they gathered around a Christmas tree
dash provided by a solicitous Soviet government dash
and sang carols and spirituals period.* Yeah, I know
I'm overfiling this story. But I got excited. Real excited.
You can see it. The impact of one culture on another
culture. And by the way, listen, I'm having a helluva
time. They're a great bunch, these *Porgy and Bess* people. Like living with a circus."

On Monday morning, the day of the première, the
cast met at Leningrad's Palace of Culture for a final
dress rehearsal with full orchestra. Originally the Soviets
had intended housing the production in the attractive
Mariinsky theatre, but the demand for tickets convinced
them they could double their profit by transferring the
opera to the huge Palace of Culture. The Palace, a pile
of muddy-orange concrete, was slapped together in the
thirties. From the outside it is not unlike one of those
decaying examples of supermarket architecture along
Hollywood and Vine. Several things about the interior
suggest a skating rink. Its temperature, for one. But
Davy Bey, and the other children in the company,
thought it was "a grand place," especially the vast
backstage with its black recesses for hiding, its fly ropes
to swing on, and where the tough backstage crew, strong
men and stronger women, caressed them, gave them
candy sticks and called them *"Aluchka,"* a term of affection.

I rode over to the rehearsal in a car shared by two
of the Ministry's interpreters, Miss Lydia and the tall,
personable youth named Sascha. Miss Lydia, a woman

who enjoys her food, was in a fine state of excitement, as though she were about to sit down to a delicious meal. "We will see it, no? Now we will *see* this *Porgy-Bess,*" she said, wiggling on the seat. And then it occurred to me that yes, of course, at last Miss Lydia and her Ministry colleagues would be able to judge for themselves "this *Porgy-Bess,*" the myth that had for so long consumed their hours and energy. Even Savchenko would be having his first glimpse. Here and there along the route, Miss Lydia happily pointed at street placards advertising the show. Breen's name, repeated often, was in bigger, bolder type than Gershwin's, and the name of his absent co-producer, Blevins Davis, was omitted altogether. The day before, Mrs. Gershwin had observed to Warner Watson that in Russia the name Gershwin seemed to be "riding in the rumble seat"; to which Watson had replied, "Look, Lee, it's got to be Robert's show this time. He wants it that way. He's just got to have it."

"How do you sit that still?" Miss Lydia inquired of Sascha. "Now we *see* it. Before the ordinary people." Sascha *was* still. He had a seasick, stricken look, and not without reason. That morning Savchenko had thrown Breen into a tailspin by telling him that the production's theatre programs were still at the printer and would not be obtainable for another few days. It was an authentic crisis because the programs contained a synopsis of the opera's plot, and Breen was afraid that without this guide the audience would have difficulty following the action. Savchenko offered a solution. Why not have one of the Ministry's translators come before the curtain and, prior to each act, outline the plot? Sascha had been chosen for the task. "How will I handle my feet?" he said, his eyes hypnotized with stage fright. "How will I speak when there is no water in my mouth?" Miss Lydia tried to soothe him. "Think only what an honor! Many important people will be present. You will be noticed. If you were *my* son, Sascha, I would be very proud."

Inside the Palace of Culture's darkened auditorium, Sascha and Miss Lydia found seats in the fourth row. I sat down behind them, between Savchenko and "Joe" Adamov, both of whom were exploring their mouths with toothpicks. Other Russians, some thirty-odd who had finagled invitations to watch the run-through, were scattered around in the first several rows. Among them were Moscow jouralists and photographers who had come to cover the première. The orchestra in the pit, an importation from Moscow's Stanislavski Theatre, was winging through the overture with confident ease. The conductor, Alexander Smallens, a Russian-born American who has made rather a life's work of *Porgy and Bess,* having maestroed its every incarnation, including the original 1935 production, said the Stanislavski was the sixty-first orchestra under his command and the best of the lot. "Superb musicians, and a joy to work with. They love the score, and they have the tempo, the rhythm. All they need now is a little more the *mood."* On stage, Breen, wearing a beret, a windbreaker, and a pair of close-fitting frontier pants, motioned the cast into place for the first scene. Flat overhead rehearsal lights shadowed the actors' faces, drained the color from the scenery and accentuated its wrinkled wornness. The set, a simple functional job, depicts a corner of Catfish Row with its balconied houses and shuttered windows. Presently, responding to a signal from Breen, a soprano leaned over a balcony and began to sing the opening song, "Summertime." Miss Lydia recognized the melody. She swayed her head and hummed with the music until Savchenko tapped her on the shoulder and growled an admonition that made her shrink in her seat. Midway through the performance, Adamov dug me with his elbow and said, "I speak pretty good English, right? Well *I* can't figure what the hell they're yelling about. All this dialect crap! I think . . ." but I never heard what he thought, for Savchenko turned round with a look that strangled Adamov. Most of the Russians were as silent as Savchenko could have wished. The rows of profiles, silhouetted in the glow

from the stage, remained as severely unmarred by expression as coin engravings. At the end, with the last
aria sung, there was a quiet drifting off to the cloakrooms.
Savchenko and Miss Lydia, Sascha and two other young
men from the Ministry, Igor and Henry, waited together while an attendant brought their coats. I walked
over and asked Miss Lydia her opinion of what she'd
seen. She bit her lower lip, her eyes darted toward Savchenko, who said firmly, "Interesting. Most interesting."
Miss Lydia nodded, but neither she nor Sascha, Igor
nor Henry, would venture a different adjective. "Yes,"
they all said, "interesting. Most interesting."

The average playing time of *Porgy and Bess* is approximately two and a half hours, but this final run-
through involving many pauses for corrections, lasted
from 10 A.M. until two in the afternoon. The cast, edgy
with hunger and anxious to return to the hotel, were
annoyed when, after the theatre had emptied of Russian
spectators, Breen informed them that the rehearsal was
not yet over. He wanted to restage the curtain calls.

As matters stood, and though only the two players
in the title roles took individual bows, the pattern of
calls already established required six minutes to complete. Not many productions can expect an audience to
sustain six minutes of applause. Breen now proposed extending these six minutes indefinitely by contriving what
amounted to "a separate little show. Just," he said, "an
impromptu thing. Sort of like an encore." It consisted
of having a drummer beat a bongo while, one at a time,
every winking, waving member of the company sash-
ayed across the stage inviting individual applause. Even
the stage manager, the wardrobe mistress, the electricians, and naturally the director himself, were set to receive homage from the audience. One had the choice of
two conclusions: either Breen was counting on an ovation of volcanic vigor, or he feared the reverse, and so
was insuring prolonged applause by staging this "impromptu" extra curtain call. Obviously under the delicate diplomatic circumstances, no audience would walk

out while the performers were still, in a sense, performing.

Private limousines had been put at the disposal of the leading players. Martha Flowers, who alternates with Ethel Ayler in the role of Bess, and who had been assigned to sing the part that evening, offered me a return ride to the Astoria. I asked if she were nervous about the première. "Me? Uh uh. I've been doing this show two years. The only thing makes me nervous is, maybe I'm ruining my voice for serious work." Miss Flowers, a young Juilliard graduate, is ambitious to make a reputation as a concert recitalist. She is small and perky. Whether smiling or not, her lips are always pursed downward, as though she'd just tasted a green persimmon. "I'm tired, though. I sure am that. This kind of climate's no good for a singer. You've really got to watch your throat," she said, massaging her own. "The other Bess, you know—Ethel, she's in bed with a bad cold. Got a temperature and everything. So I'll have to sing the matinée tomorrow and maybe the evening, too. Well, a person could ruin their voice *forever,* carrying on like that." She described her schedule between now and curtain time. "I ought to eat something. But first I'll take a bath. Can you float in your tub? Mine's so big I can float. I'll take a nap, too. We start for the theatre at six. Maybe six-thirty I'll be slipping into my costume and pinning that old red flower in my hair. Then I guess I'll have a long sit."

At six-thirty, the hour when Miss Flowers was presumably in her dressing room pinning on a paper rose, Mrs. Breen and Mrs. Gershwin were in the Bohlens' suite, where they had been asked to have drinks prior to leaving for the Palace of Culture. Breen himself, too busy to accept the Ambassador's hospitality, had already gone to the theatre.

The drinks, Scotch and tap water, were being served by Bohlen's aide, Roye L. Lowry, and Mrs. Lowry, a couple harmoniously matched in their conservative, schoolteacherish demeanor. Mrs. Bohlen's close friend, Marina Sulzberger, the quick-witted wife of the *Times* man, was also present to provide the hostess with conversational assistance. Not that Mrs. Bohlen, a serenely efficient woman with a dairymaid complexion and sensible blue eyes, gives an impression of being unable to keep any conversation afloat, however awkward. But there was, if one remembers the exceedingly reproachful letter Breen had dispatched to Bohlen a few days earlier, a certain awkwardness inherent in this meeting between representatives of Everyman Opera and the U. S. State Department. As for the Ambassador, one would not suppose, from his amiable manner, that he'd ever received such a letter. A career diplomat for more than twenty-five years, a large percentage of them spent at the Moscow Embassy, where he first held Lowry's present post, Second Secretary, and where he was ultimately appointed Ambassador in 1952, Bohlen still resembles a photograph taken the year (1927) he graduated from Harvard. Experience has harshened his sportsman's handsomeness, salted his hair and reduced, rather obliterated, a dreaming naïveté around the eyes. But the direct look of youth, of rugged stamina, has stayed with him. He lounged in his chair, sipping Scotch and talking to Mrs. Breen as though they were in a country room with a warm hearth and lazing dogs on the floor.

But Mrs. Breen couldn't relax. She sat on the edge of her seat, like an applicant for a job. "It's so sweet of you to have come. Just dear of you," she told Bohlen in a small-girl voice that was somehow not quite her own. "It means so much to the cast."

"You don't think we would've *missed* it?" said Bohlen, and his wife added, "Not for anything in the world! It's the high point of the winter. We've thought of nothing else, have we, Chip?" she said, using the Ambassador's nickname.

Mrs. Breen modestly lowered her eyes, a touch of color tinged her cheeks. "It means so much to the cast."

"It means so much to *us*," said Mrs. Bohlen. "Our life isn't so amusing that we could afford to miss something like this. Why, we'd have got here if we'd had to walk the whole way. Crawled on our hands and knees."

Mrs. Breen raised her eyes for an instant, and glanced sharply at the Ambassador's wife, as though half suspecting her of satiric intent; then, reassured by Mrs. Bohlen's straight, clear face, she dropped her gaze again. "It's just dear of you," she whispered. "And of course we're all thrilled about the party in Moscow."

"Oh, yes . . . the party," said Mrs. Bohlen, with detectable resignation. In honor of the company's Moscow première, two weeks hence, the Bohlens had promised to give an official reception at their residence, Spaso House.

"Robert and I do hope Mr. Bulganin will be there. We want to thank him personally for all the courtesy we've received. The Ministry of Culture paid Robert a lovely tribute. Seven ivory elephants." Mrs. Breen was referring to a mantelpiece parade of plastic elephants that Savchenko had presented as a gift to Breen.

"How very nice," said Mrs. Bohlen dimly, as though she'd lost the conversational thread. "Well, of course, we can't be quite sure *who's* coming to the party. We're sending out two hundred invitations, more or less, but since Russians never answer an R.S.V.P., we never know who to expect or how many."

"That's right," said the Ambassador. "You don't count on these fellows until they walk in the door. Any of them. And when they give a party themselves they almost never invite you until the last minute. Everyone in the diplomatic corps keeps the evening free when we know there's going to be a big affair at the Kremlin. We just sit around, hoping the phone will ring. Sometimes we're in the middle of dinner before they invite us. Then it's a rush. Fortunately, you never have to dress for these things," he said, reverting to a previous topic, and a painful one for Mrs. Breen, who, earlier in the day, had been chagrined to learn that Bohlen was unwilling to attend the opening in black-tie. Indeed, driven by her determination to "make everything gala," she had gone a step further and envisioned the Ambassador wearing white tie and tails, which is what her husband planned to do. But, "It never occurred to me to bring a dinner jacket," said Bohlen, fingering a button of the dark gray suit he considered proper to the occasion. "No one wears them here. Not even for a première."

Over in a corner, Mrs. Gershwin and Mrs. Sulzberger were elaborating on the same sartorial theme. "Of *course* we shouldn't dress up. That's what I've told Wilva all along. We went to a ballet the other night and looked perfectly ridiculous. Oh, there's too much fuss around here. I don't know what the fuss is all about. After all, it's *only* little old *Porgy*."

"Actually," said Mrs. Sulzberger, a Greek-born woman whose clever eyes sparkle with Mediterranean mischief, "it might not be a bad thing for the Russians to see people dressed. There's no excuse to go about looking the way they do. When we first came here, I felt sorry for them," she said, and added that she and her husband had been in the Soviet Union two weeks, staying as house guests of the Bohlens. "I thought the way they dressed, the dreariness of it all, I imagined it was because they were terribly poor. But really, you know, that's not true. They look this way because they want to. They do it on purpose."

"Yes," said Mrs. Gershwin, "that's what I think."

"I wonder," mused Mrs. Sulzberger. "I wonder. Do you suppose the Russians are so awful because they've always been beaten? Or have they always been beaten because they're so awful?"

"Yes," said Mrs. Gershwin, "that's what I think."

Lowry caught the Ambassador's eye, and glanced significantly at his watch. Outside the hotel a limousine was purring its engine, preparing to carry the Bohlens to the theatre. Other Zivs, a street-long gleam of them, waited for Mrs. Breen and Mrs. Gershwin, for Savchenko and Adamov and the employees of AP, Time-Life, CBS.

Soon the cars would start slithering across the square, like a funeral cortege.

Bohlen swallowed his Scotch and accompanied his guests to the door of the suite. "I don't think you have any thing to worry about," he told Mrs. Breen. "The Russians are very musical people. You'll have rubles coming out of your ears."

"Adorable man. And she's charming, too," Mrs. Gershwin remarked to Mrs. Breen, as the two ladies descended the stairs.

"Adorable. But," said Mrs. Breen, her shy little-girl voice suddenly maturing, "Robert and I *did* want it to be gala."

"Well, darling, we can't be gala if we're going to be conspicuous," observed Mrs. Gershwin, whose dia-monded decorations made her look as though she were moving in a spotlight. "Frankly, myself, I think it would do the Russians a world of good to see people dressed up. There's no excuse for them to go around looking the way they do. When we first came here, I felt sorry for them, but now . . ."

Across town, at the Palace of Culture, snow-sprin-kled crowds were massing on the sidewalk to watch the ticket holders arrive, and inside the theatre a sizable number, baking in a blaze of newsreel and television arc lights, were already seated. Baskets of flowers, yellow and white, flanked the stage, and crossed flags, an en-twining of stars and stripes and hammer and sickle, floated above the proscenium. Backstage, where the tun-ing orchestra's chirping flutes and moaning oboes echoed like forest sounds, Martha Flowers, costumed and com-pletely calm, despite the distant, rising audience-roar, was having, as she'd predicted, "a long sit."

And it was very long. The curtain, announced for eight, went up at nine-five and came down at eleven-forty. By midnight I was back at the Astoria waiting for a call from Henry Shapiro, the UP correspondent in Mos-cow who'd said he would telephone me after the première to find out "how it went. What really happened." There is no absolute truth in these matters, only opinion, and as I attempted to formulate my own, tried to decide what I was going to tell Shapiro, I stretched on the bed and switched out the light. My eyes smarted from the recent glare of flash bulbs, I seemed still to hear the soft clickety noise of newsreel cameras. And indeed, lying in the dark, it was as though a film were rushing through my head, a disconnected rampage of pictures: Martha Flowers tripping to the footlights to throw the audience a kiss, Savchenko striding through the lobby listening for comments, the terror in Sascha's eyes, Miss Ryan covering her face with her hands. I made a conscious effort to slow the film down, let it start at the beginning.

It began with the audience, an army standing at solemn attention while the orchestra played the national anthems of the two countries: Savchenko had courteously insisted that "The Star Spangled Banner" should be heard first. Then individual faces came into focus: Ambassador and Mrs. Bohlen, the Sulzbergers, the Lowrys, Miss Ryan and Leonard Lyons, all together in a front row. Near them, on a platform extending from the side of the stage, a squadron of photographers waited impatiently until the anthems ended: then the platform resembled a besieged fortress, photographers firing away while assistants reloaded their cameras. Some, like CBS's Dan Schorr, desperately alternated between cameras and tape recorders as they went to work documenting the pre-curtain ceremonies. There was no need for such haste. The speeches, and their translations, lasted an hour.

The Russians were brief enough. Konstantin Sergeev, the dapper young ballet master of the Leningrad Theatre, shook hands with Breen and, speaking into a microphone, said "Dear Brothers in art, welcome. We in the Soviet Union have always paid attention and tribute to the art of the United States. We know and cherish the works of such fine artists as Mark Twain, Walt Whitman, Harriet Beecher Stowe, Jack London, and Paul Robeson. We appreciate the talents of George Gershwin, and that is why this meeting is so joyous." Afterwards, apropos of this speech, Mrs. Gershwin said, "I thought I'd faint when I heard the name Gershwin being lumped in with all those Communists."

Breen bowed to Sergeev, and stepped up to the microphone, a preening, impeccable figure in his trim tuxedo and starched shirt. "He just lost his nerve," said Miss Ryan, explaining why at the last minute her employer had abandoned the idea of wearing white tie and tails. But now, watching Breen react to the applause that greeted him, one wouldn't have guessed there was a nerve in his system. His smooth blond face, bleached by the strong lights and exploding flash bulbs, possessed an inward-gazing remoteness, as though he had for so long dreamed the scene before him that it was still a dream; and when he spoke, the measured, sepulchral timbre of his actor's voice strengthened the impression that he thought himself alone on an empty stage addressing an imaginary audience, practicing, as it were, for an ego-satisfying moment that would someday come true. Imaginary audiences are notoriously submissive; but the Palace of Culture assemblage began to grow talkative themselves as Breen rambled on, the Russian translator trailing behind him. With graceful, *grand seigneur* sweepings of the hand, he introduced Ambassador and Mrs. Bohlen, who rose in their seats to acknowledge applause. The Ambassador had been expected to deliver a speech, but much to Bohlen's relief, and Breen's regret, the Soviets, extremely sensitive to protocol, had asked that this part of the program be deleted because they had no one of "comparable eminence" to make, on the Russian behalf, a rejoinder. Mrs. Gershwin was also introduced, and the conductor, Alexander Smallens, who received a sumptuous hand when Breen announced that Smallens was "born right here in Leningrad." The introductions continued as Breen presented members of the cast who were not performing that evening: Ethel Ayler, the alternate Bess, sufficiently recovered from her cold to have climbed out of bed and into a skimpy, strapless blue gown. And

Lorenzo Fuller, the alternate Sportin' Life. Fuller had a
"few" words to say, among them a Russian phrase he'd
memorized, *"Dobro poshlavat, druzya,"* which means
"Welcome, friends." The audience roared approval. But
as clock hands crept toward nine, even the frenzied
photographers paused to consult watches. "Jesus," said
one correspondent, "they ought to have a gong around
here. Like Major Bowes." It was as though Breen had
overheard him, for abruptly the ceremonial group vacated
the stage.

The theatre grew quieter than a hens' roost at sunset as the audience settled back, confident that now the
curtain would rise and reveal what they'd paid their
rubles to see, *Porgy and Bess*. Instead, Sascha appeared.
He crossed the stage stiff-legged and wobbly, as though
he were walking a plank. A sheaf of typewritten pages
quivered in his hands, and his face, bloodlessly pallid,
was drenched with sweat. The instant the audience
caught wind of why he was there, to read them the
opera's plot, the hens' roost turned into a hornets' nest.
They couldn't tolerate another syllable *about* the show,
they simply wanted to see it; and a mutiny that broke
out in the balcony, where rude voices started shouting,
spread to the orchestra: the patrons clapped, whistled,
stamped their feet. "Poor Sascha, oh, poor boy," said
Miss Ryan, covering her face with her hands. "It's too
terrible. I can't bear to watch." Several rows back
of Miss Ryan, Sascha's two friends, Igor and Henry,
slumped on their spines, but Miss Lydia, less squeamish,
glared round at her neighbors, as though she'd like to
crack them with her pocketbook. On stage, Sascha went
on reading, mumbling, as if he were whispering a prayer
against the deafening tumult; like Breen before him, he
seemed locked in a dream, a numbing, naked-in-the-
street nightmare. Smallens flicked his baton, and the
overture sounded as Sascha retreated into the wings.

It was soon evident that the audience regretted not
having paid more attention to Sascha's resumé of the

two-act tale the opera tells. In skeleton, the story is this: a crippled begger, Porgy, falls in love with a Charleston tart, Bess. Alas, this neurotic young woman is under the wicked influence of two other gentlemen. One, the devilish dope peddler, Sportin' Life, has enticed her into drug addiction, while the second, an alluringly muscular criminal named Crown, monopolizes the heroine's libidinous impulses. Porgy dispenses of the latter rival by killing him, and when he is sent to jail for the deed, Bess alleviates her woes by going on a dope binge, during which Sportin' Life persuades her to forget Porgy and traipse off with him to New York: "That's where we belong, sister," he sings as they head for the sugary lights of Harlem. In the last scene, Porgy, acquitted of Crown's murder, sets out for the North in a goat-drawn cart, believing, and leaving the spectator to believe, that he will find Bess and bring her home. Although this narrative line seems straight as a ruler, the intricate vocal-choreographic terms in which it is developed would confuse any audience where the language barrier is present, particularly if the music, the style of dancing, the directorial approach are each and all virgin territory, as they were to the overwhelming majority of those assembled in the Palace of Culture.

"Summertime" ended, and there was no applause. The entrance of Porgy went unheralded. Leslie Scott, playing the part, finished "A Woman Is a Sometimes Thing," and paused for the acclaim the number ordinarily arouses. The fact that none came caused a temporary lapse of stage action. Recovering, the cast launched into a jazzy crap-game sequence: whispering ran through the audience, as though they were asking each other what it meant, these excited men tossing dice? The whispering gathered momentum and turned into gasps, a tremor of shock, when Bess, making her initial appearance, hiked up her skirt to adjust her garter. Miss Ryan observed to Mrs. Lowry, "If they think *that's* so daring, just wait." The words weren't out of her mouth before Sportin' Life's witty, lascivious gyrations ignited fresh firecrackers of audible astonishment. The crap game concludes with Crown killing one of Porgy's neighbors; a funeral scene follows: while the murdered man's widow sings a lament, "My Man's Gone Now," the mourning inhabitants of Catfish Row sway in a tribal circle around the corpse. At this point, an important Soviet dignitary turned to a correspondent and said in Russian, "Ah, now I see! They are going to *eat* him." The deceased, undevoured, was trundled off to his grave, and the opera progressed to Porgy's optimistic "I've Got Plenty of Nothin'." Scott, a big and solidly constructed baritone, belted it across the footlights with a fervor that should've stopped the show. It didn't.

The audience's persistent silence seemed not altogether attributable to apathy; rather, for the most part, it appeared to be the result of troubled concentration, an anxious desire to understand; and so, fearful of missing the essential phrase, the significant clue that would unmask the mysteries confronting them, they listened and watched with the brooding intentness of students in a lecture hall. But the first act was almost over before the warmth that comes with comprehension wafted through the theatre. It was created by "Bess, You Is My Woman Now," a duet sung by the two principals: suddenly it was clear that Porgy and Bess were in love, that their song was a tender rejoicing, and the audience, rejoicing too, deluged the performers with applause that was brief but heavy, like tropic rain. However, the drought set in again as the music segued into the jamboree fanfare of "I Can't Sit Down," the first-act finale. The scene is peppered with folklorish humor; and, occasionally, isolated chuckles, lonely-sounding patches of laughter, indicated there were persons who appreciated it. The curtain descended. Silence. The house lights began to come up; the audience blinked, as though until this instant they hadn't known the act was over. They caught their breath, like passengers at the end of a roller-coaster ride, and began to applaud. The applause lasted thirty-two seconds.

"They're stunned," said Lowry, parroting the words, though somehow transforming the spirit, of Breen's prophecy. "They've never seen anything like it."

If the Russians were stunned, they were not alone. Several of the American journalists huddled together, comparing notes. "It's not going over," a baffled Dan Schorr complained to a bewildered Time-Life photographer. And Mrs. Bohlen, following her husband up the aisle, was poignantly pensive. Later, she told me the thought behind the expression: "I was thinking— well, we've laid an egg. Now what are we going to do about it?"

Out in the crowded lobby, Mrs. Breen smilingly expressed sentiments of a sunnier nature; according to her, the performance was going "beautifully." A correspondent interposed to ask why, in that case, the Russians were "sitting on their hands." Mrs. Breen stared at the questioner as though she thought him certifiable. "But they aren't *supposed* to applaud," she said. "Robert *planned* it that way. So that there wouldn't *be* any applause. It interrupts the mood."

The Wolferts agreed with Mrs. Breen; they felt the première was turning out a triumph. "First time we've seen the show," said Wolfert. "I don't like musicals. Got no use for them. But this one's pretty good."

Another American, the Russian-speaking Priscilla Johnson, spent the intermission eavesdropping on the customers. "They're quite shocked," she reported. "They think it's awfully immoral. But gosh, you can't blame them for not liking it. It's such a second-rate production. That's what makes me sad. If only it were *really* good, then you could blame them. Too bad, too bad," she said, ruffling her bangs, shaking her head. "This whole setup: the Breens, the publicity and all—gosh, it's just not geared for failure."

Like Miss Johnson, Savchenko and Adamov circulated about sampling opinions. "It's a very big success," was all Savchenko would admit; but Adamov, whose slang was growing richer under the company's tutelage, said: "So a lot of squares don't dig it. They don't flip. So is that big news? You got squares in New York, ain'tcha, man?"

Madame Nervitsky and her crooner-husband passed by. "Oh, we're amazed," she told me, flourishing a sword-length cigarette holder. "Nervitsky thinks it *très dépravé*. Not I. I adore the vileness of it all. The rhythm, the sweat. Really, the Negroes are too amusing. And how wonderful their teeth!" Moving closer, she said, "You did tell your friends? Room 520. Don't telephone, come quietly, bring anything. I will pay very well."

Stefan Orlov was standing at a refreshment counter, a glass of mineral water in his hand. "My friend," he said, clapping me on the shoulder. "What a night we had, yes? The next morning, my wife, she had to beat me out of bed. Tie my shoes and knot my tie. Not angry, you understand: laughing at me." He produced a pair of opera glasses, and peered through them. "I saw Nancy. I wondered, should I try to speak to her? But I said to myself: no, Nancy is sitting with fashionable people. Will you tell her that I saw her?" I said I would, and asked if he was enjoying *Porgy and Bess*. "I wish I had a ticket for every night. It's an experience. Powerful! Like Jack London. Like Gogol. I will never forget it," he said, pocketing the opera glasses. A frown creased his forehead, he opened his mouth to speak, changed his mind, took a swallow of water instead, then changed his mind again, and decided to tell me: "The question isn't whether I forget. Or what we old ones think. It's the young people who matter. It matters that they have new seeds planted in their hearts. Tonight," he said, looking around the lobby, "all these young people will stay awake. Tomorrow, they'll be whistling the music. A nuisance, humming in the classrooms. And in the summer, that's what you'll hear: young people whistling along the river. They won't forget."

Backstage, a tranquil climate prevailed as the per-

formers readied themselves for the second act. Leslie
Scott, not the least unnerved by the reception of the
previous stanza, grinned and said, "Sure, they're
kinda slow. But most audiences don't warm up until
the duet ("Bess, You Is My Woman Now"), and that
went over okay. From here on out, we'll sail." Martha
Flowers, freshening her makeup in front of a mirror,
said, "This audience, that audience, I don't know the
difference. You wouldn't either, you been doing this
show two years." But Sascha, lacking Miss Flowers'
professional *savoir,* was an alarming sight as he waited
in the wings to repeat his role of plot narrator: head
bowed, and holding to a dancer's practice bar like a
fighter on the ropes, he listened dazedly while his seconds, Igor and Henry, whispered encouragement.

To Sascha's surprise, his return bout was victori-
ous. The audience was eager to hear what would happen in the next act, and Sascha, who two weeks later
applied to the Moscow Art Theatre for a drama student fellowship, ecstatically recounted Crown's murder and Porgy's imprisonment. He walked off to one
of the largest hands of the evening; Miss Lydia was
still clapping after the house lights had dimmed.

The element in the opera which seemed most to disturb the Soviets, its sensuality, reaches a peak of
Himalayan proportions in the opening twenty minutes
of Act Two. A song "I Ain't Got No Shame" ("doin'
what I likes to do"), and the shake-that-thing brand
of choreography accompanying it, proved too aptly
titled, too graphically illustrated, for Russian comfort.
But it was the ensuing scene which contained, from a
prudish viewpoint, the real affront. The scene, a favorite of the director's and one he'd kept heightening in
rehearsal, begins with Crown's attempting to rape Bess
—he grips her to him, gropes her buttocks, her breasts;
and ends with Bess raping him—she rips off his shirt,
wraps her arms around him and writhes, sizzles like
bacon in a skillet: blackout. Areas of the audience
suffered something of a blackout, too. "Christ," said

one correspondent, his voice carrying in the hush, "they wouldn't get away with that on Broadway!" To which another American journalist, a woman, replied: "Don't be silly. It's the best thing in the show."

Leslie Scott had predicted the second act would "sail"; his forecast was almost verified during the opera's remaining forty minutes. The street-cry song of the Strawberry Woman started favorable winds blowing. Again, like the love duet, the melody and the situation, simply a peddler selling strawberries, was one the Russians could grasp, be charmed by. After that, every scene seemed to be accepted; and though the performance did not sail, perhaps because too much water had already been shipped, at least it floated, wallowed along in a current of less frigid temperature.

As the curtain fell, and the calls commenced, cameramen, scooting up and down the aisles, divided their shots between applauding Russians and salaaming actors. "They're stunned," Lowry once more pronounced, and his wife tacked on the inevitable, "They've never seen anything like it." The applause, which one experienced witness described as "nothing compared to an opening night at the Bolshoi," sustained a logical number of curtain calls, then swiftly declined. It was now, when people were leaving their seats, that Breen made his bid for a more impressive demonstration by unleashing the extra-added, "impromptu" curtain call he'd rehearsed that afternoon. On came the cast, one by one, each of them cavorting to the beat of a bongo drum. "Oh, no," groaned Miss Ryan. "They shouldn't do this. It's just begging." In the endurance test that followed, the audience compromised by substituting a chantlike pattern of clapping for authentic applause. Three minutes passed; four, five, six, seven. At last, when Miss Flowers had blown a final kiss across the footlights, and the electricians, et al, had been acknowledged, Breen, taking the ultimate bow, permitted the curtain to be lowered.

Ambassador and Mrs. Bohlen, and various Soviet

officials, were ushered backstage to shake hands with the cast. "I don't know what all the fuss is about," Mrs. Gershwin gaily cried as she squeezed through the backstage pandemonium. "It's *only* little old *Porgy*." Savchenko pushed toward Mrs. Breen; stiffly offering his hand, he said, "I want to congratulate you on a very big success." Mrs. Breen dabbed at her eyes, as though drying phantom tears. "That ovation. Wasn't it glorious?" she said, turning to gaze at her husband, who was posing for a photograph with Bohlen. "Such a tribute to Robert."

Outside, I had to walk some distance before finding a taxi. A threesome, two young men and a girl, walked ahead of me. I gathered they'd been part of the *Porgy and Bess* audience. Their voices reverberated down the shadowed, snow-silent streets. They were all talking at once, an exhilarated babble now and again mixed with humming: the strawberry street cry, a phrase of "Summertime." Then, as though she had no true understanding of the words but had memorized them phonetically, the girl sang: "There's a boat that's leavin' soon for New York, come with me, that's where we belong, sister . . ." Her friends joined in, whistling. Orlov had said, "And in the summer, that's what you'll hear: young people whistling along the river. They won't forget."

The promise of these young people who wouldn't forget, who'd been stimulated into new visions: surely, I thought, that was enough to justify my telling Henry Shapiro the première was a success. Not the "bombshell" conquest the proprietors of Everyman Opera had expected; but a victory of finer significance, one that would mature and matter. And yet, as I lay in my room thinking it over, qualms seized me when eventually the telephone rang. "How did it go? What really happened?" were questions to be answered on journalism's unsubtle level. Could I, with any honesty, give Shapiro a radiant account of the opera's overall reception? I preferred to; and suspected that it was what he, quite naturally, wanted to hear. But I let the telephone ring while a plethora of *ifs* plunged around in my head: if the Russians had been able to consult a printed program, if the fanfare and ceremonial aspects had been curtailed, if less had been demanded of the audience, if . . . I quit stalling and picked up the receiver. But the person on the line was Miss Lydia, who said she was sorry, someone had called me from Moscow and been disconnected. I had no more calls that evening.

Reviews of the production were published by two of the city's leading papers, *Smena* and *Evening Leningrad*. In Ambassador Bohlen's opinion, the articles were: "By and large, really excellent. Very thoughtful. It shows they took it seriously."

The *Evening Leningrad* critic wrote: "*Porgy and Bess* is a work stamped with brilliant talent and unusual mastery . . . warmly received by the audience." A further fifteen hundred words elaborated on that statement. He praised the score ("Gershwin's music is melodic, sincere, intentionally suffused with Negro musical folklore. There are plenty of really expressive and contrasting melodics."), Breen's direction ("The show is directed with great mastery and rivets one's attention with its dynamic sweep."), the conductor ("The musical part of the performance is on a very high level."), and the cast (" . . . plays together with a harmony rarely to be seen . . ."). The libretto, however, provoked a gentle reprimand, for the writer noticed in it "some elements of expressionism and melodrama, an abundance of the customary details regarding criminal investigation." Nor did *Evening Leningrad* forget to press the political pedal: "We, the Soviet spectators, realize the corrosive effect of the capitalistic system on the consciousness, the mentality and the moral outlook of a people oppressed by poverty. This lifts Heyward's play, as set to music by Gershwin, into the realms of social drama." But such comments seemed a mere pianissimo compared to the loud chords of propaganda that opponents of the *Porgy and Bess* tour had anticipated.

The second critic, U. Kovalyev, writing in *Smena,* mentioned a factor ignored by *Evening Leningrad.* "The astoundingly erotic coloring of some of the dancing scenes is unpleasant. And it is hard to lay the blame on a specific national dance. It is more the taste of the director and perhaps his kind of 'tradition' stemming from Broadway 'burlesques' and 'revues.' But on the whole," continues Kovalyev, *"Porgy and Bess* presents one of the most interesting events of this theatrical season. It is an excellently performed production, colorful, full of movement and music. It testifies to the high talent of the Negro people. Very possibly not all of the music and the staging will be approved by the Soviet audiences and everything will not necessarily be understandable to them. We are not used to the naturalistic details in the dance, to the excessive jazz sound of the symphony orchestra, etc. Nevertheless the performance broadens our concept of the art of contemporary America, and familiarizes us with thus far unknown facets of the musical and theatrical life of the United States."

These reviews did not appear until Thursday, three days after the opening. By then, their publication was rather an anticlimax and the company was inclined to regard them with a yawn. "Sure it's nice they write okay things, but who cares?" said one member of the cast, expressing a prevalent attitude. "It's not what the Russians think. It's the stuff they're hearing about us back home. *That's* what counts."

The company was already aware of what America was hearing, for late Tuesday afternoon, the day following the première, Breen received a cable on the subject from Everyman Opera's New York office. Miss Ryan typed copies of it, and she was about to put one of them on the company's bulletin board when we met in the lobby. "Hi," she said. "Guess what? Stefan the Bunny called. He wants to take me dancing. Do you think it'll be all right? I mean, as long as he just wants to dance? Anyway, I don't care. I'd go dancing with Jack the Ripper, anything to get away from *Porgy and Bess,*" she said, and thumbtacked her type-written version of the cable to the bulletin board.

LT ROBERT BREEN HOTEL ASTORIA LENINGRAD USSR

WONDERFUL ARTICLES HERE ALL DECEMBER 27 PAPERS STOP ALL MENTION TEN MINUTES STAND-ING OVATION STOP

JOURNALS HEADLINE—"LENINGRAD GOES WILD OVER PORGY AND BESS" STOP

AP FACTUAL RELEASE INCLUDES GREAT TICKET DEMAND AND SIZE AUDIENCE STOP

TRIBUNE STRESSES WARM AUDIENCE RECEPTION STOP

TELEGRAM HEADLINE—"PORGY WINS PRAISE FROM RUSSIA" OVER AP RELEASE STOP

MIRROR EDITORIAL "HEART TO HEART DIPLOMACY —CAST TAKING LENINGRAD BY SONG WE ARE PROUD OF THEM" STOP

AP RELEASE IN SOME PAPERS SAYS MOSCOW RADIO TERMED PREMIERE GREAT SUCCESS STOP

TIMES EDITORIAL TODAY BY SULZBERGER "PORGY BESS OPENING ANOTHER WINDOW TO WEST"

JOURNAL EDITORIAL TODAY—"MADE TREMENDOUS HIT"

NBC CBS NEWSCASTS FABULOUS

CONGRATULATIONS TO EVERY SINGLE SOUL WITH YOU

"Of course," remarked Miss Ryan, perusing the cable, "that's not *exactly* how it arrived. The Breens did a little adding and editing. There was one line: 'Times says scored moderate success.' You can bet Wilva cut that out! Well," she said with a smile, a sigh, "why not make a good thing better? Wilva just wants everybody to feel wonderful, and I think that's kind of endearing."

All afternoon members of the company, passing through the lobby, stopped to read the message from New York. It made them grin, they walked away with lightened steps. "What'cha say, man?" said Earl Bruce Jackson to Warner Watson as they stood reading the cable. "We're making history!" And Watson, rubbing his hands together, replied: "Yep, uh huh. I guess we've got *history* fenced in."

The Duke in His Domain

MOST JAPANESE GIRLS GIGGLE. The little maid on the fourth floor of the Miyako Hotel, in Kyoto, was no exception. Hilarity, and attempts to suppress it, pinked her cheeks (unlike the Chinese, the Japanese complexion more often than not has considerable color), shook her plump peony-and-pansy-kimonoed figure. There seemed to be no particular reason for this merriment; the Japanese giggle operates without apparent motivation. I'd merely asked to be directed toward a certain room. "You come see Marron?" she gasped, showing, like so many of her fellow-countrymen, an array of gold teeth. Then, with the tiny, pigeon-toed skating steps that the wearing of a kimono necessitates, she led me through a labyrinth of corridors, promising, "I knock you Marron." The "l" sound does not exist in Japanese, and by "Marron" the maid meant Marlon—Marlon Brando, the American actor, who was at that time in Kyoto doing location work for the Warner Brothers-William Goetz motion-picture version of James Michener's novel *Sayonara*.

My guide tapped at Brando's door, shrieked "Marron!," and fled away along the corridor, her kimono sleeves fluttering like the wings of a parakeet. The door was opened by another doll-delicate Miyako maid, who at once succumbed to her own fit of quaint hysteria. From an inner room, Brando called, "What is it, honey?" But the girl, her eyes squeezed shut with mirth and her fat little hands jammed into her mouth, like a bawling baby's, was incapable of reply. "Hey, honey, what is it?" Brando again inquired, and appeared in the doorway. "Oh, hi," he said when he saw me. "It's seven, huh?" We'd made a seven-o'clock date for dinner; I was nearly twenty minutes late. "Well, take off your shoes and come on in. I'm just finishing up here. And, hey, honey," he told the maid, "bring us some ice." Then, looking after the girl as she scurried off, he cocked his hands on his hips and, grinning, declared, "They kill me. They really kill me. The kids, too. Don't you think they're wonderful, don't you love them—Japanese kids?"

The Miyako, where about half of the "Sayonara" company was staying, is the most prominent of the so-called Western-style hotels in Kyoto; the majority of its rooms are furnished with sturdy, if commonplace and cumbersome, European chairs and tables, beds and couches. But, for the convenience of Japanese guests who prefer their own mode of décor while desiring the prestige of staying at the Miyako, or of those foreign travelers who yearn after authentic atmosphere yet are disinclined to endure the unheated rigors of a real Japanese inn, the Miyako maintains some suites decorated in the traditional manner, and it was in one of these that Brando had chosen to settle himself. His quarters consisted of two rooms, a bath, and a glassed-in sun porch. Without the overlying and underlying clutter of Brando's personal belongings, the rooms would have been textbook illustrations of the Japanese penchant for an ostentatious barrenness. The floors were covered with tawny *tatami* matting, with a discreet scattering of raw-silk pillows; a scroll depicting swimming golden carp hung in an alcove, and beneath it, on a stand, sat a vase filled with tall lilies and red leaves, arranged just so. The larger of the two rooms—the inner one—which the occupant was using as a sort of business office where he also dined and slept, contained a long, low lacquer table and a sleeping pallet. In these rooms, the divergent concepts of Japanese and Western decoration—the one seeking to impress by a lack of display, an absence of possession-exhibiting, the other intent on precisely the reverse—could both be observed, for Brando seemed unwilling to make use of the apartment's storage space, concealed behind sliding paper doors. All that he owned seemed to be out in the open. Shirts, ready for the laundry; socks, too; shoes and sweaters and jackets and hats and ties, flung around like the costume of a dismantled scarecrow. And cameras, a typewriter, a tape recorder, an electric heater that performed with stifling competence. Here, there, pieces of partly nibbled fruit; a box of the famous Japanese strawberries, each berry the size of an egg. And books, a deep-thought cascade, among which one saw Colin Wilson's *The Outsider* and various works on Buddhist prayer, Zen meditation, Yogi breathing, and Hindu mysticism, but no fiction, for Brando reads none. He has never, he professes, opened a novel since April 3, 1924, the day he was born, in Omaha, Nebraska. But while he may not care to read fiction, he does desire to write it, and the long lacquer table was loaded with overfilled ash trays and piled pages of his most recent creative effort, which happens to be a film script entitled *A Burst of Vermilion*.

In fact, Brando had evidently been working on his story at the moment of my arrival. As I entered the room, a subdued-looking, youngish man, whom I shall call Murray, and who had previously been pointed out to me as "the fellow that's helping Marlon with his writing," was squatted on the matting fumbling through the manuscript of *A Burst of Vermilion*. Weighing some pages on his hand, he said, "Tell ya, Mar, s'pose I go over this down in my room, and maybe we'll get together again—say, around ten-thirty?"

Brando scowled, as though unsympathetic to the idea of resuming their endeavors later in the evening. Having been slightly ill, as I learned later, he had spent the day in his room, and now seemed restive. "What's this?" he asked, pointing to a couple of oblong packages among the literary remains on the lacquer table.

Murray shrugged. The maid had delivered them; that was all he knew. "People are always sending Mar presents," he told me. "Lots of times we don't know who sent them. True, Mar?"

"Yeah," said Brando, beginning to rip open the gifts, which, like most Japanese packages—even mundane purchases from very ordinary shops—were beautifully wrapped. One contained candy, the other white rice cakes, which proved cement-hard, though they looked like puffs of cloud. There was no card in either package to identify the donor. "Every time you turn around, some Japanese is giving you a present. They're crazy about giving presents," Brando observed. Athletically crunching a rice cake, he passed the boxes to Murray and me.

Murray shook his head; he was intent on obtaining Brando's promise to meet with him again at ten-thirty. "Give me a ring around then," Brando said, finally. "We'll see what's happening."

Murray, as I knew, was only one member of what some of the *Sayonara* company referred to as "Brando's gang." Aside from the literary assistant, the gang consisted of Marlon Brando, Sr., who acts as his son's business manager; a pretty, dark-haired secretary, Miss Levin; and Brando's private makeup man. The travel expenses of this entourage, and all its living expenses while on location, were allowed for in the actor's contract with Warner Brothers. Legend to the contrary, film studios are not usually so lenient financially. A Warner man to whom I talked later explained the tolerance shown Brando by saying, "Ordinarily we wouldn't put up with it. All the demands he makes. Except—well, this picture just *had* to have a big star. Your star—that's the only thing that really counts at the box office."

Among the company were some who felt that the social protection supplied by Brando's inner circle was preventing them from "getting to know the guy" as well

as they would have liked. Brando had been in Japan for
more than a month, and during that time he had shown
himself on the set as a slouchingly dignified, amiable-
seeming young man who was always ready to co-operate
with, and even encourage, his co-workers—the actors
particularly—yet by and large was not socially availa-
ble, preferring, during the tedious lulls between scenes,
to sit alone reading philosophy or scribbling in a schoolboy notebook. After the day's work, instead of accepting
his colleagues' invitations to join a group for drinks, a
plate of raw fish in a restaurant, and a prowl through
the old geisha quarter of Kyoto, instead of contributing to the one-big-family, houseparty bonhomie that
picture-making on location theoretically generates, he
usually returned to his hotel and stayed there. Since the
most fervent of movie-star fans are the people who
themselves work in the film industry, Brando was a subject of immense interest within the ranks of the *Sayonara*
group, and the more so because his attitude of friendly
remoteness produced, in the face of such curiosity, such
wistful frustrations. Even the film's director, Joshua Logan, was impelled to say, after working with Brando for
two weeks, "Marlon's the most exciting person I've met
since Garbo. A genius. But I don't know what he's like.
I don't know anything about him."

The maid had re-entered the star's room, and Murray, on his way out, almost tripped over the train of
her kimono. She put down a bowl of ice and, with a
glow, a giggle, an elation that made her little feet, hoof-
like in their split-toed white socks, lift and lower like a
prancing pony's, announced, "Appapie! Tonight on
menu appapie."

Brando groaned. "Apple pie. That's all I need." He
stretched out on the floor and unbuckled his belt, which
dug too deeply into the swell of his stomach. "I'm supposed to be on a diet. But the only things I want to eat
are apple pie and stuff like that." Six weeks earlier, in
California, Logan had told him he must trim off ten
pounds for his role in *Sayonara,* and before arriving in

Kyoto he had managed to get rid of seven. Since reaching Japan, however, abetted not only by American-type apple pie but by the Japanese cuisine, with its delicious emphasis on the sweetened, the starchy, the fried, he'd regained, then doubled this poundage. Now, loosening his belt still more and thoughtfully massaging his midriff, he scanned the menu, which offered, in English, a wide choice of Western-style dishes, and, after reminding himself "I've *got* to lose weight," he ordered soup, beefsteak with French-fried potatoes, three supplementary vegetables, a side dish of spaghetti, rolls and butter, a bottle of *sake,* salad, and cheese and crackers.

"And appapie, Marron?"

He sighed. "With ice cream, honey."

Though Brando is not a teetotaller, his appetite is more frugal when it comes to alcohol. While we were awaiting the dinner, which was to be served to us in the room, he supplied me with a large vodka on the rocks and poured himself the merest courtesy sip. Resuming his position on the floor, he lolled his head against a pillow, dropped his eyelids, then shut them. It was as though he'd dozed off into a disturbing dream; his eyelids twitched, and when he spoke, his voice—an unemotional voice, in a way cultivated and genteel, yet surprisingly adolescent, a voice with a probing, asking, boyish quality—seemed to come from sleepy distances.

"The last eight, nine years of my life have been a mess," he said. "Maybe the last two have been a little better. Less rolling in the trough of the wave. Have you ever been analyzed? I was afraid of it at first. Afraid it might destroy the impulses that made me creative, an artist. A sensitive person receives fifty impressions where somebody else may only get seven. Sensitive people are so vulnerable; they're so easily brutalized and hurt just because they *are* sensitive. The more sensitive you are, the more certain you are to be brutalized, develop scabs. Never evolve. Never allow yourself to feel anything, because you always feel too much. Analysis helps. It

helped me. But still, the last eight, nine years I've been
pretty mixed up, a mess pretty much. . . ."

The voice went on, as though speaking to hear itself, an effect Brando's speech often has, for, like many
persons who are intensely self-absorbed, he is something
of a monologuist—a fact that he recognizes and for
which he offers his own explanation. "People around me
never say anything," he says. "They just seem to want
to hear what I have to say. That's why I do all the
talking." Watching him now, with his eyes closed, his unlined face white under an overhead light, I felt as if the
moment of my initial encounter with him were being re-
created. The year of that meeting was 1947; it was a
winter afternoon in New York, when I had occasion to
attend a rehearsal of Tennessee Williams' *A Streetcar
Named Desire,* in which Brando was to play the role of
Stanley Kowalski. It was this role that first brought him
general recognition, although among the New York
theatre's cognoscenti he had already attracted attention,
through his student work with the drama coach Stella
Adler and a few Broadway appearances—one in a
play by Maxwell Anderson, *Truckline Café,* and another as Marchbanks opposite Katharine Cornell's Can-
dida—in which he showed an ability that had been
much praised and discussed. Elia Kazan, the director
of *A Streetcar Named Desire,* said at that time, and has
recently repeated, "Marlon is just the best actor in the
world." But ten years ago, on the remembered afternoon, he was still relatively unknown; at least, I hadn't
a clue to who he might be when, arriving too early at
the *Streetcar* rehearsal, I found the auditorium deserted
and a brawny young man stretched out atop a table on
the stage under the gloomy glare of work lights, solidly
asleep. Because he was wearing a white T shirt and
denim trousers, because of his squat gymnasium phy-
sique—the weight-lifter's arms, the Charles Atlas chest
(though an opened *Basic Writings of Sigmund Freud*

was resting on it)—I took him for a stagehand. Or did until I looked closely at his face. It was as if a stranger's head had been attached to the brawny body, as in certain counterfeit photographs. For this face was so very untough, superimposing, as it did, an almost angelic refinement and gentleness upon hard-jawed good looks: taut skin, a broad, high forehead, wide-apart eyes, an aquiline nose, full lips with a relaxed, sensual expression. Not the least suggestion of Williams' unpoetic Kowalski. It was therefore rather an experience to observe, later that afternoon, with what chameleon ease Brando acquired the character's cruel and gaudy colors, how superbly, like a guileful salamander, he slithered into the part, how his own persona evaporated—just as, in this Kyoto hotel room ten years afterward, my 1947 memory of Brando receded, disappeared into his 1957 self. And the present Brando, the one lounging there on the *tatami* and lazily puffing filtered cigarettes as he talked and talked, was, of course, a different person—bound to be. His body was thicker; his forehead was higher, for his hair was thinner; he was richer (from the producers of *Sayonara* he could expect a salary of three hundred thousand dollars, plus a percentage of the picture's earnings); and he'd become, as one journalist put it, "the Valentino of the bop generation"—turned into such a world celebrity that when he went out in public here in Japan, he deemed it wise to hide his face not only by wearing dark glasses but by donning a surgeon's gauze mask as well. (The latter bit of disguise is not so *outré* in Japan as it may sound, since numerous Asians wear such masks, on the theory that they prevent the spreading of germs.) Those were some of the alterations a decade had made. There were others. His eyes had changed. Although their *caffè-espresso* color was the same, the shyness, any traces of real vulnerability that they had formerly held, had left them; now he looked at people with assurance, and with what can only be called a pitying expression, as though he dwelt in spheres of enlightenment where they, to his regret, did not. (The reactions of the people subjected to this gaze of constant commiseration range from that of a young actress who avowed that "Marlon is really a very *spiritual* person, wise and very sincere; you can see it in his eyes" to that of a Brando acquaintance who said, "The way he looks at you, like he was so damn sorry for you—doesn't it make you want to cut your throat?") Nevertheless, the subtly tender character of his face had been preserved. Or almost. For in the years between he'd had an accident that gave his face a more conventionally masculine aspect. It was just that his nose had been broken. And, maneuvering a word in edgewise, I asked, "How did you break your nose?"

". . . by which I don't mean that I'm *always* unhappy. I remember one April I was in Sicily. A hot day, and flowers everywhere. I like flowers, the ones that smell. Gardenias. Anyway, it was April and I was in Sicily, and I went off by myself. Lay down in this field of flowers. Went to sleep. That made me happy. I was happy *then*. What? You say something?"

"I was wondering how you broke your nose."

He rubbed his nose and grinned, as though remembering an experience as happy as the Sicilian nap. "That was a long time ago. I did it boxing. It was when I was in *Streetcar*. We, some of the guys backstage and me—we used to go down to the boiler room in the theatre and horse around, mix it up. One night, I was mixing it up with this guy and—crack! So I put on my coat and walked around to the nearest hospital—it was off Broadway somewhere. My nose was really busted. They had to give me an anesthetic to set it, and put me to bed. Not that I was sorry. *Streetcar* had been running about a year and I was sick of it. But my nose healed pretty quick, and I guess I would've been back in the show practically right away if I hadn't done what I did to Irene Selznick." His grin broadened as he mentioned Mrs. Selznick, who had been the producer of the Williams play. "There is one shrewd lady, Irene Selznick. When she wants something, she wants it. And she

wanted me back in the play. But when I heard she was
coming to the hospital, I went to work with bandages
and iodine and mercurochrome, and—Christ!—when
she walked in the door, I looked like my head had been
cut off. At the least. And *sounded* as though I were
dying. 'Oh, Marlon,' she said, 'you poor, *poor* boy!' And
I said, 'Don't you worry about anything, Irene. I'll be
back in the show tonight!' And she said, 'Don't you dare!
We can manage without you for—for—well, a *few* days
more.' 'No, no,' I said. 'I'm O.K. I want to work. Tell
them I'll be back tonight.' So she said, 'You're in no
condition, you poor darling. I *forbid* you to come to the
theatre.' So I stayed in the hospital and had myself a
ball." (Mrs. Selznick, recalling the incident recently,
said, "They didn't set his nose properly at all. Suddenly
his face was quite different. Kind of tough. For months
afterward, I kept telling him, 'But they've *ruined* your
face. You must have your nose broken again and reset.' Luckily for him, he didn't listen to me. Because I
honestly think that broken nose made his fortune as far
as the movies go. It gave him sex appeal. He was too
beautiful before.")

Brando made his first trip to the Coast in 1949,
when he went out there to play the leading role in *The
Men,* a picture dealing with paraplegic war veterans. He
was accused, at the time, of uncouth social conduct,
and criticized for his black-leather-jacket taste in attire,
his choice of motorcycles instead of Jaguars, and his
preference for obscure secretaries rather than movie
starlets; moreover, Hollywood columnists studded their
copy with hostile comments concerning his attitude
toward the film business, which he himself summed up
soon after he entered it by saying, "The only reason I'm
here is that I don't yet have the moral courage to turn
down the money." In interviews, he repeatedly stated
that becoming "simply a movie actor" was the thing
furthest from his thoughts. "I may do a picture now
and then," he said on one occasion, "but mostly I intend
to work on the stage." However, he followed *The Men,*

which was more of a *succès d'estime* than a commercial
triumph, by recreating Kowalski in the screen treatment of *A Streetcar Named Desire,* and this role, as it
had done on Broadway, established him as a star. (De-
fined practically, a movie star is any performer who can
account for a box-office profit regardless of the quality of
the enterprise in which he appears; the breed is so
scarce that there are fewer than ten actors today who
qualify for the title. Brando is one of them; as a box-
office draw, male division, he is perhaps outranked only
by William Holden.) In the course of the last five years,
he has played a Mexican revolutionary (*Viva Zapata!*),
Mark Antony (*Julius Caesar*), and a motorcycle-mad
juvenile delinquent (*The Wild One*); earned an Academy Award in the role of a dockyard thug (*On the
Waterfront*); impersonated Napoleon (*Désirée*); sung
and danced his way through the part of an adult delinquent (*Guys and Dolls*); and taken the part of the
Okinawan interpreter in *The Teahouse of the August
Moon,* which, like *Sayonara,* his tenth picture, was
partly shot on location in Japan. But he has never, except for a brief period in summer stock, returned to the
stage. "Why should I?" he asked with apathy when I
remarked on this. "The movies have a greater potential.
They can be a factor for good. For moral development.
At least some can—the kind of movies I want to do."
He paused, seemed to listen, as though his statement
had been tape-recorded and he were now playing it
back. Possibly the sound of it dissatisfied him; at any
rate, his jaw started working, as if he were biting down
on an unpleasant mouthful. He looked off into space
suddenly and demanded, "What's so hot about New
York? What's so hot about working for Cheryl Crawford
and Robert Whitehead?" Miss Crawford and Whitehead
are two of New York's most prominent theatrical producers, neither of whom has had occasion to employ
Brando. "Anyway, what would I be in?" he continued.
"There aren't any parts for me."

Stack them, and the playscripts offered him in any

given season by hopeful Broadway managements might very well rise to a height exceeding the actor's own. Tennessee Williams wanted him for the male lead in each of his last five plays, and the most recent of these, *Orpheus Descending,* which was pending production at the time of our talk, had been written expressly as a co-starring vehicle for Brando and the Italian actress Anna Magnani. "I can explain very easily why I didn't do *Orpheus,*" Brando said. "There are beautiful things in it, some of Tennessee's best writing, and the Magnani part is great; she stands for something, you can understand her—and she would wipe me off the stage. The character I was supposed to play, this boy, this Val, he never takes a stand. I didn't really know what he was for or against. Well, you can't act a vacuum. And I told Tennessee. So he kept trying. He rewrote it for me, maybe a couple of times. But—" He shrugged. "Well, I had no intention of walking out on any stage with Magnani. Not in that part. They'd have had to mop me up." Brando mused a moment, and added, "I think—in fact, I'm sure—Tennessee has made a fixed association between me and Kowalski. I mean, we're friends and he knows that as a person I am just the opposite of Kowalski, who was everything I'm against—totally insensitive, crude, cruel. But still Tennessee's image of me is confused with the fact that I played that part. So I don't know if he could write for me in a different color range. The only reason I did *Guys and Dolls* was to work in a lighter color—yellow. Before that, the brightest color I'd played was red. From red down. Brown. Gray. Black." He crumpled an empty cigarette package and bounced it in his hand like a ball. "There aren't any parts for me on the stage. Nobody writes them. Go on. Tell me a part I could do."

In the absence of vehicles by worthy contemporaries, might he not favor the work of older hands? Several responsible persons who appeared with him in the film had admired his reading of Mark Antony in *Julius Caesar,* and thought him equipped, provided the

will was there, to essay many of the Mount Everest
roles in stage literature—even, possibly, Oedipus.

Brando received reminders of this praise blankly
—or, rather, he seemed to be indulging his not-listening
habit. But, sensing silence again, he dissolved it: "Of
course, movies *date* so quickly. I saw *Streetcar* the other
day and it was already an old-fashioned picture. Still,
movies do have the greatest potential. You can say
important things to a lot of people. About discrimination
and hatred and prejudice. I want to make pictures that
explore the themes current in the world today. In terms
of entertainment. That's why I've started my own independent production company." He reached out affec-
tionately to finger *A Burst of Vermilion,* which will be
the first script filmed by Pennebaker Productions—the
independent company he has formed.

And did *A Burst of Vermilion* satisfy him as a
basis for the kind of lofty aims he proposed?

He mumbled something. Then he mumbled something else. Asked to speak more clearly, he said, "It's a
Western."

He was unable to restrain a smile, which expanded
into laughter. He rolled on the floor and roared. "Christ,
the only thing is, will I ever be able to look my friends
in the face again?" Sobering somewhat, he said, "Seriously, though, the first picture *has* to make money.
Otherwise, there won't be another. I'm nearly broke.
No, no kidding. I spent a year and two hundred thousand dollars of my own money trying to get some writer
to come up with a decent script. Which used my ideas.
The last one, it was so terrible I said I can do better
myself. I'm going to direct it, too."

Produced by, directed by, written by, and starring.
Charlie Chaplin has managed this, and gone it one better
by composing his own scores. But professionals of wide
experience—Orson Welles, for one—have caved in under a lesser number of chores than Brando planned to
assume. However, he had a ready answer to my suggestion that he might be loading the cart with more than

the donkey could haul. "Take producing," he said. "What does a producer do except cast? I know as much about casting as anyone does, and that's all producing is. Casting." In the trade, one would be hard put to it to find anyone who concurred in this opinion. A good producer, in addition to doing the casting—that is, assembling the writer, the director, the actors, the technical crew, and the other components of his team—must be a diplomat of the emotions, smoothing and soothing, and above all, must be a skilled mechanic when it comes to dollars-and-cents machinery. "But seriously," said Brando, now excessively sober, "*Burst isn't* just cowboys-and-Indians stuff. It's about this Mexican boy—hatred and discrimination. What happens to a community when those things exist."

Sayonara, too, has moments when it purports to attack race prejudice, telling, as it does, the tale of an American jet pilot who falls in love with a Japanese music-hall dancer, much to the dismay of his Air Force superiors, and also to the dismay of her employers, though the latter's objection is not the racial unsuitability of her beau but simply that she has a beau at all, for she is a member of an all-girl opera company—based on a real-life counterpart, the Takarazuka Company—whose management promotes a legend that offstage its hundreds of girls lead a conventlike existence, unsullied by male presences of any creed or color. Michener's novel concludes with the lovers forlornly bidding each other *sayonara,* a word meaning farewell. In the film version, however, the word, and consequently the title, has lost significance; here the fadeout reveals the twain of East and West so closely met that they are on their way to the matrimonial bureau. At a press conference that Brando conducted upon his Tokyo arrival, he informed some sixty reporters that he had contracted to do this story because "it strikes very precisely at prejudices that serve to limit our progress toward a peaceful world. Underneath the romance, it attacks prejudices that exist on the part of the Japanese as well as on our part," and also he was doing the film because it would give him the "invaluable opportunity" of working under Joshua Logan, who could teach him "what to do and what not to do."

But time had passed. And now Brando said, with a snort, "Oh, *Sayonara,* I love it! This wondrous hearts-and-flowers nonsense that was supposed to be a serious picture about Japan. So what difference does it make? I'm just doing it for the money anyway. Money to put in the kick for my own company." He pulled at his lip reflectively and snorted again. "Back in California, I sat through twenty-two hours of script conferences. Logan said to me, 'We welcome any suggestions you have, Marlon. Any changes you want to make, you just make them. If there's anything you don't like—why, re-write it, Marlon, write it your own way.'" Brando's friends boast that he can imitate anybody after fifteen minutes' observation; to judge by the eerie excellence with which he mimicked Logan's vaguely Southern voice, his sad-eyed, beaming, aquiver-with-enthusiasm manner, they are hardly exaggerating. *"Rewrite?* Man, I rewrote the whole damn script. And now out of that they're going to use maybe eight lines." Another snort. "I give up. I'm going to walk through the part, and that's that. Sometimes I think nobody knows the difference anyway. For the first few days on the set, I tried to act. But then I made an experiment. In this scene, I tried to do everything wrong I could think of. Grimaced and rolled my eyes, put in all kinds of gestures and expressions that had no relation to the part I'm supposed to be playing. What did Logan say? He just said, 'It's wonderful! Print it!'"

A phrase that often occurs in Brando's conversation, "I only mean forty per cent of what I say," is probably applicable here. Logan, a stage and film director of widely recognized and munificently rewarded accomplishments (*Mister Roberts, South Pacific, Picnic*), is a man balanced on enthusiasm, as a bird is balanced on air. A creative person's need to believe in the value

of what he is creating is axiomatic; Logan's belief in
whatever project he is engaged in approaches euphoric
faith, protecting him, as it seems designed to do, from
the nibbling nuisance of self-doubt. The joy he took in
everything connected with *Sayonara,* a film he had
been preparing for two years, was so nearly flawless
that it did not permit him to conceive that his star's enthusiasm might not equal his own. Far from it. "Marlon,"
he occasionally announced, "says he's never been as
happy with a company as he is with us." And "I've
never worked with such an exciting, inventive actor.
So pliable. He takes direction beautifully, and yet he always has something to add. He's made up this Southern
accent for the part; I never would have thought of it
myself, but, well, it's exactly right—it's perfection."
Nevertheless, by the night I had dinner in Brando's hotel
room Logan had begun to be aware that there was something lacking in his rapport with Brando. He attributed
it to the fact that at this juncture, when most of the
scenes being filmed concentrated on Japanese background (street crowds, views, spectacles) rather than
actors, he had not yet worked with Brando on material
that put either of them to much of a test. "That'll come
when we get back to California," he said. "The interior
stuff, the dramatic scenes. Brando's going to be great—
we'll get along fine."

There was another reason for Logan's inability, at
that point, to give his principal player the kind of attention that might have established closer harmony: he was
in serious disharmony with the very Japanese elements
that had contributed most to his decision to make the
picture. Long infatuated with the Japanese theatre, Logan had counted heavily on interlacing *Sayonara* with
authentic sequences taken from the classic Kabuki theatre, the masked Nō dramas, the Bunraku puppet plays;
they were to be, so to say, the highbrow-lights of the
film. And to this end Logan, along with William Goetz,
the producer, had been in negotiation for over a year

with Shochiku, the gigantic film company that controls
a major part of Japan's live theatrical activities. The
ruler of the Shochiku empire is a small, unsmiling
eminence in his eighties, known as Mr. Otani; he has a
prénom, Takejiro, but there are few men alive on such
familiar terms that they would presume to use it. The
son of a butcher (and therefore, in Japan's Buddhist
society, a member of the outcast group), Otani, together
with a brother now dead, founded Shochiku and nur-
tured it to the point where, for the last four years, its
payroll has been the biggest of any single company in
Japan. A tycoon to rival Kokichi Mikimoto, the late
cultured-pearl potentate, Otani casts a cloaklike shadow
over the entire Japanese entertainment industry; in
addition to having monopolistic control of the classic
theatre, he owns the country's most extensive chain of
movie houses and music halls, produces many films, and
has a hand in radio and television. From Otani's vantage point, any transactions with the Messrs. Logan and
Goetz must have looked like very small *sake.* However,
he was at first in sympathy with their project, largely
because he was impressed by the fervor of Logan's
veneration for Kabuki, Nō, and Bunraku, the three un-
questionably genuine gems in the old man's crown, and
the ones closest to his heart. (According to some spe-
cialists, these ancient arts owe their continued health
mainly to his generosity.) But Otani is not all philan-
thropist; when Shochiku's negotiations with the *Sayonara* management were supposedly concluded, the
former had given the latter, for a handsome price,
franchise to photograph scenes in Tokyo's famed Kabuki Theatre, and, for a still handsomer honorarium,
permission to make free use of the Kabuki troupe, the
Nō plays and players, and the Bunraku puppeteers.
Shochiku had also agreed to the participation of its
own all-girl opera company—a necessary factor in the
production of the film, since the Takarazuka troupe depicted in the novel had deeply resented Michener's "li-
bel" and refused any co-operation whatever. Logan,

leaving for Japan, was so elated he could have flown there under his own power. "Otani's given us carte blanche, and this is going to be it, the real thing," he said. "None of that fake Kabuki, that second-rate stuff, but the real thing—something that's never been put in a picture before." And was not destined to be; for, across the wide Pacific, Logan and his associates had a personal Pearl Harbor awaiting them. Otani is seldom seen; he usually appears in the person of bland assistants, and as Logan and Goetz disembarked from their plane, a group of these informed the film-makers that Shochiku had made an error in its financial reckoning; the bill was now much higher than the initial estimate. Producer Goetz objected. Otani, certain that he held the stronger cards (after all, here were these Hollywood people in Japan, accompanied by an expensive cast, an expensive crew, and expensive equipment), replied by raising the tab still more. Whereupon Goetz, himself a business-man as tough as tortoise shell, ended the negotiations and told his director they would have to make up their own Kabuki, Nō, Bunraku, and all-girl opera company from among unattached, free-lancing artists.

Meanwhile, the Tokyo press was publicizing the contretemps. Several papers, the *Japan Times* among them, implied that Shochiku was to be censured for hav-ing "acted in bad faith"; others, taking a pro-Shochiku, or perhaps simply an anti-*Sayonara,* line, expressed themselves as delighted that the Americans would not have the opportunity to "degrade our finest artistic tradi-tions" by representing them in a film version of "a vul-gar novel that is in no way a compliment to the Japanese people." The papers antagonistic to the *Sayonara* proj-ect especially relished reporting the fact that Logan had cast a Mexican actor, Ricardo Montalban, in the part of a ranking Kabuki performer (Kabuki is traditionally an all-male enterprise; the grander, more difficult roles are those of women, played by female impersonators, and Montalban's assignment was to portray one such) and then had had the "effrontery" to try and hire a genuine Kabuki star to substitute for Montalban in the dance sequences, which, one Japanese writer remarked, was much the same as "asking Ethel Barrymore to be a stand-in." All in all, the local press was touchily interested in what was taking place down in Kyoto—the city, two hundred and thirty miles south of Tokyo, in which, because of its plethora of historic temples, its photogenic blue hills and misty lakes, and its carefully preserved old-Japan atmosphere, with elegant geisha quarter and paper-lantern-lighted streets, the *Sayonara* staff had decided to take most of their location shots. And, all in all, down in Kyoto the company was encountering as many difficulties as its ill-wishers could have hoped for. In particular, the Americans were finding it a problem to muster nationals willing to appear in their film—an interesting phenomenon, considering how desirous the average Japanese is of having himself photographed. True, the movie-makers had rounded up a ragbag-picking of Nō players and puppeteers not under contract to Shochiku, but they were having the devil's own time assembling a presentable all-girl opera company. (These peculiarly Japanese institutions resemble a sort of single-sex, innocent-minded Folies-Bergère; oddly, few men attend their performances, the audiences being, on the whole, as all-girl as the cast.) In the hope of bridging this gap, the *Sayonara* management had distributed posters advertising a contest to select "the one hundred most beautiful girls in Japan." The affair, for which they expected a big turnout, was scheduled to take place at two o'clock on a Thursday afternoon in the lobby of the Kyoto Hotel. But there were no winners, because there were no contestants; none showed up. Producer Goetz, one of the disappointed judges, resorted next, and with some success, to the expedient of luring ladies out of Kyoto's cabarets and bars. Kyoto—or, for that matter, any Japanese city—is a barfly's Valhalla. Proportionately, the number of premises purveying strong liquor is higher than in New York, and the diversity of these saloons—which range from cozy bamboo closets accommodating four customers to many-storied, neon-hued temples of fun featuring, in accordance with the Japanese aptitude for imitation, cha-cha bands and rock 'n' rollers and hill-billy quartets and *chanteuses existentialistes* and Oriental vocalists who sing Cole Porter songs with American Negro accents—is extraordinary. But however low or however deluxe the establishment may be, one thing remains the same: there is always on hand a pride of hostesses to cajole and temper the clientele. Great numbers of these sleekly coifed, smartly costumed, relentlessly festive *jolies jeunes filles* sit sipping Parfaits d'Amour (a syrupy violet-colored cocktail currently fashionable in these surroundings) while performing the duties of a poor man's geisha girl; that is, lightening the spirits, without necessarily corrupting the morals, of weary married men and tense, anxious-to-be-amused bachelors. It is not unusual to see four to a customer. But when the *Sayonara* officials began to try to corral them, they had to contend with the circumstance that nightworkers, such as they were dealing with, have no taste for the early rising that picture-making demands. To acquire their talents, and see that the ladies were on the set at the proper hour, certain of the film's personnel did everything but distribute engagement rings.

Still another annoyance for the makers of *Sayonara* involved the United States Air Force, whose cooperation was vital, but which, though it had previously promised help, now had fits of shilly-shallying, because it gravely objected to one of the basic elements of the plot—that during the Korean War some American Air Force men who married Japanese were shipped home. This, the Air Force complained, may have been the *practice,* but it was not official Pentagon policy. Given the choice of cutting out the offending premise, and thereby removing a sizable section of the script's entrails, or permitting it to remain, and thereby forfeiting Air Force aid, Logan selected surgery.

Then, there was the problem of Miss Miiko Taka,

who had been cast as the Takarazuka dancer capable of arousing Air Force Officer Brando's passion. Having first tried to obtain Audrey Hepburn for the part, and found that Miss Hepburn thought not, Logan had started looking for an "unknown," and had come up with Miss Taka, poised, pleasant, an unassuming, quietly attractive nisei, innocent of acting experience, who stepped out of a clerking job with a Los Angeles travel bureau into what she called "this Cinderella fantasy." Although her acting abilities—as well as those of another *Sayonara* principal, Red Buttons, an ex-burlesque, ex-television jokester, who, like Miss Taka, had had meager dramatic training—were apparently causing her director some concern, Logan, admirably undaunted, cheerful despite all, was heard to say, "We'll get away with it. As much as possible, I'll just keep their faces straight and their mouths shut. Anyway, Brando, he's going to be so great *he'll* give us what we need." But, as for giving, "I give up," Brando repeated. "I'm going to give up. I'm going to sit back. Enjoy Japan."

At that moment, in the Miyako, Brando was presented with something Japanese to enjoy: an emissary of the hotel management, who, bowing and beaming and soaping his hands, came into the room saying "Ah, Missa Marron Brando—" and was silent, tongue-tied by the awkwardness of his errand. He'd come to reclaim the "gift" packages of candy and rice cakes that Brando had already opened and avidly sampled. "Ah, Missa Marron Brando, it is a missake. They were meant for derivery in another room. Aporogies! Aporogies!" Laughing, Brando handed the boxes over. The eyes of the emissary, observing the plundered contents, grew grave, though his smile lingered—indeed, became fixed. Here was a predicament to challenge the rightly renowned Japanese politeness. "Ah," he breathed, a solution limbering his smile, "since you rike them very much, you muss keep one box." He handed the rice cakes back. "And they"—apparently the rightful owner

—"can have the other. So, now everyone is preased."

It was just as well that he left the rice cakes, for dinner was taking a long while to simmer in the kitchen. When it arrived, I was replying to some inquiries Brando had made about an acquaintance of mine, a young American disciple of Buddhism who for five years had been leading a contemplative, if not entirely unworldly, life in a settlement inside the gates of Kyoto's Nishi-Honganji Temple. The notion of a person's retiring from the world to lead a spiritual existence—an Oriental one, at that—made Brando's face become still, in a dreaming way. He listened with surprising attention to what I could tell him about the young man's present life, and was puzzled—chagrined, really—that it was not at all, or at all, a matter of withdrawal, of silence and prayer-sore knees. On the contrary, behind Nishi-Honganji's walls my Buddhist friend occupied three snug, sunny rooms brimming with books and phonograph records; along with attending to his prayers and performing the tea ceremony, he was quite capable of mixing a Martini; he had two servants, and a Chevrolet, in which he often conveyed himself to the local cinemas. And, speaking of that, he had read that Marlon Brando was in town, and longed to meet him. Brando was little amused. The puritan streak in him, which has some width, had been touched; his conception of the truly devout could not encompass anyone as *du monde* as the young man I'd described. "It's like the other day on the set," he said. "We were working in a temple, and one of the monks came over and asked me for an autographed picture. Now, *what* would a monk want with my autograph? A picture of me?"

He stared questioningly at his scattered books, so many of which dealt with mystical subjects. At his first Tokyo press conference, he had told the journalists that he was glad to be back in Japan, because it gave him another chance to "investigate the influence of Buddhism on Japanese thought, the determining cultural factor." The reading matter on display offered proof that he was adhering to this scholarly, if somewhat obscure, program. "What I'd like to do," he presently said, "I'd like to talk to someone who *knows* about these things. Because—" But the explanation was deferred until the maid, who just then skated in balancing vast platters, had set the lacquer table and we had knelt on cushions at either end of it.

"Because," he resumed, wiping his hands on a small steamed towel, the usual preface to any meal served in Japan, "I've seriously considered—I've very *seriously* thought about—throwing the whole thing up. This business of being a successful actor. What's the point, if it doesn't evolve into anything? All right, you're a success. At last you're *accepted*, you're welcome everywhere. But that's it, that's all there is to it, it doesn't lead anywhere. You're just sitting on a pile of candy gathering thick layers of—of *crust*." He rubbed his chin with the towel, as though removing stale makeup. "Too much success can ruin you as surely as too much failure." Lowering his eyes, he looked without appetite at the food that the maid, to an accompaniment of constant giggles, was distributing on the plates. "Of course," he said hesitantly, as if he were slowly turning over a coin to study the side that seemed to be shinier, "you can't *always* be a failure. Not and survive. Van Gogh! There's an example of what can happen when a person never receives any recognition. You stop relating; it puts you outside. But I guess success does that, too. You know, it took me a long time before I was aware that that's what I was—a big success. I was so absorbed in myself, my own problems, I never looked around, took account. I used to walk in New York, miles and miles, walk in the streets late at night, and never *see* anything. I was never sure about acting, whether that was what I really wanted to do; I'm still not. Then, when I was in *Streetcar*, and it had been running a couple of months, one night—dimly, dimly—I began to hear this roar. It was like I'd been asleep, and I woke up here sitting on a pile of candy."

Before Brando achieved this sugary perch, he had known the vicissitudes of any unconnected, unfinanced, only partly educated (he has never received a high-school diploma, having been expelled before graduation from Shattuck Military Academy, in Faribault, Minnesota, an institution he refers to as "the asylum") young man who arrives in New York from more rural parts—in his case, Libertyville, Illinois. Living alone in furnished rooms, or sharing underfurnished apartments, he had spent his first city years fluctuating between acting classes and a fly-by-night enrollment in Social Security; Best's once had him on its payroll as an elevator boy. A friend of his, who saw a lot of him in those pre-candy days, corroborates to some extent the rather somnambulistic portrait Brando paints of himself. "He was a brooder, all right," the friend has said. "He seemed to have a built-in hideaway room and was always rushing off to it to worry over himself, and gloat, too, like a miser with his gold. But it wasn't all Gloomsville. When he wanted to, he could rocket right out of himself. He had a wild, kid kind of fun thing. Once, he was living in an old brownstone on Fifty-second Street, near where some of the jazz joints are. He used to go up on the roof and fill paper bags with water and throw them down at the stiffs coming out of the clubs. He had a sign on the wall of his room that said, 'You Ain't Livin' If You Don't Know It.' Yeah, there was always something jumping in that apartment—Marlon playing the bongos, records going, people around, kids from the Actors' Studio, and a lot of down-and-outers he'd picked up. And he could be sweet. He was the least opportunistic person I've ever known. He never gave a damn about anybody who could help him; you might say he went out of his way to avoid them. Sure, part of that—the kind of people he didn't like and the kind he did, both—stemmed from his insecurities, his inferiority feelings. Very few of his friends were his equals—anybody he'd have to *compete* with, if you know what I mean. Mostly they were strays, idolizers,

characters who were dependent on him one way or
another. The same with the girls he took out. Plain sort
of somebody's-secretary-type girls—nice enough but
nothing that's going to start a stampede of competitors."
(The last-mentioned preference of Brando's was true
of him as an adolescent, too, or so his grandmother has
said. As she put it, "Marlon always picked on the cross-
eyed girls.")

The maid poured *sake* into thimble-size cups, and
withdrew. Connoisseurs of this palely pungent rice wine
pretend they can discern variations in taste and quality
in over fifty brands. But to the novice all *sake* seems to
have been brewed in the same vat—a toddy, pleasant at
first, cloying afterward, and not likely to echo in your
head unless it is devoured by the quart, a habit many of
Japan's *bons vivants* have adopted. Brando ignored the
sake and went straight for his filet. The steak was excellent; Japanese take a just pride in the quality of their
beef. The spaghetti, a dish that is very popular in Japan,
was not; nor was the rest—the conglomeration of peas,
potatoes, beans. Granted that the menu was a queer one,
it is on the whole a mistake to order Western-style food
in Japan, yet there arise those moments when one
retches at the thought of more raw fish, sukiyaki, and
rice with seaweed, when, however temptingly they may
be prepared and however prettily presented, the unac-
customed stomach revolts at the prospect of eel broth
and fried bees and pickled snake and octopus arms.

As we ate, Brando returned to the possibility of
renouncing his movie-star status for the satisfactions of a
life that "led somewhere." He decided to compromise.
"Well, when I get back to Hollywood, what I *will* do, I'll
fire my secretary and move into a smaller house," he
said. He sighed with relief, as though he'd already cast off
old encumbrances and entered upon the simplicities of
his new situation. Embroidering on its charms, he said,
"I won't have a cook or maid. Just a cleaning woman
who comes in twice a week. But"—he frowned, squinted,
as if something were blurring the bliss he envisioned—

"wherever the house is, it has to have a *fence*. On account of the people with pencils. You don't know what it's like. The people with pencils. I need a fence to keep them out. I suppose there's nothing I can do about the telephone."

"Telephone?"

"It's tapped. Mine is."

"Tapped? Really? By whom?"

He chewed his steak, mumbled. He seemed reluctant to say, yet certain it was so. "When I talk to my friends, we speak French. Or else a kind of bop lingo we made up."

Suddenly, sounds came through the ceiling from the room above us—footfalls, muffled voices like the noise of water flowing through a pipe. "Sh-h-h!" whispered Brando, listening intently, his gaze alerted upward. "Keep your voice down. *They* can hear everything." They, it appeared, were his fellow actor Red Buttons and Buttons' wife, who occupied the suite overhead. "This place is made of paper," he continued, in tiptoe tones, and with the absorbed countenance of a child lost in a very earnest game—an expression that half explained his secretiveness, the looking-over-his-shoulder, coded-bop-for-telephones facet of his personality that occasionally causes conversation with him to assume a conspiratorial quality, as though one were discussing subversive topics in perilous political territory. Brando said nothing; I said nothing. Nor did Mr. and Mrs. Buttons—not anything distinguishable. During the siege of silence, my host located a letter buried among the dinner plates, and read it while he ate, like a gentleman perusing his breakfast newspaper. Presently, remembering me, he remarked, "From a friend of mine. He's making a documentary, the life of James Dean. He wants me to do the narration. I think I might." He tossed the letter aside and pulled his apple pie, topped with a melting scoop of vanilla ice cream, toward him. "Maybe not, though. I get excited about something, but it never lasts more than seven minutes. Seven minutes exactly. That's my limit.

I never know why I get up in the morning." Finishing his pie, he gazed speculatively at my portion; I passed it to him. "But I'm really considering this Dean thing. It could be important."

James Dean, the young motion-picture actor killed in a car accident in 1955, was promoted throughout his phosphorescent career as the All-American "mixed-up kid," the symbol of misunderstood hot-rodding youth with a switch-blade approach to life's little problems. When he died, an expensive film in which he had starred, *Giant,* had yet to be released, and the picture's press agents, seeking to offset any ill effects that Dean's demise might have on the commercial prospects of their product, succeeded by "glamorizing" the tragedy, and, in ironic consequence, created a Dean legend of rather necrophilic appeal. Though Brando was seven years older than Dean, and professionally more secure, the two actors came to be associated in the collective movie-fan mind. Many critics reviewing Dean's first film, *East of Eden,* remarked on the well-nigh plagiaristic resemblance between his acting mannerisms and Brando's. Offscreen, too, Dean appeared to be practicing the sincerest form of flattery; like Brando, he tore around on motorcycles, played bongo drums, dressed the role of rowdy, spouted an intellectual rigmarole, cultivated a cranky, colorful newspaper personality that mingled, to a skillfully potent degree, plain bad boy and sensitive sphinx.

"No, Dean was never a friend of mine," said Brando, in response to a question that he seemed surprised to have been asked. "That's not why I may do the narration job. I hardly knew him. But he had an *idée fixe* about me. Whatever I did he did. He was always trying to get close to me. He used to call up." Brando lifted an imaginary telephone, put it to his ear with a cunning, eavesdropper's smile. "I'd listen to him talking to the answering service, asking for me, leaving messages. But I never spoke up. I never called him back. No, when I—"

The scene was interrupted by the ringing of a real

telephone. "Yeah?" he said, picking it up. "Speaking. From where? . . . Manila? . . . Well, I don't know anybody in Manila. Tell them I'm not here. No, when I finally met Dean," he said, hanging up, "it was at a party. Where he was throwing himself around, acting the madman. So I spoke to him. I took him aside and asked him didn't he know he was sick? That he needed help?" The memory evoked an intensified version of Brando's familiar look of enlightened compassion. "He listened to me. He knew he was sick. I gave him the name of an analyst, and he went. And at least his *work* improved. Toward the end, I think he was beginning to find his own way as an actor. But this glorifying of Dean is all wrong. That's why I believe the documentary could be important. To show he wasn't a hero; show what he really was —just a lost boy trying to find himself. That ought to be done, and I'd like to do it—maybe as a kind of expiation for some of my own sins. Like making *The Wild One*." He was referring to the strange film in which he was presented as the Führer of a tribe of Fascistlike delinquents. "But. Who knows? Seven minutes is my limit."

From Dean the conversation turned to other actors, and I asked which ones, specifically, Brando respected. He pondered; though his lips shaped several names, he seemed to have second thoughts about pronouncing them. I suggested a few candidates—Laurence Olivier, John Gielgud, Montgomery Clift, Gérard Philipe, Jean-Louis Barrault. "Yes," he said, at last coming alive, "Philipe is a good actor. So is Barrault. Christ, what a wonderful picture that was—*Les Enfants du Paradis!* Maybe the best movie ever made. You know, that's the only time I ever fell in love with an actress, somebody on the screen. I was mad about Arletty." The Parisian star Arletty is well remembered by international audiences for the witty, womanly allure she brought to the heroine's part in Barrault's celebrated film. "I mean, I was really in *love* with her. My first trip to Paris, the thing I did right away, I asked to meet Arletty. I went to see her as though I were going to a shrine. My ideal woman. Wow!" He slapped the table. "Was that a mistake, was that a disillusionment! She was a tough article."

The maid came to clear the table; *en passant,* she gave Brando's shoulder a sisterly pat, rewarding him, I took it, for the cleaned-off sparkle of his plates. He again collapsed on the floor, stuffing a pillow under his head. "I'll tell you," he said, "Spencer Tracy is the kind of actor I like to watch. The way he holds back, *holds* back —then darts in to make his point, darts back. Tracy, Muni, Cary Grant. They know what they're doing. You can learn something from them."

Brando began to weave his fingers in the air, as though hoping that gestures would describe what he could not precisely articulate. "Acting is such a tenuous thing," he said. "A fragile, shy thing that a sensitive director can help lure out of you. Now, in movie-acting the important, the *sensitive* moment comes around the third take of a scene; by then you just need a whisper from the director to crystallize it for you. Gadge"—he was using Elia Kazan's nickname—"can usually do it. He's wonderful with actors."

Another actor, I suppose, would have understood at once what Brando was saying, but I found him difficult to follow. "It's what happens inside you on the third take," he said, with a careful emphasis that did not lessen my incomprehension. One of the most memorable film scenes Brando has played occurs in the Kazan-directed *On the Waterfront;* it is the car-ride scene in which Rod Steiger, as the racketeering brother, confesses he is leading Brando into a death trap. I asked if he could use the episode as an example, and tell me how his theory of the "sensitive moment" applied to it.

"Yes. Well, no. Well, let's see." He puckered his eyes, made a humming noise. "That was a seven-take scene, and I didn't like the way it was written. Lot of dissension going on there. I was fed up with the whole picture. All the location stuff was in New Jersey, and it was the dead of winter—the cold, Christ! And I was having problems at the time. Woman trouble. That scene.

Let me see. There were seven takes because Rod Steiger couldn't stop crying. He's one of those actors loves to cry. We kept doing it over and over. But I can't remember just when, just how it crystallized itself for me. The first time I saw *Waterfront,* in a projection room with Gadge, I thought it was so terrible I walked out without even speaking to him."

A month earlier, a friend of Brando's had told me, "Marlon always turns against whatever he's working on. Some element of it. Either the script or the director or somebody in the cast. Not always because of anything very rational—just because it seems to comfort him to be dissatisfied, let off steam about something. It's part of his pattern. Take *Sayonara.* A dollar gets you ten he'll develop a hoss on it somewhere along the line. A hoss on Logan, maybe. Maybe against Japan—the whole damn country. He loves Japan *now.* But with Marlon you never know from one minute to the next."

I was wondering whether I might mention this supposed "pattern" to Brando, ask if he considered it a valid observation about himself. But it was as though he had anticipated the question. "I ought to keep my mouth shut," he said. "Around here, around *Sayonara,* I've let a few people know the way I feel. But I don't always feel the same way two days running."

It was ten-thirty, and Murray called on the dot.

"I went out to dinner with the girls," he told Brando, his telephone voice so audible that I could hear it, too; it spoke above a blend of dance-band rumble and barroom roar. Obviously he was patronizing not one of the more traditional, cat-quiet Kyoto restaurants but, rather, a place where the customers wore shoes. "We're just finishing. How about it? You through?"

Brando looked at me thoughtfully, and I, in turn, at my coat. But he said, "We're still yakking. Call me back in an hour."

"O.K. Well . . . O.K. Listen. Miiko's here. She wants to know did you get the flowers she sent you?"

Brando's eyes lazily rolled toward the glassed-in sun porch, where a bowl of asters was centered on a round bamboo table. "Uh-huh. Tell her thanks very much."

"Tell her yourself. She's right here."

"No! Hey, wait a minute! Christ, *that's* not how you do it." But the protest came too late. Murray had already put down the phone, and Brando, reiterating *"That's* not how you do it," blushed and squirmed like an embarrassed boy.

The next voice to emanate from the receiver belonged to his *Sayonara* leading lady, Miss Miiko Taka. She asked about his health.

"Better, thanks. I ate the bad end of an oyster, that's all. Miiko? . . . Miiko, that was very *sweet* of you to send me the flowers. They're beautiful. I'm looking at them right now. Asters," he continued, as though shyly venturing a line of verse, "are my favorite flowers. . . ."

I retired to the sun porch, leaving Brando and Miss Taka to conduct their conversation in stricter seclusion. Below the windows, the hotel garden, with its ultra-simple and *soigné* arrangements of rock and tree, floated in the mists that crawl off Kyoto's waterways—for it *is* a watery city, crisscrossed with shallow rivers and cascading canals, dotted with pools as still as coiled snakes and mirthful little waterfalls that sound like Japanese girls giggling. Once the imperial capital and now the country's cultural museum, such an aesthetic treasure house that American bombers let it go unmolested during the war, Kyoto is surrounded by water, too; beyond the city's containing hills, thin roads run like causeways across the reflecting silver of flooded rice fields. That evening, despite the gliding mists, the blue encircling hills were discernible against the night, for the upper air had purity; a sky was there, stars were in it, and a scrap of moon. Some portions of the town could be seen. Nearest was a neighborhood of curving roofs, the dark façades of aristocratic houses fashioned from silky wood yet austere, northern, as secret-looking as any stone Siena palace. How brilliant they made the street lamps appear, and the doorway lanterns casting keen kimono colors—pink and orange, lemon and red. Farther away was a modern flatness—wide avenues and neon, a skyscraper of raw concrete that seemed less enduring, more perishable, than the papery dwellings stooping around it.

Brando completed his call. Approaching the sun porch, he looked at me looking at the view. He said, "Have you been to Nara? Pretty interesting."

I had, and yes, it was. "Ancient, old-time Nara," as a local cicerone unfailingly referred to it, is an hour's drive from Kyoto—a postcard town set in a show-place park. Here is the apotheosis of the Japanese genius for hypnotizing nature into unnatural behavior. The great shrine-infested park is a green salon where sheep graze, and herds of tame deer wander under trim pine trees and, like Venetian pigeons, gladly pose with honeymooning couples; where children yank the beards of unretaliating goats; where old men wearing black capes with mink collars squat on the shores of lotus-quilted lakes and, by clapping their hands, summon swarms of fish, speckled and scarlet carp, fat, thick as trout, who allow their snouts to be tickled, then gobble the crumbs that the old men sprinkle. That this serpentless Eden should strongly appeal to Brando was a bit surprising. With his liberal taste for the off-trail and not-overly-trammeled, one might have thought he would be unresponsive to so ruly, subjugated a landscape. Then, as though apropos of Nara, he said, "Well, I'd like to be married. I want to have children." It was not, perhaps, the non sequitur it seemed; the gentle safety of Nara just could, by the association of ideas, suggest marriage, a family.

"You've got to have love," he said. "There's no other reason for living. Men are no different from mice. They're born to perform the same function. Procreate." ("Marlon," to quote his friend Elia Kazan, "is one of the gentlest people I've ever known. Possibly the gentlest." Kazan's remark had meaning when one observed

Brando in the company of children. As far as he was concerned, Japan's youngest generation—lovely, lively, cherry-cheeked kids with bowlegs and bristling bangs—was always welcome to lark around the *Sayonara* sets. He was good with the children, at ease, playful, appreciative; he seemed, indeed, their emotional contemporary, a co-conspirator. Moreover, the condoling expression, the slight look of dispensing charitable compassion, peculiar to his contemplation of some adults was absent from his eyes when he looked at a child.)

Touching Miss Taka's floral offering, he went on, "What other reason is there for living? Except love? That has been my main trouble. My inability to love anyone." He turned back into the lighted room, stood there as though hunting something—a cigarette? He picked up a pack. Empty. He slapped at the pockets of trousers and jackets lying here and there. Brando's wardrobe no longer smacks of the street gang; as a dresser, he has graduated, or gone back, into an earlier style of outlaw chic, that of the prohibition sharpie—black snap-brim hats, striped suits and somber-hued George Raft shirts with pastel ties. Cigarettes were found; inhaling, he slumped on the pallet bed. Beads of sweat ringed his mouth. The electric heater hummed. The room was tropical; one could have grown orchids. Overhead, Mr. and Mrs. Buttons were again bumping about, but Brando appeared to have lost interest in them. He was smoking, thinking. Then, picking up the stitch of his thought, he said, "I can't. Love anyone. I can't trust anyone enough to give myself to them. But I'm ready. I want it. And I may, I'm almost on the point, I've really got to . . ." His eyes narrowed, but his tone, far from being intense, was indifferent, dully objective, as though he were discussing some character in a play—a part he was weary of portraying yet was trapped in by contract. "Because—well, what else is there? That's all it's all about. To love somebody."

(At this time, Brando was, of course, a bachelor, who had, upon occasion, indulged in engagements of a

quasi-official character—once to an aspiring authoress
and actress, by name Miss Blossom Plumb, and again,
with more public attention, to Mlle. Josanne Mariani-
Bérenger, a French fisherman's daughter. But in neither
instance were banns ever posted. One day last month,
however, in a sudden and somewhat secret ceremony at
Eagle Rock, California, Brando was married to a dark,
sari-swathed young minor actress who called herself
Anna Kashfi. According to conflicting press reports, either she was a Darjeeling-born Buddhist of the purest
Indian parentage or she was the Calcutta-born daughter
of an English couple named O'Callaghan, now living in
Wales. Brando has not yet done anything to clear up the
mystery.)

"Anyway, I have *friends*. No. No, I don't," he said,
verbally shadowboxing. "Oh, sure I do," he decided,
smoothing the sweat on his upper lip. "I have a great
many friends. Some I don't hold out on. I let them know
what's happening. You have to trust somebody. Well, not
all the way. There's nobody I rely on to tell *me* what to
do."

I asked if that included professional advisers. For
instance, it was my understanding that Brando very
much depended on the guidance of Jay Kanter, a young
man on the staff of the Music Corporation of America,
which is the agency that represents him. "Oh, Jay,"
Brando said now. "Jay does what I tell *him* to. I'm alone
like that."

The telephone sounded. An hour seemed to have
passed, for it was Murray again. "Yeah, still yakking,"
Brando told him. "Look, let *me* call *you*. . . . Oh, in an
hour or so. You be back in your room? . . . O.K."

He hung up, and said, "Nice guy. He wants to be a
director—eventually. I was saying something, though.
We were talking about friends. Do you know how I
make a friend?" He leaned a little toward me, as though
he had an amusing secret to impart. "I go about it very
gently. I circle around and around. I circle. Then, gradually, I come nearer. Then I reach out and touch them—

ah, so gently . . ." His fingers stretched forward like
insect feelers and grazed my arm. "Then," he said, one
eye half shut, the other, à la Rasputin, mesmerically
wide and shining, "I draw back. Wait awhile. Make
them wonder. At just the right moment, I move in again.
Touch them. Circle." Now his hand, broad and blunt-
fingered, traveled in a rotating pattern, as though it held
a rope with which he was binding an invisible presence.
"They don't know what's happening. Before they realize
it, they're all entangled, involved. I have them. And suddenly, sometimes, I'm all *they* have. A lot of them, you
see, are people who don't fit anywhere; they're not
accepted, they've been hurt, crippled one way or another.
But I want to help them, and they can focus on me; I'm
the duke. Sort of the duke of my domain."

(A past tenant on the ducal preserve, describing its
seigneur and his subjects, has said, "It's as though Marlon lived in a house where the doors are never locked.
When he lived in New York, the door always *was* open.
Anybody could come in, whether Marlon was there or
not, and everybody did. You'd arrive and there would
be ten, fifteen characters wandering around. It was
strange, because nobody seemed to really know anybody
else. They were just there, like people in a bus station.
Some type asleep in a chair. People reading the tabs. A
girl dancing by herself. Or painting her toenails. A comedian trying out his night-club act. Off in a corner, there'd
be a chess game going. And drums—bang, boom, bang,
boom! But there was never any drinking—nothing like
that. Once in a while, somebody would say, 'Let's go
down to the corner for an ice-cream soda.' Now, in all
this Marlon was the common denominator, the only connecting link. He'd move around the room drawing individuals aside and talking to them alone. If you've noticed,
Marlon can't, *won't,* talk to two people simultaneously.
He'll never take part in a *group* conversation. It always
has to be a cozy tête-à-tête—one person at a time. Which
is necessary, I suppose, if you use the same kind of
charm on everyone. But even when you know that's

what he's doing, it doesn't matter. Because when *your* turn comes, he makes you feel you're the only person in the room. In the world. Makes you feel that you're under his protection and that your troubles and moods concern him deeply. You have to believe it; more than anyone I've known, he radiates *sincerity*. Afterward, you may ask yourself, 'Is it an act?' If so, what's the point? What have you got to give him? Nothing except—and this *is* the point—affection. Affection that lends him authority over you. I sometimes think Marlon is like an orphan who later on in life tries to compensate by becoming the kindly head of a huge orphanage. But even outside this institution he wants everybody to love him." Although there exist a score of witnesses who might well contradict the last opinion, Brando himself is credited with having once informed an interviewer, "I can walk into a room where there are a hundred people—if there is *one* person in that room who doesn't like me, I know it and have to get out." As a footnote, it should be added that within the clique over which Brando presides he is esteemed as an intellectual father, as well as an emotional big brother. The person who probably knows him best, the comedian Wally Cox, declares him to be "a creative philosopher, a very deep thinker," and adds, "He's a real liberating force for his friends.")

Brando yawned; it had got to be a quarter past one. In less than five hours he would have to be showered, shaved, breakfasted, on the set, and ready for a makeup man to paint his pale face the mulatto tint that Technicolor requires.

"Let's have another cigarette," he said as I made a move to put on my coat.

"Don't you think you should go to sleep?"

"That just means getting up. Most mornings, I don't know why I do. I can't face it." He looked at the telephone, as though remembering his promise to call Murray. "Anyway, I may work later on. You want something to drink?"

Outside, the stars had darkened and it had started to drizzle, so the prospect of a nightcap was pleasing, especially if I should have to return on foot to my own hotel, which was a mile distant from the Miyako. I poured some vodka; Brando declined to join me. However, he subsequently reached for my glass, sipped from it, set it down between us, and suddenly said, in an offhand way that nonetheless conveyed feeling, "My mother. She broke apart like a piece of porcelain."

I had often heard friends of Brando's say, "Marlon worshiped his mother." But prior to 1947, and the première of *A Streetcar Named Desire,* few, perhaps none, of the young actor's circle had met either of his parents; they knew nothing of his background except what he chose to tell them. "Marlon always gave a very colorful picture of home life back in Illinois," one of his acquaintances told me. "When we heard that his family were coming to New York for the opening of *Streetcar,* everybody was very curious. We didn't know what to expect. On opening night, Irene Selznick gave a big party at '21.' Marlon came with his mother and father. Well, you can't imagine two more attractive people. Tall, handsome, charming as they could be. What impressed me—I think it amazed everyone—was Marlon's attitude toward them. In their presence, he wasn't the lad we knew. He was a model son. Reticent, respectful, very polite, considerate in every way."

Born in Omaha, Nebraska, where his father was a salesman of limestone products, Brando, the family's third child and only son, was soon taken to live in Libertyville, Illinois. There the Brandos settled down in a rambling house in a countrified neighborhood; at least, there was enough country around the house to allow the Brandos to keep geese and hens and rabbits, a horse, a Great Dane, twenty-eight cats, and a cow. Milking the cow was the daily chore that belonged to Bud, as Marlon was then nicknamed. Bud seems to have been an extroverted and competitive boy. Everyone who came within range of him was at once forced into some variety of contest: Who can eat fastest? Hold his breath longest? Tell the tallest tale? Bud was rebellious, too; rain or shine, he ran away from home every Sunday. But he and his two sisters, Frances and Jocelyn, were devotedly close to their mother. Many years later, Stella Adler, Brando's former drama coach, described Mrs. Brando, who died in 1954, as "a very beautiful, a heavenly, lost, girlish creature." Always, wherever she lived, Mrs. Brando had played leads in the productions of local dramatic societies, and always she had longed for a more brightly footlighted world than her surroundings provided. These yearnings inspired her children. Frances took to painting; Jocelyn, who is at present a professional actress, interested herself in the theatre. Bud, too, had inherited his mother's theatrical inclinations, but at seventeen he announced a wish to study for the ministry. (Then, as now, Brando searched for a belief. As one Brando disciple once summed it up, "He needs to find something in life, something in himself, that is permanently true, and he needs to lay down his life for it. For such an intense personality, nothing less than that will do.") Talked out of his clerical ambitions, expelled from school, rejected for military service in 1942 because of a trick knee, Brando packed up and came to New York. Whereupon Bud, the plump, towheaded, unhappy adolescent, exits, and the man-sized and very gifted Marlon emerges.

Brando has not forgotten Bud. When he speaks of the boy he was, the boy seems to inhabit him, as if time had done little to separate the man from the hurt, desiring child. "My father was indifferent to me," he said. "Nothing I could do interested him, or pleased him. I've accepted that now. We're friends now. We get along." Over the past ten years, the elder Brando has supervised his son's financial affairs; in addition to Pennebaker Productions, of which Mr. Brando, Sr., is an employee, they have been associated in a number of ventures, including a Nebraska grain-and-cattle ranch, in which a large percentage of the younger Brando's earnings was invested. "But my mother was everything to me. A whole world. I tried so hard. I used to come home from school . . ." He hesitated, as though waiting for me to picture him: Bud, books under his arm, scuffling his way along an afternoon street. "There wouldn't be anybody home. Nothing in the icebox." More lantern slides: empty rooms, a kitchen. "Then the telephone would ring. Somebody calling from some bar. And they'd say, 'We've got a lady down here. You better come get her.'" Suddenly, Brando was silent. In the silence the picture faded, or, rather, became fixed: Bud at the telephone. At last, the image moved again, leaped forward in time. Bud is eighteen, and: "I thought if she loved me enough, trusted me enough, I thought, then we can be together, in New York; we'll live together and I'll take care of her. Once, later on, that really happened. She left my father and came to live with me. In New York, when I was in a play. I tried so hard. But my love wasn't enough. She couldn't care enough. She went back. And one day"— the flatness of his voice grew flatter, yet the emotional pitch ascended until one could discern, like a sound within a sound, a wounded bewilderment—"I didn't care any more. She was there. In a room. Holding on to me. And I let her fall. Because I couldn't take it any more— watch her breaking apart, in front of me, like a piece of porcelain. I stepped right over her. I walked right out. I was indifferent. Since then, I've been indifferent."

The telephone was signaling. Its racket seemed to rouse him from a daze; he stared about, as though he'd wakened in an unknown room, then smiled wryly, then whispered, "Damn, damn, damn," as his hand lurched toward the telephone. "Sorry," he told Murray. "I was just going to call you. . . . No, he's leaving now. But look, man, let's call it off tonight. It's after one. It's nearly two o'clock. . . . Yeah. . . . Sure thing. Tomorrow."

Meanwhile, I'd put on my overcoat, and was waiting to say good night. He walked me to the door, where I put on my shoes. "Well, *sayonara*," he mockingly bade me. "Tell them at the desk to get you a taxi." Then, as I walked down the corridor, he called, "And listen! Don't pay too much attention to what I say. I don't always feel the same way."

In a sense, this was not my last sight of him that evening. Downstairs, the Miyako's lobby was deserted. There was no one at the desk, nor, outside, were there any taxis in view. Even at high noon, the fancy crochet of Kyoto's streets had played me tricks; still, I set off through the marrow-chilling drizzle in what I hoped was a homeward direction. I'd never before been abroad so late in the city. It was quite a contrast to daytime, when the central parts of the town, caroused by crowds of fiesta massiveness, jangle like the inside of a *pachinko* parlor, or to early evening—Kyoto's most exotic hours, for then, like night flowers, lanterns wreathe the side streets, and resplendent geishas, with their white ceramic faces and their ballooning lacquered wigs strewn with silver bells, their hobbled wiggle-walk, hurry among the shadows toward meticulously tasteful revelries. But at two in the morning these exquisite grotesques are gone, the cabarets are shuttered; only cats remained to keep me company, and drunks and red-light ladies, the inevitable old beggar-bundles in doorways, and, briefly, a ragged street musician who followed me playing on a flute a medieval music. I had trudged far more than a mile when, at last, one of a hundred alleys led to familiar ground—the main-street district of department stores and cinemas. It was then that I saw Brando. Sixty feet tall, with a head as huge as the greatest Buddha's, there he was, in comic-paper colors, on a sign above a theatre that advertised *The Teahouse of the August Moon.* Rather Buddha-like, too, was his pose, for he was depicted in a squatting position, a serene smile on a face that glistened in the rain and the light of a street lamp. A deity, yes; but, more than that, really, just a young man sitting on a pile of candy.

A House on the Heights

I LIVE IN BROOKLYN. By choice.

Those ignorant of its allures are entitled to wonder why. For, taken as a whole, it *is* an uninviting community. A veritable veldt of tawdriness where even the *noms des quartiers* aggravate: Flatbush and Flushing Avenue, Bushwick, Brownsville, Red Hook. Yet, in the greenless grime-gray, oases do occur, splendid contradictions, hearty echoes of healthier days. Of these seeming mirages, the purest example is the neighborhood in which I am situated, an area known as Brooklyn Heights. Heights, because it stands atop a cliff that secures a sea-gull's view of the Manhattan and Brooklyn bridges, of lower Manhattan's tall dazzle and the ship-lane waters, breeding river to bay to ocean, that encircle and seethe past posturing Miss Liberty.

I'm not much acquainted with the proper history of the Heights. However, I *believe* (but please don't trust me) that the oldest house, the oldest still extant and functioning, belongs to our back-yard neighbors, Mr. and Mrs. Philip Broughton. A silvery gray, shingle-wood Colonial shaded by trees robustly leafed, it was built in 1790, the home of a sea captain. Period prints, dated 1830, depict the Heights area as a cozy port bustling with billowed sails; and, indeed, many of the section's finer houses, particularly those of Federal design, were first intended to shelter the families of shipmasters. Cheerfully austere, as elegant and other-era as formal calling cards, these houses bespeak an age of able servants and solid fireside ease; of horses in musical harness (old rose-brick carriage houses abound hereabouts; all now, naturally, transformed into pleasant, if rather doll-pretty, dwellings); invoke specters of bearded seafaring fathers and bonneted stay-at-home wives: devoted parents to great broods of future bankers and fashionable brides. For a century or so that is how it must have been: a time of tree-shrouded streets, lanes limp with willow, August gardens brimming with bumblebees and herbaceous scent, of ship horns on the river, sails in the wind, and a country-green meadow sloping down to the harbor, a cow-grazing, butterflied meadow where children sprawled away breezy summer afternoons, where the slap of sleds resounded on December snows.

Is that how it was? Conceivably I take too Valentine a view. However it be, my Valentine assumes the stricter aspect of a steel engraving as we mosey, hand in hand, with Henry Ward Beecher, whose church once dominated the spiritual life of the Heights, through the latter half of the last century. The great Bridge, opened in 1883, now balanced above the river; and the port, each year expanding becoming a more raucous, big-business matter, chased the children out of the meadow, withered it, entirely whacked it away to make room for black palace-huge warehouses tickly with imported tarantulas and reeking of rotten bananas.

By 1910, the neighborhood, which comprises sly alleys and tucked-away courts and streets that sometimes run straight but also dwindle and bend, had undergone fiercer vicissitudes. Descendants of the Reverend Beecher's stiff-collared flock had begun removing themselves to other pastures; and immigrant tribes, who had first ringed the vicinity, at once infiltrated en masse. Whereupon a majority of what remained of genteel old stock, the sediment in the bottom of the bottle, poured forth from their homes, leaving them to be demolished or converted into eyesore-seedy rooming establishments.

So that, in 1925, Edmund Wilson, allowing a paragraph to what he considered the dead and dying Heights, disgustedly reported: "The pleasant red and pink brick houses still worthily represent the generation of Henry Ward Beecher; but an eternal Sunday is on them now; they seem sunk in a final silence. In the streets one may catch a glimpse of a solitary well-dressed old gentleman moving slowly a long way off; but in general the respectable have disappeared and only the vulgar survive. The empty quiet is broken by the shouts of shrill Italian children and by incessant mechanical pianos in dingy apartment houses, accompanied by human voices that seem almost as mechanical as they. At night, along unlighted streets, one gives a wide berth to drunkards that sprawl out across the pavement from the shadow of darkened doors; and I have known a dead horse to be left in the road—two blocks from the principal post office and not much more from Borough Hall—with no effort made to remove it, for nearly three weeks."

Gothic as this glimpse is, the neighborhood nevertheless continued to possess, cheap rents aside, some certain appeal brigades of the gifted—artists, writers—began to discover. Among those riding in on the initial wave was Hart Crane, whose poet's eye, focusing on his window view, produced *The Bridge*. Later, soon after the success of *Look Homeward, Angel,* Thomas Wolfe, noted prowler of the Brooklyn night, took quarters: an apartment, equipped with the most publicized icebox in literature's archives, which he maintained until his "overgrowed carcass" was carried home to the hills of Carolina. At one time, a stretch of years in the early forties, a single, heaven knows singular, house on Middagh Street boasted a roll call of residents that read: W. H. Auden, Richard Wright, Carson McCullers, Paul and Jane Bowles, the British composer Benjamin Britten, impresario and stage designer Oliver Smith, an authoress of murder entertainments—Miss Gypsy Rose Lee, and a Chimpanzee accompanied by Trainer. Each of the tenants in this ivory-tower boarding house contributed to its upkeep, lights, heat, the wages of a general cook (a former Cotton Club chorine), and all were present at the invitation of the owner, that very original editor, writer, *fantaisiste,* a gentleman with a guillotine tongue, yet benevolent and butter-hearted, the late, the justly lamented George Davis.

Now George is gone; and his house too: the necessities of some absurd civic project caused it to be torn down during the war. Indeed, the war years saw the neighborhood slide to its nadir. Many of the more substantial old houses were requisitioned by the military, as lodgings, as jukebox canteens, and their rural-reared, piney-woods personnel treated them quite as Sherman did those Dixie mansions. Not that it mattered; not that anyone gave a damn. No one did; until, soon after the war, the Heights commenced attracting a bright new clientele, brave pioneers bringing brooms and buckets of paint: urban, ambitious young couples, by and large mid-rung in their Doctor-Lawyer-Wall Street-Whatever careers, eager to restore to the Heights its shattered qualities of circumspect, comfortable charm.

For them, the section had much to offer: roomy big houses ready to be reconverted into private homes suitable for families of old-fashioned size; and such families are what these young people either had made or were making at stepladder rates. A good place to raise children, too, this neighborhood where the traffic is cautious, and the air has clarity, a seaside tartness; where there are gardens for games, quiet stoops for amusing; and where, above all, there is the Esplanade to roller-skate upon. (Forbidden: still the brats do it.) While far from being a butterflied meadow, the Esplanade, a wide terrace-like walk overlooking the harbor, does its contemporary best to approximate that playing pasture of long-gone girls and their brothers.

So, for a decade and longer, the experiment of reviving the Heights has proceeded: to the point where one is

tempted to term it a *fait accompli*. Window boxes bloom
with geraniums; according to the season, green foliated
light falls through the trees or gathered autumn leaves
burn at the corner; flower-loaded wagons wheel by while
the flower seller sings his wares; in the dawn one occasionally hears a cock crow, for there is a lady with a garden who keeps hens and a rooster. On winter nights, when
the wind brings the farewell callings of boats outward
bound and carries across rooftops the chimney smoke of
evening fires, there is a sense, evanescent but authentic
as the firelight's flicker, of time come circle, of ago's
sweeter glimmerings recaptured.

Though I'd long been acquainted with the neighborhood, having now and then visited there, my closer association began two years ago when a friend bought a
house on Willow Street. One mild May evening he asked
me over to inspect it. I was most impressed; exceedingly
envious. There were twenty-eight rooms, high-ceilinged,
well proportioned, and twenty-eight workable, marble-
manteled fireplaces. There was a beautiful staircase floating upward in white, swan-simple curves to a skylight of
sunny amber-gold glass. The floors were fine, the real
thing, hard lustrous timber; and the walls! In 1820,
when the house was built, men knew how to make walls
—thick as a buffalo, immune to the mightiest cold, the
meanest heat.

French doors led to a spacious rear porch reminiscent of Louisiana. A porch canopied, completely submerged, as though under a lake of leaves, by an ancient
but admirably vigorous vine weighty with grapelike
bunches of wisteria. Beyond, a garden: a tulip tree, a
blossoming pear, a perched black-and-red bird bending
a feathery branch of forsythia.

In the twilight, we talked, my friend and I. We sat
on the porch consulting Martinis—I urged him to have
one more, another. It got to be quite late, he began to
see my point: Yes, twenty-eight rooms *were* rather a lot;
and yes, it seemed only *fair* that I should have some of
them.

That is how I came to live in the yellow brick house on Willow Street.

Often a week passes without my "going to town," or "crossing the bridge," as neighbors call a trip to Manhattan. Mystified friends, suspecting provincial stagnation, inquire: "But what do you *do* over there?" Let me tell you, life can be pretty exciting around here. Remember Colonel Rudolf Abel, the Russian secret agent, the biggest spy ever caught in America, head of the whole damned apparatus? Know where they nabbed him? Right here! smack on Fulton Street! Trapped him in a building between David Semple's fine-foods store and Frank Gambuzza's television repair shop. Frank, grinning as though he'd done the job himself, had his picture in *Life;* so did the waitress at the Music Box Bar, the colonel's favorite watering hole. A peevish few of us couldn't fathom why our pictures weren't in *Life* too. Frank, the Music Box Bar girl, they weren't the only people who knew the colonel. Such a gentleman-like gentleman: one would never have *supposed*. . . .

I confess, we don't catch spies every day. But most days are supplied with stimulants: in the harbor some exotic freighter to investigate; a bird of strange plumage resting among the wisteria; or, and how exhilarating an occurrence it is, a newly arrived shipment at Knapp's. Knapp's is a set of shops, really a series of storerooms resembling caverns, clustered together on Fulton near Pineapple Street. The proprietor—that is too modest a designation for so commanding a figure—the czar, the Aga Khan of these paradisal emporiums is Mr. George Knapp, known to his friends as Father.

Father is a world traveler. Cards arrive: he is in Seville, now Copenhagen, now Milan, next week Manchester, everywhere and all the while on a gaudy spending spree. Buying: blue crockery from a Danish castle. Pink apothecary jars from an old London pharmacy. English brass, Barcelona lamps, Battersea boxes, French paperweights, Italian witch balls, Greek icons, Venetian blackamoors, Spanish saints, Korean cabinets; and junk, glorious junk, a jumble of ragged dolls, broken buttons, a stuffed kangaroo, an aviary of owls under a great glass bell, the playing pieces of obsolete games, the paper moneys of defunct governments, an ivory umbrella cane *sans* umbrella, crested chamber pots and mustache mugs and irreparable clocks, cracked violins, a sundial that weighs seven hundred pounds, skulls, snake vertebrae, elephants' hoofs, sleigh bells and Eskimo carvings and mounted swordfish, medieval milkmaid stools, rusted firearms and flaking waltz-age mirrors.

Then Father comes home to Brooklyn, his treasures trailing after him. Uncrated, added to the already perilous clutter, the blackamoors prance in the marvelous gloom, the swordfish glide through the store's Atlantic-depth dusk. Eventually they will go: fancier *antiquaires,* and anonymous mere beauty lovers, will come, cart them away. Meanwhile, poke around. You're certain to find a plum; and it may be a peach. That paperweight—the one imprisoning a Baccarat dragonfly. If you want it, take it now: tomorrow, assuredly the day after, will see it on Fifty-Seventh Street at quintuple the tariff.

Father has a partner, his wife Florence. She is from Panama, is handsome, fresh-colored and tall, trim enough to look well in the trousers she affects, a woman of proud posture and, vis-à-vis customers, of nearly eccentric curtness, take-it-or-go disdain—but then, poor soul, she is under the discipline of not being herself permitted to sell, even quote a price. Only Father, with his Macaulayan memory, his dazzling ability to immediately lay hold of any item in the dizzying maze, is so allowed. Brooklyn-born, waterfront-bred, always hatted and usually wearing a wet cold cigar, a stout, short, round power-house with one arm, with a strutting walk, a rough-guy voice, shy nervous sensitive eyes that blink when irritation makes him stutter, Father is nevertheless an aesthete. A tough aesthete who takes no guff, will not quibble over his evaluations, just declares: "Put it down!" and, "Get it Manhattan half the money, I give it yuh free." They are an excellent couple, the Knapps. I explore their museum several times a week, and toward October, when a Franklin stove in the shape of a witch hut warms the air and Florence serves cider accompanied by a damp delicious date-nut bread she bakes in discarded coffee-cans, never miss a day. Occasionally, on these festive afternoons, Father will gaze about him, blink-blink his eyes with vague disbelief, then, as though his romantic accumulations were closing round him in a manner menacing, observe: "I got to be crazy. Putting my heart in a fruitcake business like this. And the *investment*. The money alone! Honest, in your honest opinion, wouldn't you say I'm crazy?"

Certainly not. If, however, Mrs. Cornelius Oosthuizen were to beg the question——

It seems improbable that someone of Mrs. Oosthuizen's elevation should have condescended to distinguish me with her acquaintance. I owe it all to a pound of dog meat. What happened was: the butcher's boy delivered a purchase of mine which, by error, included hamburger meant to go to Mrs. O. Recognizing her name on the order slip, and having often remarked her house, a garnet-colored château in mood remindful of the old Schwab mansion on Manhattan's Riverside Drive, I thought of taking round the package myself, not dreaming to meet the fine lady, but, at most, ambitious for a moment's glance into her fortunate preserve. Fortunate, for it boasted, so I'd had confided to me, a butler and staff of six. Not that this is the Height's sole *maison de luxe:* we are blessed with several exponents of limousine life—but unarguably, Mrs. O. is *la regina di tutti*.

Approaching her property, I noticed a person in Persian lamb very vexedly punching the bell, pounding a brass knocker. "God damn you, Mabel," she said to the door; then turned, glared at me as I climbed the steps—a tall intimidating replica of frail unforbidding Miss Marianne Moore (who, it may be recalled, is a Brooklyn lady too). Pale lashless eyes, razor lips, hair a silver fuzz. "Ah, *you*. I know you," she accused me, as behind her the door was opened by an Irish crone wearing an ankle-length apron. "So. I suppose you've come to sign the petition? Very good of you, I'm sure." Mumbling an explanation, muttering servile civilities, I conveyed the butcher's parcel from my hands to hers; she, as though I'd tossed her a rather rotten fish, dangled it gingerly until the maid remarked: "Ma'am, 'tis Miss Mary's meat the good lad's brought."

"Indeed. Then don't stand there, Mabel. Take it." And, regarding me with a lessening astonishment that I could not, in her behalf, reciprocate: "Wipe your boots, come in. We will discuss the petition. Mabel, send Murphy with some Bristol and biscuit. . . . Oh? At the dentist's! When I *asked* him *not* to tamper with that tooth. What hellish nonsense," she swore, as we passed into a hatrack-vestibule. "Why didn't he go to the hypnotist, as I told him? Mary! Mary! Mary," she said when now appeared a friendly nice dog of cruel pedigree: a spaniel *cum* chow attached to the legs of a dachshund, "I believe Mabel has your lunch. Mabel, take Miss Mary to the kitchen. And we will have our biscuits in the Red Room."

The room, in which red could be discerned only in a bowl of porcelain roses and a basket of marzipan strawberries, contained velvet-swagged windows that commanded a pulse-quickening prospect: sky, skyline, far away a wooded slice of Staten Island. In other respects, the room, a heavy confection, cumbersome, humorless, a hunk of Beidermeier pastry, did not recommend itself. "It was my grandmother's bedroom; my father preferred it as a parlor. Cornelius, Mr. Oosthuizen, died here. Very suddenly: while listening at the radio to the Roosevelt person. An attack. Brought on by anger and cigars. I'm sure you won't ask permission to smoke. Sit down. . . . Not there. There, by the window. Now here, it *should* be here, somewhere, in this drawer? Could it be upstairs? Damn Murphy, horrid man always meddling with my—no, I have it: the petition."

The document stated, and objected to, the plans of a certain minor religious sect that had acquired a half-block of houses on the Heights which they planned to flatten and replace with a dormitory building for the benefit of their Believers. Appended to it were some dozen protesting signatures; the Misses Seeley had signed, and Mr. Arthur Veere Vinson, Mrs. K. Mackaye Brownlowe—descendants of the children in the meadow, the old-guard survivors of *their* neighborhood's evilest hours, those happy few who regularly attended Mrs. O.'s black-tie-sit-downs. She wasted no eloquence on the considerable merit of their complaint; simply, "Sign it," she ordered, a Lady Catherine de Brough instructing a Mr. Collins.

Sherry came; and with it an assembly of cats. Scarred battlers with leprous fur and punch-drunk eyes. Mrs. O., motioning toward the least respectable of these, a tiger-striped marauder, told me: "This is the one you may take home. He's been with us a month, we've put him in splendid condition, I'm sure you'll be devoted. Dogs? What *sort* of dogs have you? Well, I don't approve the pure breeds. Anyone will give *them* a home. I took Miss Mary off the street. And Lovely Louise, Mouse and Sweet William—my dogs, all my cats, too, came off the streets. Look below, there in the garden. Under the heaven tree. Those markings: graves are what you see, some as old as my childhood. The seashells are goldfish. The yellow coral, canaries. That white stone is a rabbit; that cross of pebbles: my favorite, the first Mary—angel girl, went bathing in the river and caught a fatal chill. I used to tease Cornelius, Mr. Oosthuizen, told him, ha-ha, told him I planned to put him there with the rest of my darlings. Ha-ha, he wasn't amused, not at all. So, I mean to say, your having dogs doesn't signify: Billy here has such spirit, *he* can hold his own. No, I insist you have him. For I can't keep him much longer, he's a disturbing influence; and if I let him loose, he'll run back to his bad old life in the St. George alley. I wouldn't want *that* on my conscience if I were you."

Her persuasions failed; in consequence our parting was cool. Yet at Christmas she sent me a card, a Cartier engraving of the heaven tree protecting the bones in its sad care. And once, encountering her at the bakery, where we both were buying brownies, we discussed the impudent disregard her petition had received: alas, the wreckers had wrecked, the brethren were building. On the same occasion, she shame-on-you informed me that Billy the cat, released from her patronage, had indeed returned to the sinful ways of the St. George alley.

The St. George alley, adjoining a small cinema, is a shadowy shelter for vagrants: wino derelicts wandered over the bridge from Chinatown and the Bowery share it with other orphaned, gone-wild creatures: cats, as many as minnows in a stream, who gather in their greatest numbers toward nightfall; for then, as darkness happens, strange-eyed women, not unlike those black-clothed fanatics who haunt the cat arenas in Rome, go stealing through the alley with caressing hisses and sacks of crumbled salmon. (Which isn't to suggest that Mrs. O. is one who indulges in this somehow unhealthy hobby: regarding animals, her actions, while perhaps a bit overboard, are kindly meant, and not untypical of the Heights, where a high percentage of the pet population has been adopted off the streets. Astonishing, really, the amount of lost strays who roam their way into the neighborhood, as though instinct informed them they'd find someone here who couldn't abide being followed through the rain, but would, instead, lead them home, boil milk, and call Dr. Wasserman, Bernie, our smart-as-they-come young vet whose immaculate hospital resounds with the music of Bach concertos and the barkings of mending beasts.)

Just now, in connection with these notes. I was hunting through a hieroglyphic shambles I call my journal. Odd, indeed the oddest, jottings—a majority of which conceal from me their meanings. God knows what "Thunder on Cobra Street" refers to. Or "A diarrhea of platitudes in seventeen tongues." Unless it is intended to describe a most tiresome local person, a linguist terribly talkative in many languages though articulate in none. However, "Took T&G to G&T" does make sense.

The first initials represent two friends, the latter a

restaurant not far away. You must have heard of it, Gage & Tollner. Like Kolb's and Antoine's in New Orleans, Gage & Tollner is a last-century enterprise that has kept in large degree its founding character. The shaky dance of its gaslight chandeliers is not a period-piece hoax; nor do the good plain marble-topped tables, the magnificent array of gold-edged mirrors, seem sentimental affectations—rather, it is a testament to the seriousness of the proprietors, who have obliged us by letting the place stay much as it was that opening day in 1874. One mightn't suppose it, for in the atmosphere there is none of the briny falderal familiar to such aquariums, but the specialty is sea food. The best. Chowders the doughtiest down-Easter must approve. Lobsters that would appease Nero. Myself, I am a soft-shelled-crab *aficionado:* a plate of sautéed crabs, a halved lemon, a glass of chilled Chablis: most satisfactory. The waiters, too, dignified but swift-to-smile Negroes who take pride in their work, contribute to the goodness of Gage & Tollner; on the sleeves of their very laundered jackets they sport military-style chevrons awarded according to the number of years each has served; and, *were* this the Army, some would be generals.

Nearby, there is another restaurant, a fraction less distinguished, but of similar vintage and virtually the same menu: Joe's—Joe being, by the way, an attractive young lady. On the far fringes of the Heights, just before Brooklyn becomes Brooklyn again, there is a street of Gypsies with Gypsy cafés (have your future foretold and be tattooed while sipping tankards of Moorish tea); there is also an Arab-Armenian quarter sprinkled with spice-saturated restaurants where one can buy, hot from the oven, a crusty sort of pancake frosted with sesame seed —once in a while I carry mine down to the waterfront, intending to share with the gulls; but, gobbling as I go, none is ever left. On a summer's evening a stroll across the bridge, with cool winds singing through the steel shrouds, with stars moving about above and ships below, can be intoxicating, particularly if you are headed toward the roasting-pork, sweet-and-sour aromas of China-town.

Another journal notation reads, "At last a face in the ghost hotel!" Which means: after months of observation, in all climates at all hours, I'd sighted someone in a window of a haunted-seeming riverfront building that stands on Water Street at the foot of the Heights. A lonely hotel I often make the destination of my walks: because I think it romantic, in aggravated moments imagine retiring there, for it is as secluded as Mt. Athos, remoter than the Krak Chevalier in the mountains of wildest Syria. Daytimes the location, a dead-end Chiricoesque piazza facing the river, is little disturbed; at night, not at all: not a sound, except foghorns and a distant traffic whisper from the bridge which bulks above. Peace, and the shivering glow of gliding-by tugs and ferries.

The hotel is three-storied. Sunstruck scraps of reflected river-shine, and broken, jigsaw images of the bridge waver across the windows; but beyond the glass nothing stirs: the rooms, despite contradictory evidence, milk bottles on sills, a hat on a hook, unmade beds and burning bulbs, appear unoccupied: never a soul to be seen. Like the sailors of the *Marie Celeste,* the guests, hearing a knock, must have opened their doors to a stranger who swallowed them whole. Could it be, perhaps it *was,* the stranger himself that I saw?—"At last a face in the ghost hotel!" I glimpsed him just the once, one April afternoon one cloudless blue day; and he, a balding man in an undershirt, hurled up a window, flexed hairy arms, yawned hugely, hugely inhaled the river breeze—was gone. No, on careful second thought, I will never set foot in that hotel. For I should either be devoured or have my mystery dispelled. As children we are sensitive to mystery: locked boxes, whisperings behind closed doors, the what-thing that lurks yonder in the trees, waits in every stretch between street lamps; but as we grow older all is too explainable, the capacity to invent pleasurable alarm recedes: too bad, a pity—throughout our lives we ought to believe in ghost hotels.

Close by the hotel begins a road that leads along the river. Silent miles of warehouses with shuttered wooden windows, docks resting on the water like sea spiders. From May through September, *la saison pour la plage,* these docks are diving boards for husky ragamuffins—while perfumed apes, potentates of the waterfront but once dock-divers themselves, cruise by steering two-toned (banana-tomato) car concoctions. Crane-carried tractors and cotton bales and unhappy cattle sway above the holds of ships bound for Bahia, for Bremen, for ports spelling their names in Oriental calligraphy. Provided one has made waterfront friends, it is sometimes possible to board the freighters, carouse and sun yourself: you may even be asked to lunch—and I, for one, am always quick to accept, embarrassingly so if the hosts are Scandinavian: they always set a superior table from larders brimming with smoked "taste thrills" and iced aquavit. Avoid the Greek ships, however: very poor cuisine, no liquor served except *ouzo,* a sickly licorice syrup; and, at least in the opinion of this panhandler, the grub on French freighters by no means meets the standards one might reasonably expect.

The tugboat people are usually good for a cup of coffee, and in wintry weather, when the river is tossing surf, what joy to take refuge in a stove-heated tug cabin and thaw out with a mug of the blackest Java. Now and again along the route minuscule beaches occur, and once, it was around sunset on a quiet Sunday, I saw on one of them something that made me look twice, and twice more: still it seemed a vision. Every kind of sailor is common enough here, even saronged East Indians, even the giant Senegalese, their onyx arms afire with blue, with yellow tattooed flowers, with saucy torsos and garish *graffitti* (Je t'aime, Hard Luck, Mimi Chang, Adios Amigo). Runty Russians, too—one sees them about, flap-flapping in their pajama-like costumes. But the barefooted sailors on the beach, the three I saw reclining there, profiles set against the sundown, seemed mythical as mermen: more exactly, mermaids—for their hair, striped with albino streaks, was lady-length, a savage fiber falling to their shoulders; and in their ears gold rings glinted. Whether plenipotentiaries from the pearl-floored palace of Poseidon or mariners merely, Viking-tressed seamen out of the Gothic North languishing after a long and barberless voyage, they are included permanently in my memory's curio cabinet: an object to be revolved in the light that way and this, like those crystal lozenges with secretive carvings sealed inside.

After consideration, "Thunder on Cobra Street" does become decipherable. On the Heights there is no Cobra Street, though a street exists that suits the name, a steep downhill incline leading to a dark sector of the dockyards. Not a true part of the Heights neighborhood, it lies, like a serpent at the gates, on the outmost periphery. Seedy hangouts, beer-sour bars and bitter candy stores mingle among the eroding houses, the multifamily dwellings that architecturally range from time-blackened brownstone to magnified concepts of Mississippi privy.

Here, the gutters are acrawl with Cobras; that is, a gang of "juvenile" delinquents: COBRA, the word is stamped on their sweat shirts, painted, sometimes in letters that shine with a fearful phosphorescence, across the backs of their leather jackets. The steep street is within their ugly estate, a bit of their "turf," as they term it; an infinitesimal bit, for the Cobras, a powerful cabala, cast owning eyes on acres of metropolitan terrain. I am not brave—*au contraire;* quite frankly these fellows, may they be twelve years old or twenty, set my heart thumping like a sinner's at Sunday meeting. Nevertheless, when it has been a matter of convenience to pass through this section of their domain, I've compelled my nerves to accept the challenge.

On the last venture, and perhaps it will remain the last, I was carrying a good camera. The sun was unseen in a sky that ought to either rumble or rain. Rackety children played skip-rope, while a lamppost-lot of idle elders looked on, dull-faced and drooping: a denim-painted, cowboy-booted gathering of Cobras. Their eyes, their asleep sick insolent eyes, swerved on me as I climbed the street. I crossed to the opposite curb; then *knew,* without needing to verify it, that the Cobras had uncoiled and were sliding toward me. I heard them whistling; and the children hushed, the skip-rope ceased swishing. Someone —a pimpled purple birthmark bandit-masked the lower half of his face—said, "Hey yuh, Whitey, lemmeseeduh-camra." Quicken one's step? Pretend not to hear? But every alternative seemed explosive. "Hey, Whitey, hey yuh, takemuhpitchawantcha?"

Thunder salvaged the moment. Thunder that rolled, crashed down the street like a truck out of control. We all looked up, a sky ripe for storm stared back. I shouted, "Rain! Rain!" and ran. Ran for the Heights, that safe cita-del, that bourgeois bastion. Tore along the Esplanade— where the nice young mothers were racing their carriages against the coming disaster. Caught my breath under the thrashing leaves of troubled elms, rushed on: saw the flower-wagon man struggling with his thunder-frightened horse. Saw, twenty yards ahead, then ten, five, then none, the yellow house on Willow Street. Home! And happy to be.